Literature for
INTERPRETATION

WALLACE A. BACON
ROBERT S. BREEN

The School of Speech
Northwestern University

Literature for
INTERPRETATION

HOLT, RINEHART AND WINSTON · NEW YORK
CHICAGO · SAN FRANCISCO · TORONTO

ACKNOWLEDGMENTS

For permission to use the copyrighted works reproduced in this volume acknowledgment is made to the following:

"Young Goodman Brown," from *Mosses from an Old Manse* by Nathaniel Hawthorne. Reprinted with permission from Houghton Mifflin Company, Boston.

"The Real Thing," Copyright 1921 by Henry James. From *Henry James: Selected Short Stories*, published by John Farquharson Ltd., London; also from *The Soft Side*, published by Paul R. Reynolds & Son, New York; and The Macmillan Company, New York. Reprinted with permission from John Farquharson Ltd., The Macmillan Company, and Paul R. Reynolds & Son.

"The Mezzotint," from *Collected Ghost Stories* by M. J. James. Reprinted with permission from Edward Arnold (Publishers) Ltd., London.

"The Burglar," from *Simple Stories* by Archibald Marshall. Copyright 1927 by Harper & Brothers; copyright renewed 1955 by Archibald Marshall. Reprinted by permission of Harper & Brothers.

"The Grave," from *The Leaning Tower and Other Stories*, copyright, 1944, by Katherine Anne Porter. Used by permission of Harcourt, Brace and Company, Inc.

"The Baby Party," Copyright 1925 Hearst International Magazine Co., Inc.; renewal copyright 1953 Frances S. F. Lanahan. Reprinted from *All the Sad Young Men* by F. Scott Fitzgerald with the permission of Charles Scribner's Sons.

"The Patented Gate and the Mean Hamburger," Copyright, 1947, by Robert Penn Warren. Reprinted from his volume *The Circus in the Attic and Other Stories* by permission of Harcourt, Brace and Company, Inc.

"Lilly Daw and the Three Ladies," Copyright, 1937, by Eudora Welty. Reprinted from her volume, *A Curtain of Green and Other Stories*, by permission of Harcourt, Brace and Company, Inc.

"Death of a Traveling Salesman," Copyright, 1936, by Eudora Welty. Reprinted from her volume, *A Curtain of Green and Other Stories*, by permission of Harcourt, Brace and Company, Inc.

"A Story," from *Quite Early One Morning*, by Dylan Thomas. Copyright 1954 by New Directions. Reprinted by permission of New Directions and of J. M. Dent & Sons, Ltd.

"A Christmas Memory," © Copyright 1956 by Truman Capote. Reprinted from *Breakfast at Tiffany's*, by Truman Capote, by permission of Random House, Inc.

"When Lilacs Last in the Dooryard Bloom'd" and "Out of the Cradle Endlessly Rocking," from *The Wound Dresser* by Walt Whitman. Reprinted with permission from The Bodley Book Shop, New York.

"Lucifer in Starlight" is reprinted with the permission of Charles Scribner's Sons from *The Poetical Works of George Meredith*.

Three Sonnets, from *Modern Love* by George Meredith are reprinted with the permission of Charles Scribner's Sons.

"A Narrow Fellow in the Grass," "I Never Saw a Moor," "Parting," "The Soul Selects Her Own Society," "They Say That Time Assuages," "I Had Been Hungry All the Years," and "Because I Could Not Stop for Death," from *The Poems of Emily Dickinson*. Reprinted by permission of Little, Brown & Company.

"Channel Firing," "Ah, Are You Digging on My Grave?" and "The Oxen," from *Collected Poems of Thomas Hardy* Copyright 1925 by The Macmillan Company, New York. Reprinted with permission of The Macmillan Company and of the Trustees of the Hardy Estate, The Macmillan Company of Canada Limited, and Macmillan and Company Ltd., London.

"Pied Beauty," from *Poems of Gerard Manley Hopkins*. Third edition edited by W. H. Gardner. Copyright 1948 by Oxford University Press, Inc. Reprinted by permission.

'When I Was One-and-Twenty," "Reveille," "Loveliest of Trees, the Cherry Now," "With Rue My Heart Is Laden," and "To an Athlete Dying Young," from *Complete Poems* by A. E. Housman. Copyright 1940, © 1959 by Henry Holt and Company, Inc., New York. By permission of Holt, Rinehart and Winston, Inc., New York.

"Leda and the Swan" and "Sailing to Byzantium," from *Collected Poems* by William Butler Yeats. Copyright 1928 by The Macmillan Company, New York, and used with their permission. Also from *Collected Poems of W. B. Yeats* with their permission. Also from *Collected Poems of W. B. Yeats* with permission from The Macmillan Co. of Canada, Ltd., A. P. Watt & Son, London, and Mrs. Yeats.

The Collected Poetry of W. H. Auden by permission of Random House, Inc., New York, and Faber & Faber Ltd., London.

"I Think Continually of Those Who Were Truly Great," Copyright 1934 by The Modern Library, Inc. Reprinted from *Collected Poems 1928–1953* by Stephen Spender, by permission of Random House, Inc., and of Faber & Faber, Ltd., London.

"Poem in October" and "In Memory of Ann Jones," from *The Collected Poems of Dylan Thomas.* Copyright 1939, 1942, 1946 by New Directions. Copyright 1952, 1953 by Dylan Thomas. Reprinted by permission of New Directions, and of J. M. Dent and Sons Ltd., London.

"To Sir William Temple," from *The Love Letters of Dorothy Osborne* by Dorothy Osborne. Reprinted with permission of Dodd, Mead & Company, New York; E. P. Dutton & Co., Inc., New York; and Clarendon Press, Oxford.

"To Alexander Pope," from *The Correspondence of Jonathan Swift,* edited by Elrington Ball. Reprinted with permission from G. Bell & Sons, Ltd.

"To Mary Scurlock," from *The Correspondence of Richard Steele,* edited by Rae Blanchard. Reprinted with permission from The Clarendon Press, Oxford. Also, from *The Letters of Richard Steele,* edited by R. Brimley Johnson, reprinted with permission of Dodd, Mead & Company, New York.

"To Lady Mary Wortley Montagu," from *The Correspondence of Alexander Pope,* edited by George Sherburn. Reprinted with permission from The Clarendon Press, Oxford.

"Letters on Mrs. Thrale's Marriage to Piozzi," from *The Portable Johnson & Boswell,* edited by Louise Kronenberger. Copyright 1947. Reprinted with permission from The Viking Press, Inc., New York.

"To West," from *The Correspondence of Gray, Walpole, West and Ashton,* edited by Dr. Paget Toynbee. Reprinted with permission of The Clarendon Press, Oxford.

"To Mr. Hogarth," from *Pineapples of Finest Flavor* by David Garrick. Copyright 1930 by The President and Fellows of Harvard College. Reprinted with permission of Harvard University Press, Cambridge.

"To the Countess of Ossory," from *Letters of Horace Walpole,* edited by Mrs. Paget Toynbee. Reprinted with permission of The Clarendon Press, Oxford.

"From her diary," from *The Diary of Fanny Burney,* edited by Lewis Gibbs. Reprinted with permission from J. M. Dent & Sons, Ltd., London, and E. P. Dutton & Co., Inc., New York.

"From her Grasmere journal," from the *Journals of Dorothy Wordsworth,* edited by E. de Selincourt. Reprinted with permission from Macmillan & Co., Ltd., London and of St. Martin's Press, Inc., New York.

"From his journal," from *The Autobiography and Journals of Benjamin Robert Haydon,* edited by Malcolm Elwin. Reprinted with permission from MacDonald & Co. (Publishers) Ltd., London.

"To the Countess of ———" and "To Lady Byron," from the book *Letters of Lord Byron,* edited by R. G. Howarth, Everyman's Library. Reprinted by permission of E. P. Dutton & Co., Inc., New York and the Everyman's Library edition of *Byron's Letters,* with permission to reprint from J. M. Dent & Sons, Ltd., London.

"To Fanny Brawne," from *The Letters of John Keats,* edited by Maurice Buxton Forman. Reprinted with permission from Oxford University Press, London.

"To John Welsh," from *Letters and Memorials of Jane Welsh Carlyle.* Copyright 1947. Reprinted with permission from Charles Scribner's Sons, New York.

"To Effie Gray (9 November 1847)," "To Effie Gray (11 November 1847)," "To Effie Gray (30 November 1847)," and "To Effie Gray's Father (5 July 1849)," from *John Ruskin and Effie Gray,* edited by Sir William James, copyright 1947 Charles Scribner's Sons. Used by permission of Charles Scribner's Sons and John Murray, Ltd., London.

"To Olivia Langdon," from *The Love Letters of Mark Twain,* edited by Dixon Wecter. Copyright 1947, 1959 by The Mark Twain Company. Reprinted by permission of Harper & Brothers, New York.

"A Correspondence," from *The Letters between Samuel Butler and E. M. A. Savage,* edited by Keynes and Hill. Reprinted with permission from Jonathan Cape Limited, London.

"To his wife (2 December 1873)" and "To his wife (8 February 1874)," from *The Letters of Sidney Lanier.* Copyright 1947. Reprinted with permission from Charles Scribner's Sons, New York.

"To his father," from *The Letters of William James,* edited by Henry James. Copyright 1948 by William James and Margaret James Porter. Reprinted by permission of Paul R. Reynolds & Son, New York.

"To his sister, Kate Hopkins," from *Further Letters of Gerard Manley Hopkins,* edited by Claude Collier Abbott. Copyright 1956, Oxford University Press. Reprinted with permission of Oxford University Press with agreement by the Society of Jesus.

"To Edmund Gosse," from *Letters and Miscellanies of Robert Louis Stevenson,* edited by Sidney Colvin. Copyright 1947 Charles Scribner's Sons. Reprinted with permission from Charles Scribner's Sons, New York.

"To Mrs. Patrick Campbell," from *Letters of James M. Barrie,* edited by Viola Meynell, copyright 1947 Lady Cynthia Asquith. Used by permission of Charles Scribner's Sons, New York and David Higham Associates, Ltd., London.

"From her diary," from Virginia Woolf: *A Writer's Diary,* edited and copyright, 1953, 1954, by Leonard Woolf. Reprinted by permission of Harcourt, Brace and Company, New York.

"To Ezra Pound," from *Selected Letters of William Carlos Williams.* Copyright 1957. Reprinted with permission from Ivan Obolensky, Inc., New York.

"To J. M. Murry," from *The Selected Letters of D. H. Lawrence,* edited by Diana Trilling. Copyright 1932 by the Estate of D. H. Lawrence. Reprinted by permission of The Viking Press, Inc., New York.

"To Mrs. Elizabeth Glendower Evans," from *The Letters of Sacco and Vanzetti*, editors Marion Denman Frankfurter & Gardner Jackson. Copyright 1928, 1956 by The Viking Press, Inc. and reprinted by their permission.

"To Mrs. Cerise Jack," from *The Letters of Sacco and Vanzetti*, editors Marion Denman Frankfurter & Gardner Jackson. Copyright 1928, 1956 by The Viking Press, Inc. and reprinted by their permission.

"To the Millay family and friends," from *Letters of Edna St. Vincent Millay*, Harper & Brothers. Copyright 1952 by Norman Millay Ellis. By permission of Norma Millay Ellis.

"From *Eimi*, a journal of a trip to Russia in 1931," from *Eimi*, copyright, 1933, by E. E. Cummings. Reprinted by permission of the author. Published by Harcourt, Brace and Company, Inc., New York.

"To Aline Bernstein," reprinted with the permission of Charles Scribner's Sons from *The Letters of Thomas Wolfe*, edited by Elizabeth Nowell, copyright © 1956 Edward C. Aswell.

"To his wife, Gweno, written from Burma, undated," from *In the Green Tree* by Alun Lewis. Reprinted with permission from George Allen & Unwin Ltd., London.

"From his Journal, *The Sign of Jonas*," from *The Sign of Jonas* by Thomas Merton, copyright 1953, by The Abbey of Our Lady of Gethsemani. Reprinted with permission from Harcourt, Brace and Company, Inc., New York.

Excerpt from *Pygmalion* by George Bernard Shaw. Reprinted with permission from the Public Trustee and The Society of Authors, London.

Selection from *Long Day's Journey into Night* by Eugene O'Neill. Copyright 1956. Reprinted with permission from the Yale University Press.

Selection from *Key Largo* by Maxwell Anderson. Copyright 1939. Reprinted by arrangement with Anderson House, Hillsdale, New York.

Excerpt from *Of Mice and Men* by John Steinbeck. Copyright 1938 by John Steinbeck. Reprinted with permission from The Viking Press, Inc., New York.

Excerpt from *The Time of Your Life* by William Saroyan, copyright, 1939, by Harcourt, Brace and Company, Inc., New York. Reprinted with permission of Harcourt, Brace and Company, Inc.

Selection from *A Streetcar Named Desire* by Tennessee Williams. Copyright 1947 by Tennessee Williams. Reprinted by permission of New Directions, Norfolk, Connecticut.

Preface

ANY ANTHOLOGY of imaginative literature welcomes all readers who love to read. But *Literature for Interpretation,* while it will serve the general reader, has in mind in particular the oral reader. While not every piece will suit every performer or every audience, the collection embraces a wide range of kinds and modes and tastes; it can be used in the classroom to supplement a textbook in interpretation, or used apart from such a textbook. Those students and teachers interested in a rationale upon which the oral expression of this literature may be based can find one considered in detail in the editors' earlier volume, *Literature as Experience,* New York, 1959.

Literature is instructive, though it works largely by indirection; but most of all, it is a delight, and reading aloud is, or ought to be, first and last a pleasure, though the pleasure may consist at first in fun and at last in wisdom. How this pleasurable instruction is to be managed varies greatly from classroom to classroom and from teacher to teacher. Hence the anthology is arranged in conventional order, beginning with prose fiction and ending with drama, beginning with the earliest authors and ending with contemporaries, to leave the teacher and the students as free as possible to proceed in their own way. The order does not mean to suggest that the pieces need be taught chronologically, nor that students ought always to begin with prose; but the order here followed seemed better than the alternatives—as, for example, organization by types, by subject or themes, or by "performance problems." The collection is inclusive enough to serve for either a single semester or quarter course, or for a course running throughout the year.

All the materials chosen are English and American. Literature in translation provides special problems in the analysis of language and style, and it seemed best in this volume to avoid it. Furthermore, the editors have made no attempt to produce a collection startling for its novelty; there is some virtue in training students in standard authors and standard selections. On the other hand, there are pieces which do not often appear in a general anthology, and it is hoped that students will be encouraged to increase the range of their tastes. All the pieces, however, can yield pleasure in oral performance.

The stories in the collection begin with one by Hawthorne, who represents a strong moral vein in the history of American fiction, and conclude with one by Truman Capote, whose "A Christmas Memory," besides being a memorable story, may well serve readers who are asked to perform at the Christmas season. The stories in between these two range from high to low in tone, from serious to comic; there is even a tale of mystery. There are stories in which symbolism plays a heavy part; there are stories in which the symbolism, where it exists at all, is transparent. There are various points of view represented, and there is a variety of kinds of characterization. Texture ranges from the loose nonsense-language of Archibald Marshall to the meticulous detail of Henry James.

Among the poems, American poetry of earlier centuries is represented somewhat more fully than is usual in interpretation books; the same is true of sixteenth- and seventeenth-century English poetry. In the expectation that teachers may wish to study a few writers in closer detail, we have included a number of poems by Keats, Dickinson, Robinson, Frost, Auden, and certain others. There are ballads, sonnets, religious and dramatic lyrics, odes, narratives, and comic poems—many types, indeed, in a variety of levels of difficulty.

The drama is represented only by scenes from plays, since to include whole play texts would mean a volume of greater proportions than now seems possible. It is true that excerpts are not the best vehicle for instructing students in dramatic structure, and doubtless students should be urged to find the whole play text whenever possible and to put the excerpt in its proper context before settling on a final interpretation. Nevertheless, most of the scenes chosen have a certain "wholeness" which makes them useful as assignments in the interpretation of dramatic literature. Once again, the selections have been chosen with reference to diversities of interests among both students and teachers. There are scenes for women and scenes for men, and of course the majority of the scenes may be read without any particular reference to the sex of the reader. The plays range from comedy to satire to tragedy; from poetic and lyric dialogue to realistic prose. There are scenes from both traditional and modern poetic plays for those who wish to compare modes.

Finally, something should be said of that section of the anthology which seems least customary—the section made up of letters and selections from diaries. Those letter writers who endear themselves most to readers and whose reputations stand principally on their abilities as letter writers (Lady Mary Wortley Montagu, for example, or Horace Walpole) are those whose correspondence is characterized by wit and a taste for gossip, occasionally by imprudence or even indiscretion, and now and then by some painful intimacy. What is said in a letter is to be understood not only in the light of the character of the writer, but in the light of his relation to the correspondent. The manner in which the writer approaches the receiver of the letter is modified to meet the receiver's age, temperament, sex, and so forth. When William James addresses letters to his wife, to his children, tc his colleagues, he alters his style and content to suit their interests and also to suit his own interest in them. Hence the characterization of a writer of letters becomes an extraordinarily rich exercise for the interpreter. Many of the letters represented here come from the golden age of English letter writing—somewhere between 1750 and 1850, when the improvement of roads and the establishment of mail routes opened up the possibilities of a somewhat more rapid exchange of letters. In that day, writers still found time for the elegance, grace, and courtesy which made for the well-expressed letter; yet these writers had a reputation for honesty and humor, two remarkable virtues which, when coupled with an elegance of style, are sure to make for excellence. The period from 1850 to the present is also represented extensively, to increase the range in styles and in subject matters.

The selections from diaries provide still another reader-audience relationship. Diarists are cursed with an "itch to record," and talk more or less to themselves, though some diarists dramatize their relationship with themselves by creating a fictive character to address, and frequently diaries begun in a spirit of private communion become for the writer testaments of a somewhat more public character. Compare, for example, the text of Dorothy Wordsworth's journal of her trip to Scotland with the text she prepared in answer to pleas from her friends for publication. There is significance in the generalization that the best diarists are rarely men of action; the writing of diaries is a sedentary habit cultivated by people whom one critic regards as "bores." But once the reader accepts the human condition of these bores and learns to have patience with the slow unfolding of their daily existence, he is rewarded by a gradual realization of their striking reality.

In the compilation of the anthology, Wallace A. Bacon has been responsible for the choice of poems, stories, and plays; Robert S. Breen has been responsible for the choice of letters and diaries. Both the editors concur in the suitability of the total collection for the study of interpretation, and will be interested in comments from teachers using the volume.

W. A. B.
R. S. B.

Evanston, Illinois
March, 1961

Contents

LETTERS AND DIARIES

DRAMA

It is scarce necessary to note that the highest test of any literary form conceived in the light of "poetry"—to apply that term in its largest literary sense —hangs back unpardonably from its office when it fails to lend itself to *vivâ-voce* treatment. . . . The essential property of such a form as that is to give out its finest and most numerous secrets, and to give them out most gratefully, under the closest pressure—which is of course the pressure of the attention articulately *sounded*. Let it reward as much as it will and can the soundless, the "quiet" reading, it still deplorably "muffs" its chance and its success, still trifles with the roused appetite to which it can never honestly be indifferent, by not having so arranged itself as to owe the flower of its effect to the act and process of apprehension that so beautifully asks most from it.

—Henry James
Preface to *The Golden Bowl*

PROSE FICTION

NATHANIEL HAWTHORNE

Young Goodman Brown

YOUNG GOODMAN BROWN came forth at sunset into the street at Salem village; but put his head back, after crossing the threshold, to exchange a parting kiss with his young wife. And Faith, as the wife was aptly named, thrust her own pretty head into the street, letting the wind play with the pink ribbons of her cap while she called to Goodman Brown.

"Dearest heart," whispered she, softly and rather sadly, when her lips were close to his ear, "prithee put off your journey until sunrise and sleep in your own bed to-night. A lone woman is troubled with such dreams and such thoughts that she's afeard of herself sometimes. Pray tarry with me this night, dear husband, of all nights in the year."

"My love and my Faith," replied young Goodman Brown, "of all nights in the year, this one night must I tarry away from thee. My journey, as thou callest it, forth and back again, must needs be done 'twixt now and sunrise. What, my sweet, pretty wife, dost thou doubt me already, and we but three months married?"

"Then God bless you!" said Faith, with the pink ribbons; "and may you find all well when you come back."

"Amen!" cried Goodman Brown. "Say thy prayers, dear Faith, and go to bed at dusk, and no harm will come to thee."

So they parted; and the young man pursued his way until, being about to turn the corner by the meeting-house, he looked back and saw the head of Faith still peeping after him with a melancholy air, in spite of her pink ribbons.

"Poor little Faith!" thought he, for his heart smote him. "What a wretch am I to leave her on such an errand! She talks of dreams, too. Methought as she spoke there was trouble in her face, as if a dream had warned her what work is to be done to-night. But no, no; 'twould kill her to think it. Well, she's a blessed angel on earth; and after this one night I'll cling to her skirts and follow her to heaven."

With this excellent resolve for the future, Goodman Brown felt

3

himself justified in making more haste on his present evil purpose. He had taken a dreary road, darkened by all the gloomiest trees of the forest, which barely stood aside to let the narrow path creep through, and closed immediately behind. It was all as lonely as could be; and there is this peculiarity in such a solitude, that the traveller knows not who may be concealed by the innumerable trunks and the thick boughs overhead; so that with lonely footsteps he may yet be passing through an unseen multitude.

"There may be a devilish Indian behind every tree," said Goodman Brown to himself; and he glanced fearfully behind him as he added, "What if the devil himself should be at my very elbow!"

His head being turned back, he passed a crook of the road, and, looking forward again, beheld the figure of a man, in grave and decent attire, seated at the foot of an old tree. He arose at Goodman Brown's approach and walked onward side by side with him.

"You are late, Goodman Brown," said he. "The clock of the Old South was striking as I came through Boston, and that is full fifteen minutes agone."

"Faith kept me back a while," replied the young man, with a tremor in his voice, caused by the sudden appearance of his companion, though not wholly unexpected.

It was now deep dusk in the forest, and deepest in that part of it where these two were journeying. As nearly as could be discerned, the second traveller was about fifty years old, apparently in the same rank of life as Goodman Brown, and bearing a considerable resemblance to him, though perhaps more in expression than features. Still they might have been taken for father and son. And yet, though the elder person was as simply clad as the younger, and as simple in manner too, he had an indescribable air of one who knew the world, and who would not have felt abashed at the governor's dinner table or in King William's court, were it possible that his affairs should call him thither. But the only thing about him that could be fixed upon as remarkable was his staff, which bore the likeness of a great black snake, so curiously wrought that it might almost be seen to twist and wriggle itself like a living serpent. This, of course, must have been an ocular deception, assisted by the uncertain light.

"Come, Goodman Brown," cried his fellow-traveller, "this is a dull pace for the beginning of a journey. Take my staff, if you are so soon weary."

"Friend," said the other, exchanging his slow pace for a full stop, "having kept covenant by meeting thee here, it is my purpose now to return whence I came. I have scruples touching the matter thou wot'st of."

"Sayest thou so?" replied he of the serpent, smiling apart. "Let us walk on, nevertheless, reasoning as we go; and if I convince thee not thou shalt turn back. We are but a little way in the forest yet."

"Too far! too far!" exclaimed the goodman, unconsciously resuming his walk. "My father never went into the woods on such an errand, nor his father before him. We have been a race of honest men and good Christians since the days of the martyrs; and shall I be the first of the name of Brown that ever took this path and kept——"

"Such company, thou wouldst say," observed the elder person, interpreting his pause. "Well said, Goodman Brown! I have been as well acquainted with your family as with ever a one among the Puritans; and that's no trifle to say. I helped your grandfather, the constable, when he lashed the Quaker woman so smartly through the streets of Salem; and it was I that brought your father a pitch-pine knot, kindled at my own hearth, to set fire to an Indian village, in King Philip's war. They were my good friends, both; and many a pleasant walk have we had along this path, and returned merrily after midnight. I would fain be friends with you for their sake."

"If it be as thou sayest," replied Goodman Brown, "I marvel they never spoke of these matters; or, verily, I marvel not, seeing that the least rumor of the sort would have driven them from New England. We are a people of prayer, and good works to boot, and abide no such wickedness."

"Wickedness or not," said the traveller with the twisted staff, "I have a very general acquaintance here in New England. The deacons of many a church have drunk the communion wine with me; the selectmen of divers towns make me their chairman; and a majority of the Great and General Court are firm supporters of my interest. The governor and I, too——But these are state secrets."

"Can this be so?" cried Goodman Brown, with a stare of amazement at his undisturbed companion. "Howbeit, I have nothing to do with the governor and council; they have their own ways, and are no rule for a simple husbandman like me. But, were I to go on with thee, how should I meet the eye of that good old man, our minister, at Salem village? Oh, his voice would make me tremble both Sabbath day and lecture day."

Thus far the elder traveller had listened with due gravity; but now burst into a fit of irrepressible mirth, shaking himself so violently that his snake-like staff actually seemed to wriggle in sympathy.

"Ha! ha! ha!" shouted he again and again; then composing himself, "Well, go on, Goodman Brown, go on; but, prithee, don't kill me with laughing."

"Well, then, to end the matter at once," said Goodman Brown, considerably nettled, "there is my wife, Faith. It would break her dear little heart; and I'd rather break my own."

"Nay, if that be the case," answered the other, "e'en go thy ways, Goodman Brown. I would not for twenty old women like the one hobbling before us that Faith should come to any harm."

As he spoke he pointed his staff at a female figure on the path, in whom Goodman Brown recognized a very pious and exemplary dame, who had taught him his catechism in youth, and was still his moral and spiritual adviser, jointly with the minister and Deacon Gookin.

"A marvel, truly, that Goody Cloyse should be so far in the wilderness at nightfall," said he. "But with your leave, friend, I shall take a cut through the woods until we have left this Christian woman behind. Being a stranger to you, she might ask whom I was consorting with and whither I was going."

"Be it so," said his fellow-traveller. "Betake you to the woods, and let me keep the path."

Accordingly the young man turned aside, but took care to watch his companion, who advanced softly along the road until he had come within a staff's length of the old dame. She, meanwhile, was making the best of her way, with singular speed for so aged a woman, and mumbling some indistinct words—a prayer, doubtless—as she went. The traveller put forth his staff and touched her withered neck with what seemed the serpent's tail.

"The devil!" screamed the pious old lady.

"Then Goody Cloyse knows her old friend?" observed the traveller, confronting her and leaning on his writhing stick.

"Ah, forsooth, and is it your worship indeed?" cried the good dame. "Yea, truly is it, and in the very image of my old gossip, Goodman Brown, the grandfather of the silly fellow that now is. But—would your worship believe it?—my broomstick hath strangely disappeared, stolen, as I suspect, by that unhanged witch, Goody Cory, and that, too, when I was all anointed with the juice of smallage, and cinquefoil, and wolf's bane——"

"Mingled with fine wheat and the fat of a new-born babe," said the shape of old Goodman Brown.

"Ah, your worship knows the recipe," cried the old lady, cackling aloud. "So, as I was saying, being all ready for the meeting, and no horse to ride on, I made up my mind to foot it; for they tell me there is a nice young man to be taken into communion to-night. But now your good worship will lend me your arm, and we shall be there in a twinkling."

"That can hardly be," answered her friend. "I may not spare you my arm, Goody Cloyse; but here is my staff, if you will."

So saying, he threw it down at her feet, where, perhaps, it assumed life, being one of the rods which its owner had formerly lent to the Egyptian magi. Of this fact, however, Goodman Brown could not take cognizance. He had cast up his eyes in astonishment, and, looking down again, beheld neither Goody Cloyse nor the serpentine staff, but his fellow-traveller alone, who waited for him as calmly as if nothing had happened.

"That old woman taught me my catechism," said the young man; and there was a world of meaning in this simple comment.

They continued to walk onward, while the elder traveller exhorted his companion to make good speed and persevere in the path, discoursing so aptly that his arguments seemed rather to spring up in the bosom of his auditor than to be suggested by himself. As they went, he plucked a branch of maple to serve for a walking stick, and began to strip it of the twigs and little boughs, which were wet with evening dew. The moment his fingers touched them they became strangely withered and dried up as with a week's sunshine. Thus the pair proceeded, at a good free pace, until suddenly, in a gloomy hollow of the road, Goodman Brown sat himself down on the stump of a tree and refused to go any farther.

"Friend," said he, stubbornly, "my mind is made up. Not another step will I budge on this errand. What if a wretched old woman do choose to go to the devil when I thought she was going to heaven: is that any reason why I should quit my dear Faith and go after her?"

"You will think better of this by and by," said his acquaintance, composedly. "Sit here and rest yourself a while; and when you feel like moving again, there is my staff to help you along."

Without more words, he threw his companion the maple stick, and was as speedily out of sight as if he had vanished into the deepening gloom. The young man sat a few moments by the roadside, applauding himself greatly, and thinking with how clear a conscience he should meet the minister in his morning walk, nor shrink from the eye of good old Deacon Gookin. And what calm sleep would be his that very night, which was to have been spent so wickedly, but so purely and sweetly now, in the arms of Faith! Amidst these pleasant and praiseworthy meditations, Goodman Brown heard the tramp of horses along the road, and deemed it advisable to conceal himself within the verge of the forest, conscious of the guilty purpose that had brought him thither, though now so happily turned from it.

On came the hoof tramps and the voices of the riders, two grave old voices, conversing soberly as they drew near. These mingled sounds appeared to pass along the road, within a few yards of the young man's hiding-place; but, owing doubtless to the depth of the gloom at that particular spot, neither the travellers nor their steeds were visible. Though their figures brushed the small boughs by the wayside, it could not be seen that they intercepted, even for a moment, the faint gleam from the strip of bright sky athwart which they must have passed. Goodman Brown alternately crouched and stood on tiptoe, pulling aside the branches and thrusting forth his head as far as he durst without discerning so much as a shadow. It vexed him the more, because he could have sworn, were such a thing possible, that he recognized the voices of the minister and Deacon Gookin, jogging along quietly, as they were wont to do, when bound to some ordination or ecclesiastical council. While yet within hearing, one of the riders stopped to pluck a switch.

"Of the two, reverend sir," said the voice like the deacon's, "I had rather miss an ordination dinner than to-night's meeting. They tell me that some of our community are to be here from Falmouth and beyond, and others from Connecticut and Rhode Island, besides several of the Indian powwows, who, after their fashion, know almost as much deviltry as the best of us. Moreover, there is a goodly young woman to be taken into communion."

"Mighty well, Deacon Gookin!" replied the solemn old tones of the minister. "Spur up, or we shall be late. Nothing can be done, you know, until I get on the ground."

The hoofs clattered again; and the voices, talking so strangely in the empty air, passed on through the forest, where no church had ever been gathered or solitary Christian prayed. Whither, then, could these holy men be journeying so deep into the heathen wilderness? Young Goodman Brown caught hold of a tree for support, being ready to sink down on the ground, faint and over-burdened with the heavy sickness of his heart. He looked up to the sky, doubting whether there really was a heaven above him. Yet there was the blue arch, and the stars brightening in it.

"With heaven above and Faith below, I will yet stand firm against the devil!" cried Goodman Brown.

While he still gazed upward into the deep arch of the firmament and had lifted his hands to pray, a cloud, though no wind was stirring, hurried across the zenith and hid the brightening stars. The blue sky was still visible, except directly overhead, where this black mass of cloud was sweeping swiftly northward. Aloft in the air, as if from the depths of the cloud, came a confused and doubtful sound of voices. Once the listener fancied that he could distinguish the accents of townspeople of his own, men and women, both pious and ungodly, many of whom he had met at the communion table, and had seen others rioting at the tavern. The next moment, so indistinct were the sounds, he doubted whether he had heard aught but the murmur of the old forest, whispering without a wind. Then came a stronger swell of those familiar tones, heard daily in the sunshine at Salem village, but never until now from a cloud of night. There was one voice, of a young woman, uttering lamentations, yet with an uncertain sorrow, and entreating for some favor, which, perhaps, it would grieve her to obtain; and all the unseen multitude, both saints and sinners, seemed to encourage her onward.

"Faith!" shouted Goodman Brown, in a voice of agony and desperation; and the echoes of the forest mocked him, crying, "Faith! Faith!" as if bewildered wretches were seeking her all through the wilderness.

The cry of grief, rage, and terror was yet piercing the night, when the unhappy husband held his breath for a response. There was a scream, drowned immediately in a louder murmur of voices, fading into far-off laughter, as the dark cloud swept away, leaving the clear and silent sky above Goodman Brown. But something fluttered lightly down through the air and caught on the branch of a tree. The young man seized it, and beheld a pink ribbon.

"My Faith is gone!" cried he, after one stupefied moment. "There is no good on earth; and sin is but a name. Come, devil; for to thee is this world given."

And, maddened with despair, so that he laughed loud and long, did Goodman Brown grasp his staff and set forth again, at such a rate that he seemed to fly along the forest path rather than to walk or run. The road grew wilder and drearier and more faintly traced, and vanished at length, leaving him in the heart of the dark wilderness, still rushing onward with the instinct that guides mortal man to evil. The whole forest was peopled with frightful sounds—the creaking of the trees, the howling of wild beasts, and the yell of Indians; while some-times the wind tolled like a distant church bell, and sometimes gave a broad roar around the traveller, as if all Nature were laughing him to scorn. But he was himself the chief horror of the scene, and shrank not from its other horrors.

"Ha! ha! ha!" roared Goodman Brown when the wind laughed at him. "Let us hear which will laugh loudest. Think not to frighten me with your deviltry. Come witch, come wizard, come Indian powwow, come devil himself, and here comes Goodman Brown. You may as well fear him as he fear you."

In truth, all through the haunted forest there could be nothing more frightful than the figure of Goodman Brown. On he flew among the black pines, brandishing his staff with frenzied gestures, now giving vent to an inspiration of horrid blasphemy, and now shouting forth such laughter as set all the echoes of the forest laughing like demons around him. The fiend in his own shape is less hideous than when he rages in the breast of man. Thus sped the demoniac on his course, until, quivering among the trees, he saw a red light before him, as when the felled trunks and branches of a clearing have been set on fire, and throw up their lurid blaze against the sky, at the hour of midnight. He paused, in a lull of the tempest that had driven him onward, and heard the swell of what seemed a hymn, rolling solemnly from a distance with the weight of many voices. He knew the tune; it was a familiar one in the choir of the village meeting-house. The verse died heavily away, and was lengthened by a chorus, not of human voices, but of all the sounds of the benighted wilderness pealing in awful harmony together. Good-man Brown cried out, and his cry was lost to his own ear by its unison with the cry of the desert.

In the interval of silence he stole forward until the light glared full upon his eyes. At one extremity of an open space, hemmed in by the dark wall of the forest, arose a rock, bearing some rude, natural resem-blance either to an altar or a pulpit, and surrounded by four blazing pines, their tops aflame, their stems untouched, like candles at an eve-ning meeting. The mass of foliage that had overgrown the summit of the rock was all on fire, blazing high into the night and fitfully illumi-nating the whole field. Each pendent twig and leafy festoon was in a blaze. As the red light arose and fell, a numerous congregation alter-nately shone forth, then disappeared in shadow, and again grew, as it were, out of the darkness, peopling the heart of the solitary woods at once.

"A grave and dark-clad company," quoth Goodman Brown.

In truth they were such. Among them, quivering to and fro between gloom and splendor, appeared faces that would be seen next day at the council board of the province, and others which, Sabbath after Sabbath, looked devoutly heavenward, and benignantly over the crowded pews, from the holiest pulpits in the land. Some affirm that the lady of the governor was there. At least there were high dames well known to her, and wives of honored husbands, and widows, a great multitude, and ancient maidens, all of excellent repute, and fair young girls, who trembled lest their mothers should espy them. Either the sudden gleams of light flashing over the obscure field bedazzled Goodman Brown, or he recognized a score of the church members of Salem village famous for their especial sanctity. Good old Deacon Gookin had arrived, and waited at the skirts of that venerable saint, his revered pastor. But, irreverently consorting with these grave, reputable, and pious people, these elders of the church, these chaste dames and dewy virgins, there were men of dissolute lives and women of spotted fame, wretches given over to all mean and filthy vice, and suspected even of horrid crimes. It was strange to see that the good shrank not from the wicked, nor were the sinners abashed by the saints. Scattered also among their pale-faced enemies were the Indian priests, or powwows, who had often scared their native forest with more hideous incantations than any known to English witchcraft.

"But where is Faith?" thought Goodman Brown; and, as hope came into his heart, he trembled.

Another verse of the hymn arose, a slow and mournful strain, such as the pious love, but joined to words which expressed all that our nature can conceive of sin, and darkly hinted at far more. Unfathomable to mere mortals is the lore of fiends. Verse after verse was sung; and still the chorus of the desert swelled between like the deepest tone of a mighty organ; and with the final peal of that dreadful anthem there came a sound, as if the roaring wind, the rushing streams, the howling beasts, and every other voice of the unconcerted wilderness were mingling and according with the voice of guilty man in homage to the prince of all. The four blazing pines threw up a loftier flame, and obscurely discovered shapes and visages of horror on the smoke wreaths above the impious assembly. At the same moment the fire on the rock shot redly forth and formed a glowing arch above its base, where now appeared a figure. With reverence be it spoken, the figure bore no slight similitude, both in garb and manner, to some grave divine of the New England churches.

"Bring forth the converts!" cried a voice that echoed through the field and rolled into the forest.

At the word, Goodman Brown stepped forth from the shadow of the trees and approached the congregation, with whom he felt a loathful brotherhood by the sympathy of all that was wicked in his heart. He could have well-nigh sworn that the shape of his own dead father beckoned him to advance, looking downward from a smoke wreath, while a woman, with dim features of despair, threw out her hand to warn him back. Was it his mother? But he had no power to retreat one step, nor to resist, even in thought, when the minister and good old Deacon Gookin seized his arms and led him to the blazing rock. Thither came also the slender form of a veiled female, led between Goody Cloyse, that pious teacher of the catechism, and Martha Carrier, who had received the devil's promise to be queen of hell. A rampant hag was she. And there stood the proselytes beneath the canopy of fire.

"Welcome, my children," said the dark figure, "to the communion of your race. Ye have found thus young your nature and your destiny. My children, look behind you!"

They turned; and flashing forth, as it were, in a sheet of flame, the fiend worshippers were seen; the smile of welcome gleamed darkly on every visage.

"There," resumed the sable form, "are all whom ye have reverenced from youth. Ye deemed them holier than yourselves, and shrank from your own sin, contrasting it with their lives of righteousness and prayerful aspirations heavenward. Yet here are they all in my worshipping assembly. This night it shall be granted you to know their secret deeds: how hoary-bearded elders of the church have whispered wanton words to the young maids of their households; how many a woman, eager for widows' weeds, has given her husband a drink at bedtime and let him sleep his last sleep in her bosom; how beardless youths have made haste to inherit their fathers' wealth; and how fair damsels—blush not, sweet ones—have dug little graves in the garden, and bidden me, the sole guest, to an infant's funeral. By the sympathy of your human hearts for sin ye shall scent out all the places—whether in church, bed-chamber, street, field, or forest—where crime has been committed, and shall exult to behold the whole earth one stain of guilt, one mighty blood spot. Far more than this. It shall be yours to penetrate, in every bosom, the deep mystery of sin, the fountain of all wicked arts, and which inexhaustibly supplies more evil impulses than human power—than my power at its utmost—can make manifest in deeds. And now, my children, look upon each other."

They did so; and, by the blaze of the hell-kindled torches, the wretched man beheld his Faith, and the wife her husband, trembling before that unhallowed altar.

"Lo, there ye stand, my children," said the figure, in a deep and solemn tone, almost sad with its despairing awfulness, as if his once angelic nature could yet mourn for our miserable race. "Depending upon one another's hearts, ye had still hoped that virtue were not all a dream. Now are ye undeceived. Evil is the nature of mankind. Evil must be your only happiness. Welcome again, my children, to the communion of your race."

"Welcome," repeated the fiend worshippers, in one cry of despair and triumph.

And there they stood, the only pair, as it seemed, who were yet hesitating on the verge of wickedness in this dark world. A basin was hollowed, naturally, in the rock. Did it contain water, reddened by the lurid light? or was it blood? or, perchance, a liquid flame? Herein did the shape of evil dip his hand and prepare to lay the mark of baptism upon their foreheads, that they might be partakers of the mystery of sin, more conscious of the secret guilt of others, both in deed and thought, than they could now be of their own. The husband cast one look at his pale wife, and Faith at him. What polluted wretches would the next glance show them to each other, shuddering alike at what they disclosed and what they saw!

"Faith! Faith!" cried the husband, "look up to heaven, and resist the wicked one."

Whether Faith obeyed he knew not. Hardly had he spoken when he found himself amid calm night and solitude, listening to a roar of the wind which died heavily away through the forest. He staggered against the rock, and felt it chill and damp; while a hanging twig, that had been all on fire, besprinkled his cheek with the coldest dew.

The next morning young Goodman Brown came slowly into the street of Salem village, staring around him like a bewildered man. The good old minister was taking a walk along the graveyard to get an appetite for breakfast and meditate his sermon, and bestowed a blessing, as he passed, on Goodman Brown. He shrank from the venerable saint as if to avoid an anathema. Old Deacon Gookin was at domestic worship, and the holy words of his prayer were heard through the open window. "What God doth the wizard pray to?" quoth Goodman Brown. Goody Cloyse, that excellent old Christian, stood in the early sunshine at her own lattice, catechizing a little girl who had brought her a pint of morning's milk. Goodman Brown snatched away the child as from the grasp of the fiend himself. Turning the corner by the meeting-house, he spied the head of Faith, with the pink ribbons, gazing anxiously forth, and bursting into such joy at sight of him that she skipped along the street and almost kissed her husband before the whole village. But Goodman Brown looked sternly and sadly into her face, and passed on without a greeting.

Had Goodman Brown fallen asleep in the forest and only dreamed a wild dream of a witch-meeting?

Be it so if you will; but, alas! it was a dream of evil omen for young Goodman Brown. A stern, a sad, a darkly meditative, a distrustful, if not a desperate man did he become from the night of that fearful dream. On the Sabbath day, when the congregation were singing a holy psalm, he could not listen because an anthem of sin rushed loudly upon his ear and drowned all the blessed strain. When the minister spoke from the pulpit with power and fervid eloquence, and, with his hand on the open Bible, of the sacred truth of our religion, and of saint-like lives and triumphant deaths, and of future bliss or misery unutterable, then did Goodman Brown turn pale, dreading lest the roof should thunder down upon the gray blasphemer and his hearers. Often, awaking suddenly at midnight, he shrank from the bosom of Faith; and at morning or eventide, when the family knelt down at prayer, he scowled and muttered to himself, and gazed sternly at his wife, and turned away. And when he had lived long, and was borne to his grave a hoary corpse, followed by Faith, an aged woman, and children and grandchildren, a goodly procession, besides neighbors not a few, they carved no hopeful verse upon his tombstone, for his dying hour was gloom.

HENRY JAMES

The Real Thing

I

WHEN THE PORTER'S WIFE, who used to answer the house-bell, announced "A gentleman and a lady, sir," I had, as I often had in those days—the wish being father to the thought—an immediate vision of sitters. Sitters my visitors in this case proved to be; but not in the sense I should have preferred. There was nothing at first however to indicate that they mightn't have come for a portrait. The gentleman, a man of fifty, very high and very straight, with a moustache slightly grizzled and a dark grey walking-coat admirably fitted, both of which I noted professionally—I don't mean as a barber or yet as a tailor—would have struck me as a celebrity if celebrities often were striking. It was a truth of which I had for some time been conscious that a figure with a good deal of frontage was, as one might say, almost never a public institution. A glance at the lady helped to remind me of this paradoxical law: she also looked too distinguished to be a "personality." Moreover one would scarcely come across two variations together.

Neither of the pair immediately spoke—they only prolonged the preliminary gaze suggesting that each wished to give the other a chance. They were visibly shy; they stood there letting me take them in—which, as I afterwards perceived, was the most practical thing they could have done. In this way their embarrassment served their cause. I had seen people painfully reluctant to mention that they desired anything so gross as to be represented on canvas; but the scruples of my new friends appeared almost insurmountable. Yet the gentleman might have said "I should like a portrait of my wife," and the lady might have said "I should like a portrait of my husband." Perhaps they weren't husband and wife—this naturally would make the matter more delicate. Perhaps they wished to be done together—in which case they ought to have brought a third person to break the news.

"We come from Mr. Rivet," the lady finally said with a dim smile that had the effect of a moist sponge passed over a "sunk" piece of painting, as well as of a vague allusion to vanished beauty. She was as tall and straight, in her degree, as her companion, and with ten years less to carry. She looked as sad as a woman could look whose face was not charged with expression; that is her tinted oval mask showed waste as an exposed surface shows friction. The hand of time had played over her freely, but to an effect of elimination. She was slim and stiff, and so well-dressed, in dark blue cloth, with lappets and pockets and buttons, that it was clear she employed the same tailor as her husband. The couple had an indefinable air of prosperous thrift—they evidently got a good deal of luxury for their money. If I was to be one of their luxuries it would behoove me to consider my terms.

"Ah Claude Rivet recommended me?" I echoed; and I added that it was very kind of him, though I could reflect that, as he only painted landscape, this wasn't a sacrifice.

The lady looked very hard at the gentleman, and the gentleman looked round the room. Then staring at the floor a moment and stroking his moustache, he rested his pleasant eyes on me with the remark: "He said you were the right one."

"I try to be, when people want to sit."

"Yes, we should like to," said the lady anxiously.

"Do you mean together?"

My visitors exchanged a glance. "If you could do anything with *me* I suppose it would be double," the gentleman stammered.

"Oh yes, there's naturally a higher charge for two figures than for one."

"We should like to make it pay," the husband confessed.

"That's very good of you," I returned, appreciating so unwonted a sympathy—for I supposed he meant pay the artist.

A sense of strangeness seemed to dawn on the lady. "We mean for the illustrations—Mr. Rivet said you might put one in."

"Put in—an illustration?" I was equally confused.

"Sketch her off, you know," said the gentleman, colouring.

It was only then that I understood the service Claude Rivet had rendered me; he had told them how I worked in black-and-white, for magazines, for storybooks, for sketches of contemporary life, and consequently had copious employment for models. These things were true, but it was not less true—I may confess it now; whether because the aspiration was to lead to everything or to nothing I leave the reader to guess—that I couldn't get the honours, to say nothing of the emoluments, of a great painter of portraits out of my head. My "illustrations" were my pot-boilers; I looked to a different branch of art—far and away the most interesting it had always seemed to me—to perpetuate my fame. There was no shame in looking to it also to make my fortune; but that fortune was by so much further from being made from the moment my visitors wished to be "done" for nothing. I was disappointed; for in the pictorial sense I had immediately *seen* them. I had seized their type—I had already settled what I would do with it. Something that wouldn't absolutely have pleased them, I afterwards reflected.

"Ah you're—you're—a?" I began as soon as I had mastered my surprise. I couldn't bring out the dingy word "models": it seemed so little to fit the case.

"We haven't had much practice," said the lady.

"We've got to *do* something, and we've thought that an artist in your line might perhaps make something of us," her husband threw off. He further mentioned that they didn't know many artists and that they had gone first, on the off-chance—he painted views of course, but sometimes put in figures; perhaps I remembered—to Mr. Rivet, whom they had met a few years before at a place in Norfolk where he was sketching.

"We used to sketch a little ourselves," the lady hinted.

"It's very awkward, but we absolutely *must* do something," her husband went on.

"Of course we're not so *very* young," she admitted with a wan smile.

With the remark that I might as well know something more about them the husband had handed me a card extracted from a neat new pocket-book—their appurtenances were all of the freshest—and inscribed with the words "Major Monarch." Impressive as these words were they didn't carry my knowledge much further; but my visitor presently added: "I've left the army and we've had the misfortune to lose our money. In fact our means are dreadfully small."

"It's awfully trying—a regular strain," said Mrs. Monarch.

They evidently wished to be discreet—to take care not to swagger because they were gentlefolk. I felt them willing to recognise this as something of a drawback, at the same time that I guessed at an underlying sense—their consolation in adversity—that they *had* their points. They certainly had; but these advantages struck me as preponderantly social; such for instance as would help to make a drawing-room look well. However, a drawing-room was always, or ought to be, a picture.

In consequence of his wife's allusion to their age Major Monarch observed: "Naturally it's more for the figure that we thought of going in. We can still hold ourselves up." On the instant I saw that the figure was indeed their strong point. His "naturally" didn't sound vain, but it lighted up the question. "*She* has the best one," he continued, nodding at his wife with a pleasant after-dinner absence of circumlocution. I could only reply, as if we were in fact sitting over our wine, that this didn't prevent his own from being very good; which led him in turn to make answer: "We thought that if you ever have to do people like us we might be something like it. *She* particularly—for a lady in a book, you know."

I was so amused by them that, to get more of it, I did my best to take their point of view; and though it was an embarrassment to find myself appraising physically, as if they were animals on hire or useful blacks, a pair whom I should have expected to meet only in one of the relations in which criticism is tacit, I looked at Mrs. Monarch judicially enough to be able to exclaim after a moment with conviction: "Oh yes, a lady in a book!" She was singularly like a bad illustration.

"We'll stand up, if you like," said the Major; and he raised himself before me with a really grand air.

I could take his measure at a glance—he was six feet two and a perfect gentleman. It would have paid any club in process of formation and in want of a stamp to engage him at a salary to stand in the principal window. What struck me at once was that in coming to me they had rather missed their vocation; they could surely have been turned to better account for advertising purposes. I couldn't of course see the thing in detail, but I could see them make somebody's fortune—I don't mean their own. There was something in them for a waistcoat-maker, an hotel-keeper or a soap-vendor. I could imagine "We always use it" pinned on their bosoms with the greatest effect; I had a vision of the brilliancy with which they would launch a table d'hôte.

Mrs. Monarch sat still, not from pride but from shyness, and presently her husband said to her: "Get up, my dear, and show how smart you are." She obeyed, but she had no need to get up to show it. She walked to the end of the studio and then came back blushing, her fluttered eyes on the partner of her appeal. I was reminded of an incident I had accidentally had a glimpse of in Paris—being with a friend there, a dramatist about to produce a play, when an actress came to him to ask to be entrusted with a part. She went through her paces before him, walked up and down as Mrs. Monarch was doing. Mrs. Monarch did it quite as well, but I abstained from applauding. It was very odd to see such people apply for such poor pay. She looked as if she had ten thousand a year. Her husband had used the word that described her: she was in the London current jargon essentially and typically "smart." Her figure was, in the same order of ideas, conspicuously and irreproachably "good." For a woman of her age her waist was surprisingly small; her elbow moreover had the orthodox crook. She held her head at the conventional angle, but why did she come to *me*? She ought to have tried on jackets at a big shop. I feared my visitors were not only destitute but "artistic"—which would be a great complication. When she sat down again I thanked her, observing that what a draughtsman most valued in his model was the faculty of keeping quiet.

"Oh *she* can keep quiet," said Major Monarch. Then he added jocosely: "I've always kept her quiet."

"I'm not a nasty fidget, am I?" It was going to wring tears from me, I felt, the way she hid her head, ostrich-like, in the other broad bosom.

The owner of this expanse addressed his answer to me. "Perhaps it isn't out of place to mention—because we ought to be quite business-like, oughtn't we?—that when I married her she was known as the Beautiful Statue."

"Oh dear!" said Mrs. Monarch ruefully.

"Of course I should want a certain amount of expression," I rejoined.

"Of *course!*"—and I had never heard such unanimity.

"And then I suppose you know that you'll get awfully tired."

"Oh we *never* get tired!" they eagerly cried.

"Have you had any kind of practice?"

They hesitated—they looked at each other. "We've been photographed—*immensely,*" said Mrs. Monarch.

"She means the fellows have asked us themselves," added the Major.

"I see—because you're so good-looking."

"I don't know what they thought, but they were always after us."

"We always got our photographs for nothing," smiled Mrs. Monarch.

"We might have brought some, my dear," her husband remarked.

"I'm not sure we have any left. We've given quantities away," she explained to me.

"With our autographs and that sort of thing," said the Major.

"Are they to be got in the shops?" I enquired as a harmless pleasantry.

"Oh, yes, *hers*—they used to be."

"Not now," said Mrs. Monarch with her eyes on the floor.

II

I could fancy the "sort of thing" they put on the presentation copies of their photographs, and I was sure they wrote a beautiful hand. It was odd how quickly I was sure of everything that concerned them. If they were now so poor as to have to earn shillings and pence they could never have had much of a margin. Their good looks had been their capital, and they had good-humouredly made the most of the career that this resource marked out for them. It was in their faces, the blankness, the deep intellectual repose of the twenty years of country-house visiting that had given them pleasant intonations. I could see the sunny drawing-rooms, sprinkled with periodicals she didn't read, in which Mrs. Monarch had continuously sat; I could see the wet shrubberies in which she had walked, equipped to admiration for either exercise. I could see the rich covers the Major had helped to shoot and the wonderful garments in which, late at night, he repaired to the smoking-room to talk about them. I could imagine their leggings and waterproofs, their knowing tweeds and rugs, their rolls of sticks and cases of tackle and neat umbrellas; and I could evoke the exact appearance of their servants and the compact variety of their luggage on the platforms of country stations.

They gave small tips, but they were liked; they didn't do anything themselves, but they were welcome. They looked so well everywhere; they gratified the general relish for stature, complexion and "form." They knew it without fatuity or vulgarity, and they respected themselves in consequence. They weren't superficial; they were thorough and kept themselves up—it had been their line. People with such a taste for activity had to have some line. I could feel how even in a dull house they could have been counted on for the joy of life. At present something had happened—it didn't matter what, their little income had grown less, it had grown least—and they had to do something for pocket-money. Their friends could like them, I made out, without liking to support them. There was something about them that represented credit—their clothes, their manners, their type; but if credit is a large empty pocket in which an occasional chink reverberates, the chink at least must be audible. What they wanted of me was to help to make it so. Fortunately they had no children—I soon divined that. They would also perhaps wish our relations to be kept secret: this was why it was "for the figure"—the reproduction of the face would betray them.

I liked them—I felt, quite as their friends must have done—they were so simple; and I had no objection to them if they would suit. But somehow with all their perfections I didn't easily believe in them. After all they were amateurs, and the ruling passion of my life was the detestation of the amateur. Combined with this was another perversity—an innate preference for the represented subject over the real one: the defect of the real one was so apt to be a lack of representation. I liked things that appeared; then one was sure. Whether they *were* or not was a subordinate and almost always a profitless question. There were other considerations, the first of which was that I already had two or three recruits in use, notably a young person with big feet, in alpaca, from Kilburn, who for a couple of years had come to me regularly for my illustrations and with whom I was still—perhaps ignobly—satisfied. I frankly explained to my visitors how the case stood, but they had taken more precautions than I supposed. They had reasoned out their opportunity, for Claude Rivet had told them of the projected *édition de luxe* of one of the writers of our day—the rarest of the novelists—who, long neglected by the multitudinous vulgar and dearly prized by the attentive (need I mention Philip Vincent?) had had the happy fortune of seeing, late in life, the dawn and then the full light of a higher criticism; an estimate in which on the part of the public there was something really of expiation. The edition preparing, planned by a publisher of taste, was practically an act of high reparation; the wood-cuts with which it was to be enriched were the homage of English art to one of the most independent representatives of English letters. Major and Mrs. Monarch confessed to me they had hoped I might be able to work *them* into my branch of the enterprise. They knew I was to do the first of the books, "Rutland Ramsay," but I had to make clear to them that my participation in the rest of the affair—this first book was to be a test— must depend on the satisfaction I should give. If this should be limited my employers would drop me with scarce common forms. It was therefore a crisis for me, and naturally I was making special preparations, looking about for new people, should they be necessary, and securing the best types. I admitted however that I should like to settle down to two or three good models who would do for everything.

"Should we have often to—a—put on special clothes?" Mrs. Monarch timidly demanded.

"Dear yes—that's half the business."

"And should we be expected to supply our own costumes?"

"Oh no; I've got a lot of things. A painter's models put on—or put off—anything he likes."

"And you mean—a—the same?"

"The same?"

Mrs. Monarch looked at her husband again.

"Oh she was just wondering," he explained, "if the costumes are in *general* use." I had to confess that they were, and I mentioned further that some of them—I had a lot of genuine greasy last-century things— had served their time, a hundred years ago, on living world-stained men and women; on figures not perhaps so far removed, in that vanished world, from *their* type, the Monarchs', *quoi!* of a breeched and bewigged age. "We'll put on anything that *fits*," said the Major.

"Oh I arrange that—they fit in the pictures."

"I'm afraid I should do better for the modern books. I'd come as you like," said Mrs. Monarch.

"She has got a lot of clothes at home: they might do for contemporary life," her husband continued.

"Oh I can fancy scenes in which you'd be quite natural." And indeed I could see the slipshod rearrangements of stale properties—the stories I tried to produce pictures for without the exasperation of reading them—whose sandy tracts the good lady might help to people. But I had to return to the fact that for this sort of work—the daily mechanical grind—I was already equipped: the people I was working with were fully adequate.

"We only thought we might be more like *some* characters," said Mrs. Monarch mildly, getting up.

Her husband also rose; he stood looking at me with a dim wistfulness that was touching in so fine a man. "Wouldn't it be rather a pull sometimes to have—a—to have—?" He hung fire; he wanted me to help him by phrasing what he meant. But I couldn't—I didn't know. So he brought it out awkwardly: "The *real* thing; a gentleman, you know, or a lady." I was quite ready to give a general assent—I admitted that there was a great deal in that. This encouraged Major Monarch to say, following up his appeal with an unacted gulp: "It's awfully hard—we've tried everything." The gulp was communicative; it proved too much for his wife. Before I knew it Mrs. Monarch had dropped again upon a divan and burst into tears. Her husband sat down beside her, holding one of her hands; whereupon she quickly dried her eyes with the other, while I felt embarrassed as she looked up at me. "There isn't a confounded job I haven't applied for—waited for—prayed for. You can fancy we'd be pretty bad first. Secretaryships and that sort of thing? You might as well ask for a peerage. I'd be *anything*—I'm strong; a messenger or a coalheaver. I'd put on a gold-laced cap and open carriage-doors in front of the haberdasher's; I'd hang about a station to carry portmanteaux; I'd be a postman. But they won't *look* at you; there are thousands as good as yourself already on the ground. *Gentlemen,* poor beggars, who've drunk their wine, who've kept their hunters!"

I was as reassuring as I knew how to be, and my visitors were presently on their feet again while, for the experiment, we agreed on an hour. We were discussing it when the door opened and Miss Churm came in with a wet umbrella. Miss Churm had to take the omnibus to Maida Vale and then walk half a mile. She looked a trifle blowsy and slightly splashed. I scarcely ever saw her come in without thinking afresh how odd it was that, being so little in herself, she should yet be so much in others. She was a meagre little Miss Churm, but was such an ample heroine of romance. She was only a freckled cockney, but she could represent everything, from a fine lady to a shepherdess; she had the faculty as she might have had a fine voice or long hair. She couldn't spell and she loved beer, but she had two or three "points," and practice, and a knack, and mother-wit, and a whimsical sensibility, and a love of the theatre, and seven sisters, and not an ounce of respect, especially for the *h*. The first thing my visitors saw was that her umbrella was wet, and in their spotless perfection they visibly winced at it. The rain had come on since their arrival.

"I'm all in a soak; there *was* a mess of people in the 'bus. I wish you lived near a stytion," said Miss Churm. I requested her to get ready as quickly as possible, and she passed into the room in which she always changed her dress. But before going out she asked me what she was to get into this time.

"It's the Russian princess, don't you know?" I answered; "the one with the 'golden eyes,' in black velvet, for the long thing in the *Cheapside*."

"Golden eyes? I *say!*" cried Miss Churm, while my companions watched her with intensity as she withdrew. She always arranged herself, when she was late, before I could turn round; and I kept my visitors a little on purpose, so that they might get an idea, from seeing her, what would be expected of themselves. I mentioned that she was quite my notion of an excellent model—she was really very clever.

"Do you think she looks like a Russian princess?" Major Monarch asked with lurking alarm.

"When I make her, yes."

"Oh if you have to *make* her—!" he reasoned, not without point.

"That's the most you can ask. There are so many who are not makeable."

"Well now, *here's* a lady"—and with a persuasive smile he passed his arm into his wife's—"who's already made!"

"Oh I'm not a Russian princess," Mrs. Monarch protested a little coldly. I could see she had known some and didn't like them. There at once was a complication of a kind I never had to fear with Miss Churm.

This young lady came back in black velvet—the gown was rather rusty and very low on her lean shoulders—and with a Japanese fan in her red hands. I reminded her that in the scene I was doing she had to look over some one's head. "I forget whose it is; but it doesn't matter. Just look over a head."

"I'd rather look over a stove," said Miss Churm; and she took her station near the fire. She fell into position, settled herself into a tall attitude, gave a certain backward inclination to her head and a certain forward droop to her fan, and looked, at least to my prejudiced sense, distinguished and charming, foreign and dangerous. We left her looking so while I went downstairs with Major and Mrs. Monarch.

"I believe I could come about as near it as that," said Mrs. Monarch.

"Oh you think she's shabby, but you must allow for the alchemy of art."

However, they went off with an evident increase of comfort founded on their demonstrable advantage in being the real thing. I could fancy them shuddering over Miss Churm. She was very droll about them when I went back, for I told her what they wanted.

"Well, if *she* can sit I'll tyke to book-keeping," said my model.

"She's very ladylike," I replied as an innocent form of aggravation.

"So much of the worse for *you*. That means she can't turn round."

"She'll do for the fashionable novels."

"Oh yes, she'll *do* for them!" my model humourously declared. "Ain't they bad enough without her?" I had often sociably denounced them to Miss Churm.

III

It was for the elucidation of a mystery in one of these works that I first tried Mrs. Monarch. Her husband came with her, to be useful if necessary—it was sufficiently clear that as a general thing he would prefer to come with her. At first I wondered if this were for "propriety's" sake—if he were going to be jealous and meddling. The idea was too tiresome, and if it had been confirmed it would speedily have brought our acquaintance to a close. But I soon saw there was nothing in it and that if he accompanied Mrs. Monarch it was—in addition to the chance of being wanted—simply because he had nothing else to do. When they were separate his occupation was gone and they never *had* been separate. I judged rightly that in their awkward situation their close union was their main comfort and that this union had no weak spot. It was a real marriage, an encouragement to the hesitating, a nut for pessimists to crack. Their address was humble—I remember afterwards thinking it had been the only thing about them that was really professional—and I could fancy the lamentable lodgings in which the Major would have been left alone. He could sit there more or less grimly with his wife—he couldn't sit there anyhow without her.

He had too much tact to try and make himself agreeable when he couldn't be useful; so when I was too absorbed in my work to talk he simply sat and waited. But I liked to hear him talk—it made my work, when not interrupting it, less mechanical, less special. To listen to him was to combine the excitement of going out with the economy of staying at home. There was only one hindrance—that I seemed not to know any of the people this brilliant couple had known. I think he wondered extremely, during the term of our intercourse, whom the deuce I *did* know. He hadn't a stray sixpence of an idea to fumble for, so we didn't spin it very fine; we confined ourselves to questions of leather and even of liquor—saddlers and breeches-makers and how to get excellent claret cheap—and matters like "good trains" and the habits of small game. His lore on these last subjects was astonishing—he managed to interweave the station-master with the ornithologist. When he couldn't talk about greater things he could talk cheerfully about smaller, and since I couldn't accompany him into reminiscences of the fashionable world he could lower the conversation without a visible effort to my level.

So earnest a desire to please was touching in a man who could so easily have knocked one down. He looked after the fire and had an opinion on the draught of the stove without my asking him, and I could see that he thought many of my arrangements not half knowing. I remember telling him that if I were only rich I'd offer him a salary to come and teach me how to live. Sometimes he gave a random sigh of which the essence might have been: "Give me even such a bare old barrack as *this*, and I'd do something with it!" When I wanted to use him he came alone; which was an illustration of the superior courage of women. His wife could bear her solitary second floor, and she was in general more discreet; showing by various small reserves that she was alive to the propriety of keeping our relations markedly professional—not letting them slide into sociability. She wished it to remain clear that she and the Major were employed, not cultivated, and if she approved of me as a superior, who could be kept in his place, she never thought me quite good enough for an equal.

She sat with great intensity, giving the whole of her mind to it, and was capable of remaining for an hour almost as motionless as before a photographer's lens. I could see she had been photographed often, but somehow the very habit that made her good for that purpose unfitted her for mine. At first I was extremely pleased with her ladylike air, and it was a satisfaction, on coming to follow her lines, to see how good they were and how far they could lead the pencil. But after a little skirmishing I began to find her too insurmountably stiff; do what I would with it my drawing looked like a photograph or a copy of a photograph. Her figure had no variety of expression— she herself had no sense of variety. You may say that this was my business and was only a question of placing her. Yet I placed her in every conceivable position and she managed to obliterate their differences. She was always a lady certainly, and into the bargain was always the same lady. She was the real thing, but always the same thing. There were moments when I rather writhed under the serenity of her confidence that she *was* the real thing. All her dealings with me and all her husband's were an implication that this was lucky for *me*. Meanwhile I found myself trying to invent types that approached her own, instead of making her own transform itself—in the clever way that was not impossible for instance to poor Miss Churm. Arrange as I would and take the precautions I would, she always came out, in my pictures, too tall—landing me in the dilemma of having represented a fascinating woman as seven feet high, which (out of respect perhaps to my own very much scantier inches) was far from my idea of such a personage.

The case was worse with the Major—nothing I could do would keep *him* down, so that he became useful only for the representation of brawny giants. I adored variety and range, I cherished human accidents, the illustrative note; I wanted to characterise closely, and the thing in the world I most hated was the danger of being ridden by a type. I had quarrelled with some of my friends about it; I had parted company with them for maintaining that one *had* to be, and that if the type was beautiful—witness Raphael and Leonardo—the servitude was only a gain. I was neither Leonardo nor Raphael—I might only be a presumptuous young modern searcher; but I held that everything was to be sacrificed sooner than character. When they claimed that the obsessional form could easily *be* character I retorted, perhaps superficially, "Whose?" It couldn't be everybody's—it might end in being nobody's.

After I had drawn Mrs. Monarch a dozen times I felt surer even than before that the value of such a model as Miss Churm resided precisely in the fact that she had no positive stamp, combined of course with the other fact that what she did have was a curious and inexplicable talent for imitation. Her usual appearance was like a curtain which she could draw up at request for a capital performance. This performance was simply suggestive; but it was a word to the wise—it was vivid and pretty. Sometimes even I thought it, though she was plain herself, too insipidly pretty; I made it a reproach to her that the figures drawn from her were monotonously (*bêtement,* as we used to say) graceful. Nothing made her more angry; it was so much her pride to feel she could sit for characters that had nothing in common with each other. She would accuse me at such moments of taking away her "reputytion."

It suffered a certain shrinkage, this queer quantity, from the repeated visits of my new friends. Miss Churm was greatly in demand, never in want of employment, so I had no scruple in putting her off occasionally, to try them more at my ease. It was certainly amusing at first to do the real thing—it was amusing to do Major Monarch's trousers. They *were* the real thing, even if he did come out colossal. It was amusing to do his wife's black hair—it was so mathematically neat —and the particular "smart" tension of her tight stays. She lent herself especially to positions in which the face was somewhat averted or blurred; she abounded in ladylike back views and *profils perdus.* When she stood erect she took naturally one of the attitudes in which court-painters represent queens and princesses; so that I found myself wondering whether, to draw out this accomplishment, I couldn't get the editor of the *Cheapside* to publish a really royal romance, "A Tale of Buckingham Palace." Sometimes however the real thing and the make-believe came into contact; by which I mean that Miss Churm, keeping an appointment or coming to make one on days when I had much work in hand, encountered her invidious rivals. The encounter was not on their part, for they noticed her no more than if she had been the housemaid; not from intentional loftiness, but simply because as yet, professionally, they didn't know how to fraternise, as I could imagine they would have liked—or at least that the Major would. They couldn't talk about the omnibus—they always walked; and they didn't know what else to try—she wasn't interested in good trains or cheap claret. Besides, they must have felt—in the air—that she was amused at them, secretly derisive of their ever knowing how. She wasn't a person to conceal the limits of her faith if she had had a chance to show them.

On the other hand Mrs. Monarch didn't think her tidy; for why else did she take pains to say to me—it was going out of the way, for Mrs. Monarch—that she didn't like dirty women?

One day when my young lady happened to be present with my other sitters—she even dropped in, when it was convenient, for a chat—I asked her to be so good as to lend a hand in getting tea, a service with which she was familiar and which was one of a class that, living as I did in a small way, with slender domestic resources, I often appealed to my models to render. They liked to lay hands on my property, to break the sitting, and sometimes the china—it made them feel Bohemian. The next time I saw Miss Churm after this incident she surprised me greatly by making a scene about it—she accused me of having wished to humiliate her. She hadn't resented the outrage at the time, but had seemed obliging and amused, enjoying the comedy of asking Mrs. Monarch, who sat vague and silent, whether she would have cream and sugar, and putting an exaggerated simper into the question. She had tried intonations—as if she too wished to pass for the real thing—till I was afraid my other visitors would take offence.

Oh they were determined not to do this, and their touching patience was the measure of their great need. They would sit by the hour, uncomplaining, till I was ready to use them; they would come back on the chance of being wanted and would walk away cheerfully if it failed. I used to go to the door with them to see in what magnificent order they retreated. I tried to find other employment for them—I introduced them to several artists. But they didn't "take," for reasons I could appreciate, and I became rather anxiously aware that after such disappointments they fell back upon me with a heavier weight. They did me the honour to think me most *their* form. They weren't romantic enough for the painters, and in those days there were few serious workers in black-and-white. Besides, they had an eye to the great job I had mentioned to them—they had secretly set their hearts on supplying the right essence for my pictorial vindication of our fine novelist. They knew that for this undertaking I should want no costume-effects, none of the frippery of past ages—that it was a case in which everything would be contemporary and satirical and presumably genteel. If I could work them into it their future would be assured, for the labour would of course be long and the occupation steady.

One day Mrs. Monarch came without her husband—she explained his absence by his having had to go to the City. While she sat there in her usual relaxed majesty there came at the door a knock which I immediately recognized as the subdued appeal of a model out of work. It was followed by the entrance of a young man whom I at once saw to be a foreigner and who proved in fact an Italian acquainted with no English word but my name, which he uttered in a way that made it seem to include all others. I hadn't then visited his country, nor was I proficient in his tongue; but as he was not so meanly constituted—what Italian is?—as to depend only on that member for expression he conveyed to me, in familiar but graceful mimicry, that he was in search of exactly the employment in which the lady before me was engaged. I was not struck with him at first, and while I continued to draw I dropped few signs of interest or encouragement. He stood his ground however—not importunately, but with a dumb dog-like fidelity in his eyes that amounted to innocent impudence, the manner of a devoted servant—he might have been in the house for years—unjustly suspected. Suddenly it struck me that this very attitude and expression made a picture; whereupon I told him to sit down and wait till I should be free. There was another picture in the way he obeyed me, and I observed as I worked that there were others still in the way he looked wonderingly, with his head thrown back, about the high studio. He might have been crossing himself in Saint Peter's. Before I finished I said to myself "The fellow's a bankrupt orange-monger, but a treasure."

When Mrs. Monarch withdrew he passed across the room like a flash to open the door for her, standing there with the rapt pure gaze of the young Dante spellbound by the young Beatrice. As I never insisted, in such situations, on the blankness of the British domestic, I reflected that he had the making of a servant—and I needed one, but couldn't pay him to be only that—as well as of a model; in short I resolved to adopt my bright adventurer if he would agree to officiate in the double capacity. He jumped at my offer, and in the event my rashness—for I had really known nothing about him—wasn't brought home to me. He proved a sympathetic though a desultory ministrant, and had in a wonderful degree the *sentiment de la pose*. It was uncultivated, instinctive, a part of the happy instinct that had guided him to my door and helped him to spell out my name on the card nailed to it. He had had no other introduction to me than a guess, from the shape of my high north window, seen outside, that my place was a studio and that as a studio it would contain an artist. He had wandered to England in search of fortune, like other itinerants, and had embarked, with a partner and a small green hand-cart, on the sale of penny ices. The ices had melted away and the partner had dissolved in their train. My young man wore tight yellow trousers with reddish stripes and his name was Oronte. He was shallow but fair, and when I put him into some old clothes of my own he looked like an Englishman. He was as good as Miss Churm, who could look, when requested, like an Italian.

IV

I thought Mrs. Monarch's face slightly convulsed when, on her coming back with her husband, she found Oronte installed. It was strange to have to recognise in a scrap of a lazzarone a competitor to her magnificent Major. It was she who scented danger first, for the Major was anecdotically unconscious. But Oronte gave us tea, with a hundred eager confusions—he had never been concerned in so queer a process—and I think she thought better of me for having at last an "establishment." They saw a couple of drawings that I had made of the establishment, and Mrs. Monarch hinted that it never would have struck her he had sat for them. "Now the drawings you make from *us*, they look exactly like us," she reminded me, smiling in triumph; and I recognised that this was indeed just their defect. When I drew the Monarchs I couldn't anyhow get away from them—get into the character I wanted to represent; and I hadn't the least desire my model should be discoverable in my picture. Miss Churm never was, and Mrs. Monarch thought I hid her, very properly, because she was vulgar; whereas if she was lost it was only as the dead who go to heaven are lost—in the gain of an angel the more.

By this time I had got a certain start with "Rutland Ramsay," the first novel in the great projected series; that is I had produced a dozen drawings, several with the help of the Major and his wife, and I had sent them in for approval. My understanding with the publishers, as I have already hinted, had been that I was to be left to do my work, in this particular case, as I liked, with the whole book committed to me; but my connexion with the rest of the series was only contingent. There were moments when, frankly, it *was* a comfort to have the real thing under one's hand; for there were characters in "Rutland Ramsay" that were very much like it. There were people presumably as erect as the Major and women of as good a fashion as Mrs. Monarch. There was a great deal of country-house life—treated, it is true, in a fine fanciful ironical generalised way—and there was a considerable implication of knickerbockers and kilts. There were certain things I had to settle at the outset; such things for instance as the exact appearance of the hero and the particular bloom and figure of the heroine. The author of course gave me a lead, but there was a margin for interpretation. I took the Monarchs into my confidence, I told them frankly what I was about, I mentioned my embarrassments and alternatives. "Oh take *him!*" Mrs. Monarch murmured sweetly, looking at her husband; and "What could you want better than my wife?" the Major enquired with the comfortable candour that now prevailed between us.

I wasn't obliged to answer these remarks—I was only obliged to place my sitters. I wasn't easy in mind, and I postponed a little timidly perhaps the solving of my question. The book was a large canvas, the other figures were numerous, and I worked off at first some of the episodes in which the hero and the heroine were not concerned. When once I had set *them* up I should have to stick to them—I couldn't make my young man seven feet high in one place and five feet nine in another. I inclined on the whole to the latter measurement, though the Major more than once reminded me that *he* looked about as young as any one. It was indeed quite possible to arrange him, for the figure, so that it would have been difficult to detect his age. After the spontaneous Oronte had been with me a month, and after I had given him to understand several times over that his native exuberance would presently constitute an insurmountable barrier to our further intercourse, I waked to a sense of his heroic capacity. He was only five feet seven, but the remaining inches were latent. I tried him almost secretly at first, for I was really rather afraid of the judgement my other models would pass on such a choice. If they regarded Miss Churm as little better than a snare what would they think of the representation by a person so little the real thing as an Italian street-vendor of a protagonist formed by a public school?

If I went a little in fear of them it wasn't because they bullied me, because they had got an oppressive foothold, but because in their really pathetic decorum and mysteriously permanent newness they counted on me so intensely. I was therefore very glad when Jack Hawley came home: he was always of such good counsel. He painted badly himself, but there was no one like him for putting his finger on the place. He had been absent from England for a year; he had been somewhere—I don't remember where—to get a fresh eye. I was in a good deal of dread of any such organ, but we were old friends; he had been away for months and a sense of emptiness was creeping into my life. I hadn't dodged a missile for a year.

He came back with a fresh eye, but with the same old black velvet blouse, and the first evening he spent in my studio we smoked cigarettes till the small hours. He had done no work himself, he had only got the eye; so the field was clear for the production of my little things. He wanted to see what I had produced for the *Cheapside,* but he was disappointed in the exhibition. That at least seemed the meaning of two or three comprehensive groans which, as he lounged on my big divan, his leg folded under him, looking at my latest drawings, issued from his lips with the smoke of the cigarette.

"What's the matter with you?" I asked.

"What's the matter with *you?*"

"Nothing save that I'm mystified."

"You are indeed. You're quite off the hinge. What's the meaning of this new fad?" And he tossed me, with visible irreverence, a drawing in which I happened to have depicted both my elegant models. I asked if he didn't think it good, and he replied that it struck him as execrable, given the sort of thing I had always represented myself to him as wishing to arrive at; but I let that pass—I was so anxious to see exactly what he meant. The two figures in the picture looked colossal, but I supposed this was *not* what he meant, inasmuch as, for aught he knew to the contrary, I might have been trying for some such effect. I maintained that I was working exactly in the same way as when he last had done me the honour to tell me I might do something some day. "Well, there's a screw loose somewhere," he answered; "wait a bit and I'll discover it." I depended upon him to do so: where else was the fresh eye? But he produced at last nothing more luminous than "I don't know—I don't like your types." This was lame for a critic who had never consented to discuss with me anything but the question of execution, the direction of strokes and the mystery of values.

"In the drawings you've been looking at I think my types are very handsome."

"Oh they won't do!"

"I've been working with new models."

"I see you have. *They* won't do."

"Are you very sure of that?"

"Absolutely—they're stupid."

"You mean *I* am—for I ought to get round that."

"You *can't*—with such people. Who are they?"

I told him, so far as was necessary, and he concluded heartlessly: "Ce sont des gens qu'il faut mettre à la porte."

"You've never seen them; they're awfully good"—I flew to their defence.

"Not seen them? Why all this recent work of yours drops to pieces with them. It's all I want to see of them."

"No one else has said anything against it—the *Cheapside* people are pleased."

"Every one else is an ass, and the *Cheapside* people the biggest asses of all. Come, don't pretend at this time of day to have pretty illusions about the public, especially about publishers and editors. It's not for *such* animals you work—it's for those who know, *coloro che sanno;* so keep straight for *me* if you can't keep straight for yourself. There was a certain sort of thing you used to try for—and a very good thing it was. But this twaddle isn't *in* it." When I talked with Hawley later about "Rutland Ramsay" and its possible successors he declared that I must get back into my boat again or I should go to the bottom. His voice in short was the voice of warning.

I noted the warning, but I didn't turn my friends out of doors. They bored me a good deal; but the very fact that they bored me admonished me not to sacrifice them—if there was anything to be done with them—simply to irritation. As I look back at this phase they seem to me to have pervaded my life not a little. I have a vision of them as most of the time in my studio, seated against the wall on an old velvet bench to be out of the way, and resembling the while a pair of patient courtiers in a royal ante-chamber. I'm convinced that during the coldest weeks of the winter they held their ground because it saved them fire. Their newness was losing its gloss, and it was impossible not to feel them objects of charity. Whenever Miss Churm arrived they went away, and after I was fairly launched in "Rutland Ramsay" Miss Churm arrived pretty often. They managed to express to me tacitly that they supposed I wanted her for the low life of the book, and I let them suppose it, since they had attempted to study the work—it was lying about the studio—without discovering that it dealt only with the highest circles. They had dipped into the most brilliant of our novelists without deciphering many passages. I still took an hour from them, now and again, in spite of Jack Hawley's warning: it would be time enough to dismiss them, if dismissal should be necessary, when the rigour of the season was over. Hawley had made their acquaintance —he had met them at my fireside—and thought them a ridiculous pair. Learning that he was a painter they tried to approach him, to show him too that they were the real thing; but he looked at them, across the big room, as if they were miles away: they were a compendium of everything he most objected to in the social system of his country. Such people as that, all convention and patent-leather, with ejaculations that stopped conversation, had no business in a studio. A studio was a place to learn to see, and how could you see through a pair of feather-beds?

The main inconvenience I suffered at their hands was that at first I was shy of letting it break upon them that my artful little servant had begun to sit to me for "Rutland Ramsay." They knew I had been odd enough—they were prepared by this time to allow oddity to artists —to pick a foreign vagabond out of the streets when I might have had a person with whiskers and credentials; but it was some time before they learned how high I rated his accomplishments. They found him in an attitude more than once, but they never doubted I was doing him as an organ-grinder. There were several things they never guessed, and one of them was that for a striking scene in the novel, in which a footman briefly figured, it occurred to me to make use of Major Monarch as the menial. I kept putting this off, I didn't like to ask him to don the livery—besides the difficulty of finding a livery to fit him. At last, one day late in the winter, when I was at work on the despised Oronte, who caught one's idea on the wing, and was in the glow of feeling myself go very straight, they came in, the Major and his wife, with their society laugh about nothing (there was less and less to laugh at); came in like country-callers—they always reminded me of that—who have walked across the park after church and are presently persuaded to stay to luncheon. Luncheon was over, but they could stay to tea—I knew they wanted it. The fit was on me, however, and I couldn't let my ardour cool and my work wait, with the fading daylight, while my model prepared it. So I asked Mrs. Monarch if she would mind laying it out—a request which for an instant brought all the blood to her face. Her eyes were on her husband's for a second, and some mute telegraphy passed between them. Their folly was over the next instant; his cheerful shrewdness put an end to it. So far from pitying their wounded pride, I must add, I was moved to give it as complete a lesson as I could. They bustled about together and got out the cups and saucers and made the kettle boil. I know they felt as if they were waiting on my servant, and when the tea was prepared I said: "He'll have a cup, please—he's tired." Mrs. Monarch brought him one where he stood, and he took it from her as if he had been a gentleman at a party squeezing a crush-hat with an elbow.

Then it came over me that she had made a great effort for me—made it with a kind of nobleness—and that I owed her a compensation. Each time I saw her after this I wondered what the compensation could be. I couldn't go on doing the wrong thing to oblige them. Oh it *was* the wrong thing, the stamp of the work for which they sat—Hawley was not the only person to say it now. I sent in a large number of the drawings I had made for "Rutland Ramsay," and I received a warning that was more to the point than Hawley's. The artistic adviser of the house for which I was working was of opinion that many of my illustrations were not what had been looked for. Most of these illustrations were the subjects in which the Monarchs had figured. Without going into the question of what *had* been looked for, I had to face the fact that at this rate I shouldn't get the other books to do. I hurled myself in despair on Miss Churm—I put her through all her paces. I not only adopted Oronte publicly as my hero, but one morning when the Major looked in to see if I didn't require him to finish a *Cheapside* figure for which he had begun to sit the week before, I told him I had changed my mind—I'd do the drawing from my man. At this my visitor turned pale and stood looking at me. "Is *he* your idea of an English gentleman?" he asked.

I was disappointed, I was nervous, I wanted to get on with my work; so I replied with irritation: "Oh my dear Major—I can't be ruined for *you!*"

It was a horrid speech, but he stood another moment—after which, without a word, he quitted the studio. I drew a long breath, for I said to myself that I shouldn't see him again. I hadn't told him definitely that I was in danger of having my work rejected, but I was vexed at his not having felt the catastrophe in the air, read with me the moral of our fruitless collaboration, the lesson that in the deceptive atmosphere of art even the highest respectability may fail of being plastic.

I didn't owe my friends money, but I did see them again. They reappeared together three days later, and, given all the other facts, there was something tragic in that one. It was a clear proof they could find nothing else in life to do. They had threshed the matter out in a dismal conference—they had digested the bad news that they were not in for the series. If they weren't useful to me even for the *Cheapside* their function seemed difficult to determine, and I could only judge at first that they had come, forgivingly, decorously, to take a last leave. This made me rejoice in secret that I had little leisure for a scene; for I had placed both my other models in position together and I was pegging away at a drawing from which I hoped to derive glory. It had been suggested by the passage in which Rutland Ramsay, drawing up a chair to Artemisia's piano-stool, says extraordinary things to her while she ostensibly fingers out a difficult piece of music. I had done Miss Churm at the piano before—it was an attitude in which she knew how to take on an absolutely poetic grace. I wished the two figures to "compose" together with intensity, and my little Italian had entered perfectly into my conception. The pair were vividly before me, the piano had been pulled out; it was a charming show of blended youth and murmured love, which I had only to catch and keep. My visitors stood and looked at it, and I was friendly to them over my shoulder.

They made no response, but I was used to silent company and went on with my work, only a little disconcerted—even though exhilarated by the sense that *this* was at least the ideal thing—at not having got rid of them after all. Presently I heard Mrs. Monarch's sweet voice beside or rather above me: "I wish her hair were a little better done." I looked up and she was staring with a strange fixedness at Miss Churm, whose back was turned to her. "Do you mind my just touching it?" she went on—a question which made me spring up for an instant as with the instinctive fear that she might do the young lady a harm. But she quieted me with a glance I shall never forget—I confess I should like to have been able to paint *that*—and went for a moment to my model. She spoke to her softly, laying a hand on her shoulder and bending over her; and as the girl, understanding, gratefully assented, she disposed her rough curls, with a few quick passes, in such a way as to make Miss Churm's head twice as charming. It was one of the most heroic personal services I've ever seen rendered. Then Mrs. Monarch turned away with a low sigh and, looking about her as if for something to do, stooped to the floor with a noble humility and picked up a dirty rag that dropped out of my paint-box.

The Major meanwhile had also been looking for something to do, and, wandering to the other end of the studio, saw before him my breakfast-things neglected, unremoved. "I say, can't I be useful *here*?" he called out to me with an irrepressible quaver. I assented with a laugh that I fear was awkward, and for the next ten minutes, while I worked, I heard the light clatter of china and the tinkle of spoons and glass. Mrs. Monarch assisted her husband—they washed up my crockery, they put it away. They wandered off into my little scullery, and I afterwards found that they had cleaned my knives and that my slender stock of plate had an unprecedented surface. When it came over me, the latent eloquence of what they were doing, I confess that my drawing was blurred for a moment—the picture swam. They had accepted their failure, but they couldn't accept their fate. They had bowed their heads in bewilderment to the perverse and cruel law in virtue of which the real thing could be so much less precious than the unreal; but they didn't want to starve. If my servants were my models, then my models might be my servants. They would reverse the parts— the others would sit for the ladies and gentlemen and *they* would do the work. They would still be in the studio—it was an intense dumb appeal to me not to turn them out. "Take us on," they wanted to say— "we'll do *anything*."

My pencil dropped from my hand; my sitting was spoiled and I got rid of my sitters, who were also rather mystified and awestruck. Then, alone with the Major and his wife I had a most uncomfortable moment. He put their prayer into a single sentence: "I say, you know— just let *us* do for you, can't you?" I couldn't—it was dreadful to see them emptying my slops; but I pretended I could, to oblige them, for about a week. Then I gave them a sum of money to go away, and I never saw them again. I obtained the remaining books, but my friend Hawley repeats that Major and Mrs. Monarch did me a permanent harm, got me into false ways. If it be true I'm content to have paid the price—for the memory.

M. R. JAMES

The Mezzotint

SOME TIME AGO I believe I had the pleasure of telling you the story of an adventure which happened to a friend of mine by the name of Dennistoun, during his pursuit of objects of art for the museum at Cambridge.

He did not publish his experiences very widely upon his return to England; but they could not fail to become known to a good many of his friends, and among others to the gentleman who at that time presided over an art museum at another University. It was to be expected that the story should make a considerable impression on the mind of a man whose vocation lay in lines similar to Dennistoun's, and that he should be eager to catch at any explanation of the matter which tended to make it seem improbable that he should ever be called upon to deal with so agitating an emergency. It was, indeed, somewhat consoling to him to reflect that he was not expected to acquire ancient MSS. for his institution; that was the business of the Shelburnian Library. The authorities of that institution might, if they pleased, ransack obscure corners of the Continent for such matters. He was glad to be obliged at the moment to confine his attention to enlarging the already unsurpassed collection of English topographical drawings and engravings possessed by his museum. Yet, as it turned out, even a department so homely and familiar as this may have its dark corners, and to one of these Mr. Williams was unexpectedly introduced.

Those who have taken even the most limited interest in the acquisition of topographical pictures are aware that there is one London dealer whose aid is indispensable to their researches. Mr. J. W. Britnell publishes at short intervals very admirable catalogues of a large and constantly changing stock of engravings, plans, and old sketches of mansions, churches, and towns in England and Wales. These catalogues were, of course, the ABC of his subject to Mr. Williams: but as his museum already contained an enormous accumulation of topographical pictures, he was a regular, rather than a copious, buyer; and he rather looked to Mr. Britnell to fill up gaps in the rank and file of his collection than to supply him with rarities.

Now, in February of last year there appeared upon Mr. Williams's desk at the museum a catalogue from Mr. Britnell's emporium, and accompanying it was a typewritten communication from the dealer himself. This latter ran as follows:

Dear Sir,
We beg to call your attention to No. 978 in our accompanying catalogue, which we shall be glad to send on approval.
Yours faithfully,
J. W. Britnell.

To turn to No. 978 in the accompanying catalogue was with Mr. Williams (as he observed to himself) the work of a moment, and in the place indicated he found the following entry:

978 — *Unknown.* Interesting mezzotint: View of a manor-house, early part of the century. 15 by 10 inches; black frame. £2 2s.

It was not specially exciting, and the price seemed high. However, as Mr. Britnell, who knew his business and his customer, seemed to set store by it, Mr. Williams wrote a postcard asking for the article to be sent on approval, along with some other engravings and sketches which appeared in the same catalogue. And so he passed without much excitement of anticipation to the ordinary labours of the day.

A parcel of any kind always arrives a day later than you expect it, and that of Mr. Britnell proved, as I believe the right phrase goes, no exception to the rule. It was delivered at the museum by the afternoon post of Saturday, after Mr. Williams had left his work, and it was accordingly brought round to his rooms in college by the attendant, in order that he might not have to wait over Sunday before looking through it and returning such of the contents as he did not propose to keep. And here he found it when he came in to tea, with a friend.

The only item with which I am concerned was the rather large, black-framed mezzotint of which I have already quoted the short description given in Mr. Britnell's catalogue. Some more details of it will have to be given, though I cannot hope to put before you the look of the picture as clearly as it is present to my own eye. Very nearly the exact duplicate of it may be seen in a good many old inn parlours, or in the passages of undisturbed country mansions at the present moment. It was a rather indifferent mezzotint, and an indifferent mezzotint is, perhaps, the worst form of engraving known. It presented a full-face view of a not very large manor-house of the last century, with three rows of plain sashed windows with rusticated masonry about them, a parapet with balls or vases at the angles, and a small portico in the centre. On either side were trees, and in front a considerable expanse of lawn. The legend A. W. F. *sculpsit* was engraved on the narrow margin; and there was no further inscription. The whole thing gave the impression that it was the work of an amateur. What in the world Mr. Britnell could mean by affixing the price of £2 2s. to such an object was more than Mr. Williams could imagine. He turned it over with a good deal of contempt; upon the back was a paper label, the left-hand half of which had been torn off. All that remained were the ends of two lines of writing; the first had the letters—*ngley Hall;* the second,—*ssex.*

It would, perhaps, be just worth while to identify the place represented, which he could easily do with the help of a gazetteer, and then he would send it back to Mr. Britnell, with some remarks reflecting upon the judgement of that gentleman.

He lighted the candles, for it was now dark, made the tea, and supplied the friend with whom he had been playing golf (for I believe the authorities of the University I write of indulge in that pursuit by way of relaxation); and tea was taken to the accompaniment of a discussion which golfing persons can imagine for themselves, but which the conscientious writer has no right to inflict upon any non-golfing persons.

The conclusion arrived at was that certain strokes might have been better, and that in certain emergencies neither player had experienced that amount of luck which a human being has a right to expect. It was now that the friend—let us call him Professor Binks—took up the framed engraving, and said:

"What's this place, Williams?"

"Just what I am going to try to find out," said Williams, going to the shelf for a gazetteer. "Look at the back. Somethingley Hall, either in Sussex or Essex. Half the name's gone, you see. You don't happen to know it, I suppose?"

"It's from that man Britnell, I suppose, isn't it?" said Binks. "Is it for the museum?"

"Well, I think I should buy it if the price was five shillings," said Williams; "but for some unearthly reason he wants two guineas for it. I can't conceive why. It's a wretched engraving, and there aren't even any figures to give it life."

"It's not worth two guineas, I should think," said Binks; "but I don't think it's so badly done. The moonlight seems rather good to me; and I should have thought there *were* figures, or at least a figure, just on the edge in front."

"Let's look," said Williams. "Well, it's true the light is rather cleverly given. Where's your figure? Oh, yes! Just the head, in the very front of the picture."

And indeed there was—hardly more than a black blot on the extreme edge of the engraving—the head of a man or woman, a good deal muffled up, the back turned to the spectator, and looking towards the house.

Williams had not noticed it before.

"Still," he said, "though it's a cleverer thing than I thought, I can't spend two guineas of museum money on a picture of a place I don't know."

Professor Binks had his work to do, and soon went; and very nearly up to Hall time Williams was engaged in a vain attempt to identify the subject of his picture. "If the vowel before the *ng* had only been left, it would have been easy enough," he thought; "but as it is, the name may be anything from Guestingley to Langley, and there are many more names ending like this than I thought; and this rotten book has no index of terminations."

Hall in Mr. Williams's college was at seven. It need not be dwelt upon; the less so as he met there colleagues who had been playing golf during the afternoon, and words with which we have no concern were freely bandied across the table—merely golfing words, I would hasten to explain.

I suppose an hour or more to have been spent in what is called common-room after dinner. Later in the evening some few retired to Williams's rooms, and I have little doubt that whist was played and tobacco smoked. During a lull in these operations Williams picked up the mezzotint from the table without looking at it, and handed it to a person mildly interested in art, telling him where it had come from, and the other particulars which we already know.

The gentleman took it carelessly, looked at it, then said, in a tone of some interest:

"It's really a very good piece of work, Williams; it has quite a feeling of the romantic period. The light is admirably managed, it seems to me, and the figure, though it's rather too grotesque, is some-how very impressive."

"Yes, isn't it?" said Williams, who was just then busy giving whisky and soda to others of the company, and was unable to come across the room to look at the view again.

It was by this time rather late in the evening, and the visitors were on the move. After they went Williams was obliged to write a letter or two and clear up some odd bits of work. At last, some time past midnight, he was disposed to turn in, and he put out his lamp after lighting his bedroom candle. The picture lay face upwards on the table where the last man who looked at it had put it, and it caught his eye as he turned the lamp down. What he saw made him very nearly drop the candle on the floor, and he declares now that if he had been left in the dark at that moment he would have had a fit. But, as that did not happen, he was able to put down the light on the table and take a good look at the picture. It was indubitable—rankly impossible, no doubt, but absolutely certain. In the middle of the lawn in front of the unknown house there was a figure where no figure had been at five o'clock that afternoon. It was crawling on all fours towards the house, and it was muffled in a strange black garment with a white cross on the back.

I do not know what is the ideal course to pursue in a situation of this kind. I can only tell you what Mr. Williams did. He took the picture by one corner and carried it across the passage to a second set of rooms which he possessed. There he locked it up in a drawer, sported the doors of both sets of rooms, and retired to bed; but first he wrote out and signed an account of the extraordinary change which the picture had undergone since it had come into his possession.

Sleep visited him rather late; but it was consoling to reflect that the behaviour of the picture did not depend upon his own unsupported testimony. Evidently the man who had looked at it the night before had seen something of the same kind as he had, otherwise he might have been tempted to think that something gravely wrong was happening either to his eyes or his mind. This possibility being fortunately precluded, two matters awaited him on the morrow. He must take stock of the picture very carefully, and call in a witness for the purpose, and he must make a determined effort to ascertain what house it was that was represented. He would therefore ask his neighbour Nisbet to breakfast with him, and he would subsequently spend a morning over the gazetteer.

Nisbet was disengaged, and arrived about 9.20. His host was not quite dressed, I am sorry to say, even at this late hour. During breakfast nothing was said about the mezzotint by Williams, save that he had a picture on which he wished for Nisbet's opinion. But those who are familiar with University life can picture for themselves the wide and delightful range of subjects over which the conversation of two Fellows of Canterbury College is likely to extend during a Sunday morning breakfast. Hardly a topic was left unchallenged, from golf to lawn-tennis. Yet I am bound to say that Williams was rather distraught; for his interest naturally centred in that very strange picture which was now reposing face downwards, in the drawer in the room opposite.

The morning pipe was at last lighted, and the moment had arrived for which he looked. With very considerable—almost tremulous—excitement he ran across, unlocked the drawer, and, extracting the picture—still face downwards—ran back, and put it into Nisbet's hands.

"Now," he said, "Nisbet, I want you to tell me exactly what you see in that picture. Describe it, if you don't mind, rather minutely. I'll tell you why afterwards."

"Well," said Nisbet, "I have here a view of a country-house—English, I presume—by moonlight."

"Moonlight? You're sure of that?"

"Certainly. The moon appears to be on the wane, if you wish for details, and there are clouds in the sky."

"All right. Go on. I'll swear," added Williams in an aside, "there was no moon when I saw it first."

"Well, there's not much more to be said," Nisbet continued. "The house has one—two—three rows of windows, five in each row, except at the bottom, where there's a porch instead of the middle one, and——"

"But what about figures?" said Williams, with marked interest.

"There aren't any," said Nisbet; "but——"

"What! No figure on the grass in front?"

"Not a thing."

"You'll swear to that?"

"Certainly I will. But there's just one other thing."

"What?"

"Why, one of the windows on the ground-floor—left of the door —is open."

"Is it really so? My goodness! he must have got in," said Williams, with great excitement; and he hurried to the back of the sofa on which Nisbet was sitting, and, catching the picture from him, verified the matter for himself.

It was quite true. There was no figure, and there was the open window. Williams, after a moment of speechless surprise, went to the writing-table and scribbled for a short time. Then he brought two papers to Nisbet, and asked him first to sign one—it was his own description of the picture, which you have just heard—and then to read the other which was Williams's statement written the night before.

"What can it all mean?" said Nisbet.

"Exactly," said Williams. "Well, one thing I must do—or three things, now I think of it. I must find out from Garwood"—this was his last night's visitor—"what he saw, and then I must get the thing photographed before it goes further, and then I must find out what the place is."

"I can do the photographing myself," said Nisbet, and I will. But, you know, it looks very much as if we were assisting at the working out of a tragedy somewhere. The question is, has it happened already, or is it going to come off? You must find out what the place is. Yes," he said, looking at the picture again, "I expect you're right: he has got in. And if I don't mistake there'll be the devil to pay in one of the rooms upstairs."

"I'll tell you what," said Williams: "I'll take the picture across to old Green" (this was the senior Fellow of the College, who had been Bursar for many years). "It's quite likely he'll know it. We have property in Essex and Sussex, and he must have been over the two counties a lot in his time."

"Quite likely he will," said Nisbet; "but just let me take my photograph first. But look here, I rather think Green isn't up today. He wasn't in Hall last night, and I think I heard him say he was going down for the Sunday."

"That's true, too," said Williams; "I know he's gone to Brighton. Well, if you'll photograph it now, I'll go across to Garwood and get his statement, and you keep an eye on it while I'm gone. I'm beginning to think two guineas is not a very exorbitant price for it now."

In a short time he had returned, and brought Mr. Garwood with him. Garwood's statement was to the effect that the figure, when he had seen it, was clear of the edge of the picture, but had not got far across the lawn. He remembered a white mark on the back of its drapery, but could not have been sure it was a cross. A document to this effect was then drawn up and signed, and Nisbet proceeded to photograph the picture.

"Now what do you mean to do?" he said. "Are you going to sit and watch it all day?"

"Well, no, I think not," said Williams. "I rather imagine we're meant to see the whole thing. You see, between the time I saw it last night and this morning there was time for lots of things to happen, but the creature only got into the house. It could easily have got through its business in the time and gone to its own place again; but the fact of the window being open, I think, must mean that it's in there now. So I feel quite easy about leaving it. And besides, I have a kind of idea that it wouldn't change much, if at all, in the daytime. We might go out for a walk this afternoon, and come in to tea, or whenever it gets dark. I shall leave it out on the table here, and sport the door. My skip can get in, but no one else."

The three agreed that this would be a good plan; and, further, that if they spent the afternoon together they would be less likely to talk about the business to other people; for any rumour of such a transaction as was going on would bring the whole of the Phasmatological Society about their ears.

We may give them a respite until five o'clock.

At or near that hour the three were entering Williams's staircase. They were at first slightly annoyed to see that the door of his rooms was unsported; but in a moment it was remembered that on Sunday the skips came for orders an hour or so earlier than on weekdays. However, a surprise was awaiting them. The first thing they saw was the picture leaning up against a pile of books on the table, as it had been left, and the next thing was Williams's skip, seated on a chair opposite, gazing at it with undisguised horror. How was this? Mr. Filcher (the name is not my own invention) was a servant of considerable standing, and set the standard of etiquette to all his own college and to several neighbouring ones, and nothing could be more alien to his practice than to be found sitting on his master's chair, or appearing to take any particular notice of his master's furniture or pictures. Indeed, he seemed to feel this himself. He started violently when the three men were in the room, and got up with a marked effort. Then he said:

"I ask your pardon, sir, for taking such a freedom as to set down."

"Not at all, Robert," interposed Mr. Williams. "I was meaning to ask you some time what you thought of that picture."

"Well, sir, of course I don't set up my opinion against yours, but it ain't the pictur I should 'ang where my little girl could see it, sir."

"Wouldn't you, Robert? Why not?"

"No, sir. Why, the pore child, I recollect once she see a Door Bible, with pictures not 'alf what that is, and we 'ad to set up with her three or four nights afterwards, if you'll believe me; and if she was to ketch a sight of this skelinton here, or whatever it is, carrying off the pore baby, she would be in a taking. You know 'ow it is with children; 'ow nervish they git with a little thing and all. But what I should say, it don't seem a right pictur to be laying about, sir, not where anyone that's liable to be startled could come on it. Should you be wanting anything this evening, sir? Thank you, sir."

With these words the excellent man went to continue the round of his masters, and you may be sure the gentlemen whom he left lost no time in gathering round the engraving. There was the house, as before under the waning moon and the drifting clouds. The window that had been open was shut, and the figure was once more on the lawn: but not this time crawling cautiously on hands and knees. Now it was erect and stepping swiftly, with long strides, towards the front of the picture. The moon was behind it, and the black drapery hung down over its face so that only hints of that could be seen, and what was visible made the spectators profoundly thankful that they could see no more than a white dome-like forehead and a few straggling hairs. The head was bent down, and the arms were tightly clasped over an object which could be dimly seen and identified as a child, whether dead or living it was not possible to say. The legs of the appearance alone could be plainly discerned, and they were horribly thin.

From five to seven the three companions sat and watched the picture by turns. But it never changed. They agreed at last that it would be safe to leave it, and that they would return after Hall and await further developments.

When they assembled again, at the earliest possible moment, the engraving was there, but the figure was gone, and the house was quiet under the moonbeams. There was nothing for it but to spend the evening over gazetteers and guide-books. Williams was the lucky one at last, and perhaps he deserved it. At 11.30 P.M. he read from Murray's *Guide to Essex* the following lines:

16½ miles, *Anningley.* The church has been an interesting building of Norman date, but was extensively classicized in the last century. It contains the tomb of the family of Francis, whose mansion, Anningley Hall, a solid Queen Anne house, stands immediately beyond the churchyard in a park of about 80 acres. The family is now extinct, the last heir having disappeared mysteriously in infancy in the year 1802. The father, Mr Arthur Francis, was locally known as a talented amateur engraver in mezzotint. After his son's disappearance he lived in complete retirement at the Hall, and was found dead in his studio on the third anniversary of the disaster, having just completed an engraving of the house, impressions of which are of considerable rarity.

This looked like business, and, indeed, Mr. Green on his return at once identified the house as Anningley Hall.

"Is there any kind of explanation of the figure, Green?" was the question which Williams naturally asked.

"I don't know, I'm sure, Williams. What used to be said in the place when I first knew it, which was before I came up here, was just this: old Francis was always very much down on these poaching fellows, and whenever he got a chance he used to get a man whom he suspected of it turned off the estate, and by degrees he got rid of them all but one. Squires could do a lot of things then that they daren't think of now. Well, this man that was left was what you find pretty often in that country—the last remains of a very old family. I believe they were Lords of the Manor at one time. I recollect just the same thing in my own parish."

"What, like the man in *Tess o' the Durbervilles?*" Williams put in.

"Yes, I dare say; it's not a book I could ever read myself. But this fellow could show a row of tombs in the church there that belonged to his ancestors, and all that went to sour him a bit; but Francis, they said, could never get at him—he always kept just on the right side of the law—until one night the keepers found him at it in a wood right at the end of the estate. I could show you the place now; it marches with some land that used to belong to an uncle of mine. And you can imagine there was a row; and this man Gawdy (that was the name to be sure—Gawdy; I thought I should get it—Gawdy), he was unlucky enough, poor chap! to shoot a keeper. Well, that was what Francis wanted, and grand juries—you know what they would have been then—and poor Gawdy was strung up in double-quick time; and I've been shown the place he was buried in, on the north side of the church—you know the way in that part of the world: anyone that's been hanged or made away with themselves, they bury them that side. And the idea was that some friend of Gawdy's—not a relation, because he had none, poor devil! he was the last of his line: kind of *spes ultima gentis*—must have planned to get hold of Francis's boy and put an end to *his* line, too. I don't know—it's rather an out-of-the-way thing for an Essex poacher to think of—but, you know, I should say now it looks more as if old Gawdy had managed the job himself. Booh! I hate to think of it! have some whisky, Williams!"

The facts were communicated by Williams to Dennistoun, and by him to a mixed company, of which I was one, and the Sadducean Professor of Ophiology another. I am sorry to say that the latter when asked what he thought of it, only remarked: "Oh, those Bridgeford people will say anything"—a sentiment which met with the reception it deserved.

I have only to add that the picture is now in the Ashleian Museum; that it has been treated with a view to discovering whether sympathetic ink has been used in it, but without effect; that Mr. Britnell knew nothing of it save that he was sure it was uncommon; and that, though carefully watched, it has never been known to change again.

ARCHIBALD MARSHALL

The Burglar

ONCE THERE WAS a burglar called Arthur Pomegranate, and he had not been born a burglar, he had played the flute, but he couldn't earn enough money by that, so he had fallen on evil ways instead.

Well, one night he thought he would burgle No. 41 Wellington

Terrace, so he waited until everybody was asleep and then he climbed up a water-pipe and got into a bedroom as quietly as he could so as not to wake anybody.

But he made more noise than he meant to and he woke Mr and Mrs Willoughby who lived at No. 41 Wellington Terrace and were sleeping in that room.

So Mr Willoughby sat up in bed and he said who are you?

And he said I am Arthur Pomegranate.

And Mrs Willoughby, who hadn't sat up yet because she was rather frightened, said are you the son of my cousin Emily who married Mr Pomegranate?

And he said he was.

So Mr Willoughby said well I am very glad to hear that because when you came in just now I thought you were a burglar, especially because of your black mask, it is rather an awkward time to come, but we are pleased to see you and if you will go down into the dining-room we will put on our dressing-gowns and come and have a nice talk.

So Arthur Pomegranate went down into the dining-room and there was some silver plate on the sideboard which he thought he would like to have, and he said it wouldn't be a bad idea to go away with this before they come down.

But then he said to himself oh well I suppose I had better not as the lady upstairs is a cousin of mother's, I can easily come again if I don't like her, and I dare say there are some silver spoons and forks too, I might see about that before they come down.

So he opened the drawers of the sideboard and there were plenty of silver spoons and forks there, and he said they seem to be rather rich, I wish I had known of them before.

Well, Mr and Mrs Willoughby came down in their dressing-gowns, and they were very kind to Arthur Pomegranate and gave him some cake and lemonade because they thought he might be hungry, and they asked him how his mother was and he said she was quite well but he hadn't seen her for some time.

And Mrs Willoughby said well you don't look as if you were very rich, what do you do for a living?

And he said well I play the flute, because he didn't want them to know he was a burglar, and he had taken off his black mask.

And Mr Willoughby said I have always wished I could play the flute, would you like to come and live here and teach me?

So he said he would, and Mrs Willoughby said your mother could come too, because we haven't any children and there would be plenty of room for all of us.

So Arthur Pomegranate said he would ask his mother if she would like that, and then Mr Willoughby said well it is getting rather late and we should like to go to bed now if you don't mind, so I will just let you out at the front door, and next time you come if you just ring the bell they will let you in and you needn't take the trouble to climb up the water-pipe.

Well, Arthur Pomegranate went to see his mother, and she was very poor, because her husband was dead and she thought she wouldn't have another one, so she was pleased to go and live with Mr and Mrs Willoughby.

And they all liked each other, and Arthur Pomegranate taught Mr Willoughby to play the flute and his mother and Mrs Willoughby went shopping together, and they had very nice dinners and teas, and sometimes they went to the Pictures.

Well, that went on for some time, and one day Arthur Pomegranate said to Mr Willoughby, I suppose you are very rich, how do you make all your money?

And he said well I was in business, but I retired from it when I began to get old.

And Arthur Pomegranate said what business?

And he said well I was a burglar.

And Arthur Pomegranate was rather surprised at that and he said well it only shows how small the world is because I was a burglar too before I came here.

And Mr Willoughby said oh were you?

And he said yes I was.

And Mr Willoughby laughed and said now isn't that funny, do you remember when you first came to see us I said I thought you were a burglar?

And Arthur Pomegranate thought he wouldn't tell him that he had come to No. 41 Wellington Terrace as a burglar because he might not like it. So he said I would rather you didn't tell mother I was a burglar if you don't mind.

And Mr Willoughby said oh no I won't, and I would rather you didn't tell Mrs Willoughby I was one either, because she thinks I had something to do with ships.

So Mr Willoughby and Arthur Pomegranate liked each other more than ever after that, and they often used to talk over what they had done when they were burglars, but they both said that they were glad they weren't burglars any longer because it wasn't really honest and they would be ashamed to do it now.

Well, that went on for some time, and then one night another burglar came to No. 41 Wellington Terrace, and Arthur Pomegranate went down into the dining-room and found him putting the silver spoons and forks and the other things into a suit-case which he had brought with him.

And Arthur Pomegranate said now I have caught you and it is a good thing I heard you come in.

And the burglar said well I don't think it is a good thing, because I have a wife and a little girl who haven't got enough to eat, and if you hadn't caught me I should have sold these silver spoons and forks and things for plenty of money and then I should have been able to give them some nice food and buy them some clothes, but as I haven't done you any harm I suppose you will let me go away again now.

And Arthur Pomegranate said well I don't know about that, I should have to ask Mr Willoughby, because they are his things and not mine.

Well, just then Mr Willoughby came in, because he had heard them talking downstairs and had only just waited to put on his dressing-gown. And when he had heard about the burglar's wife and little girl he said well I don't mind letting you go this time if you promise not to do it again, because it isn't really honest, Arthur Pomegranate and I were both burglars once but we have given it up and should be ashamed to do it any more.

And the burglar said well I shouldn't mind giving it up myself, I am not very good at it, I make too much noise, but it is difficult to get honest work.

And Mr Willoughby said well how would you and your wife and your little girl like to come and live here? you could clean the boots and knives and your wife could cook, because the cook we have now gets tipsy sometimes and we thought of getting rid of her, and your little girl could go to school.

So the burglar said well I could ask her, it would be better than nothing, but I would rather you didn't tell her about me being a burglar if you don't mind, because she thinks I have something to do with carrying people's suit-cases for them outside stations.

And Mr Willoughby said that would be all right and he would rather nobody knew about him and Arthur Pomegranate being burglars either.

So they all lived together at No. 41 Wellington Terrace, and were very happy. And the burglar's little girl won prizes at the school she went to, and when she grew up Arthur Pomegranate married her, and when Mr Willoughby died he left them all his money.

KATHERINE ANNE PORTER

The Grave

THE GRANDFATHER, dead for more than thirty years, had been twice disturbed in his long repose by the constancy and possessiveness of his widow. She removed his bones first to Louisiana and then to Texas as if she had set out to find her own burial place, knowing well she would never return to the places she had left. In Texas she set up a small cemetery in a corner of her first farm, and as the family connection grew, and oddments of relations came over from Kentucky to settle, it contained at last about twenty graves. After the grandmother's death, part of her land was to be sold for the benefit of certain of her children, and the cemetery happened to lie in the part set aside for sale. It was necessary to take up the bodies and bury them again in the family plot in the big new public cemetery, where the grandmother had been buried. At last her husband was to lie beside her for eternity, as she had planned.

The family cemetery had been a pleasant small neglected garden of tangled rose bushes and ragged cedar trees and cypress, the simple flat stones rising out of uncropped sweet-smelling wild grass. The graves were lying open and empty one burning day when Miranda and her brother Paul, who often went together to hunt rabbits and doves, propped their twenty-two Winchester rifles carefully against the rail fence, climbed over and explored among the graves. She was nine years old and he was twelve.

They peered into the pits all shaped alike with such purposeful accuracy, and looking at each other with pleased adventurous eyes, they said in solemn tones: "These were graves!" trying by words to shape a special, suitable emotion in their minds, but they felt nothing except an agreeable thrill of wonder: they were seeing a new sight, doing something they had not done before. In them both there was also a small disappointment at the entire commonplaceness of the actual spectacle. Even if it had once contained a coffin for years upon years, when the coffin was gone a grave was just a hole in the ground. Miranda leaped into the pit that had held her grandfather's bones. Scratching around aimlessly and pleasurably as any young animal, she scooped up a lump of earth and weighed it in her palm. It had a pleasantly sweet, corrupt smell, being mixed with cedar needles and small leaves, and as the crumbs fell apart, she saw a silver dove no larger than a hazel nut, with spread wings and a neat fan-shaped tail. The breast had a deep round hollow in it. Turning it up to the fierce sunlight, she saw that the inside of the hollow was cut in little whorls. She scrambled out, over the pile of loose earth that had fallen back into one end of the grave, calling to Paul that she had found something, he must guess what . . . His head appeared smiling over the rim of another grave. He waved a closed hand at her. "I've got something too!" They ran to compare treasures, making a game of it, so many guesses each, all wrong, and a final show-down with opened palms. Paul had found a thin wide gold ring carved with intricate flowers and leaves. Miranda was smitten at sight of the ring and wished to have it. Paul seemed more impressed by the dove. They made a trade, with some little bickering. After he had got the dove in his hand, Paul said, "Don't you know what this is? This is a screw head for a *coffin!* . . . I'll bet nobody else in the world has one like this!"

Miranda glanced at it without covetousness. She had the gold ring on her thumb; it fitted perfectly. "Maybe we ought to go now," she said, "maybe one of the niggers 'll see us and tell somebody." They knew the land had been sold, the cemetery was no longer theirs, and they felt like trespassers. They climbed back over the fence, slung their rifles loosely under their arms—they had been shooting at targets with various kinds of firearms since they were seven years old—and set out to look for the rabbits and doves or whatever small game might happen along. On these expeditions Miranda always followed at Paul's heels along the path, obeying instructions about handling her gun when going through fences; learning how to stand it up properly so it would not slip and fire unexpectedly; how to wait her time for a shot and not just bang away in the air without looking, spoiling shots for Paul, who really could hit things if given a chance. Now and then, in her excitement at seeing birds whizz up suddenly before her face, or a rabbit leap across her very toes, she lost her head, and almost without sighting she flung her rifle up and pulled the trigger. She hardly ever hit any sort of mark. She had no proper sense of hunting at all. Her brother would be often completely disgusted with her. "You don't care whether you get your bird or not," he said. "That's no way to hunt." Miranda could not understand his indignation. She had seen him smash his hat and yell with fury when he had missed his aim. "What I like about shooting," said Miranda, with exasperating inconsequence, "is pulling the trigger and hearing the noise."

"Then, by golly," said Paul, "whyn't you go back to the range and shoot at bulls-eyes?"

"I'd just as soon," said Miranda, "only like this, we walk around more."

"Well, you just stay behind and stop spoiling my shots," said Paul, who, when he made a kill, wanted to be certain he had made it. Miranda, who alone brought down a bird once in twenty rounds, always claimed as her own any game they got when they fired at the same moment. It was tiresome and unfair and her brother was sick of it.

"Now, the first dove we see, or the first rabbit, is mine," he told her. "And the next will be yours. Remember that and don't get smarty."

"What about snakes?" asked Miranda idly. "Can I have the first snake?"

Waving her thumb gently and watching her gold ring glitter, Miranda lost interest in shooting. She was wearing her summer roughing outfit: dark blue overalls, a light blue shirt, a hired-man's straw hat, and thick brown sandals. Her brother had the same outfit except his was a sober hickory-nut color. Ordinarily Miranda preferred her overalls to any other dress, though it was making rather a scandal in the countryside, for the year was 1903, and in the back country the law of female decorum had teeth in it. Her father had been criticized for letting his girls dress like boys and go careering around astride barebacked horses. Big sister Maria, the really independent and fearless one, in spite of her rather affected ways, rode at a dead run with only a rope knotted around her horse's nose. It was said the motherless family was running down, with the Grandmother no longer there to hold it together. It was known that she had discriminated against her son Harry in her will, and that he was in straits about money. Some of his old neighbors reflected with vicious satisfaction that now he would probably not be so stiffnecked, nor have any more high-stepping horses either. Miranda knew this, though she could not say how. She had met along the road old women of the kind who smoked corn-cob pipes, who had treated her grandmother with most sincere respect. They slanted their gummy old eyes side-ways at the granddaughter and said, "Ain't you ashamed of yoself, Missy? It's aginst the Scriptures to dress like that. Whut yo Pappy thinkin about?" Miranda, with her powerful social sense, which was like a fine set of antennae radiating from every pore of her skin, would feel ashamed because she knew well it was rude and ill-bred to shock anybody, even bad-tempered old crones, though she had faith in her father's judgment and was perfectly comfortable in the clothes. Her father had said, "They're just what you need, and they'll save your dresses for school . . ." This sounded quite simple and natural to her. She had been brought up in rigorous economy. Wastefulness was vulgar. It was also a sin. These were truths; she had heard them repeated many times and never once disputed.

Now the ring, shining with the serene purity of fine gold on her rather grubby thumb, turned her feelings against her overalls and sockless feet, toes sticking through the thick brown leather straps. She wanted to go back to the farmhouse, take a good cold bath, dust herself with plenty of Maria's violet talcum powder—provided Maria was not present to object, of course—put on the thinnest, most becoming dress she owned, with a big sash, and sit in a wicker chair under the trees . . . These things were not all she wanted, of course; she had vague stirrings of desire for luxury and a grand way of living which could not take precise form in her imagination but were founded on family legend of past wealth and leisure. These immediate comforts were what she could have, and she wanted them at once. She lagged rather far behind Paul, and once she thought of just turning back without a word and going home. She stopped, thinking that Paul would never do that to her, and so she would have to tell him. When a rabbit leaped, she let Paul have it without dispute. He killed it with one shot.

When she came up with him, he was already kneeling, examining the wound, the rabbit trailing from his hands. "Right through the head," he said complacently, as if he had aimed for it. He took out his sharp, competent bowie knife and started to skin the body. He did it very cleanly and quickly. Uncle Jimbilly knew how to prepare the skins so that Miranda always had fur coats for her dolls, for though she never cared much for her dolls she liked seeing them in fur coats. The children knelt facing each other over the dead animal. Miranda watched admiringly while her brother stripped the skin away as if he were taking off a glove. The flayed flesh emerged dark scarlet, sleek, firm; Miranda with thumb and finger felt the long fine muscles with the silvery flat strips binding them to the joints. Brother lifted the oddly bloated belly.

"Look," he said, in a low amazed voice. "It was going to have young ones."

Very carefully he slit the thin flesh from the center ribs to the flanks, and a scarlet bag appeared. He slit again and pulled the bag open, and there lay a bundle of tiny rabbits, each wrapped in a thin scarlet veil. The brother pulled these off and there they were, dark gray, their sleek wet down lying in minute even ripples, like a baby's head just washed, their unbelievably small delicate ears folded close, their little blind faces almost featureless.

Miranda said, "Oh, I want to *see*," under her breath. She looked and looked—excited but not frightened, for she was accustomed to the sight of animals killed in hunting—filled with pity and astonishment and a kind of shocked delight in the wonderful little creatures for their own sakes, they were so pretty. She touched one of them ever so carefully, "Ah, there's blood running over them," she said and began to tremble without knowing why. Yet she wanted most deeply to see and to know. Having seen, she felt at once as if she had known all along. The very memory of her former ignorance faded, she had always known just this. No one had ever told her anything outright, she had been rather unobservant of the animal life around her because she was so accustomed to animals. They seemed simply disorderly and unaccountably rude in their habits, but altogether natural and not very interesting. Her brother had spoken as if he had known about everything all along. He may have seen all this before. He had never said a word to her, but she knew now a part at least of what he knew. She understood a little of the secret, formless intuitions in her own mind and body, which had been clearing up, taking form, so gradually and so steadily she had not realized that she was learning what she had to know. Paul said cautiously, as if he were talking about something forbidden: "They were just about ready to be born." His voice dropped on the last word. "I know," said Miranda, "like kittens. I know, like babies." She was quietly and terribly agitated, standing again with her rifle under her arm, looking down at the bloody heap. "I don't want the skin," she said, "I won't have it." Paul buried the young rabbits again in their mother's body, wrapped the skin around her, carried her to a clump of sage bushes, and hid her away. He came out again at once and said to Miranda, with an eager friendliness, a confidential tone quite unusual in him, as if he were taking her into an important secret on equal terms: "Listen now. Now you listen to me, and don't ever forget. Don't you ever tell a living soul that you saw this. Don't tell a soul. Don't tell Dad because I'll get into trouble. He'll say I'm leading you into things you ought not to do. He's always saying that. So now don't you go and forget and blab out sometime the way you're always doing . . . Now, that's a secret. Don't you tell."

Miranda never told, she did not even wish to tell anybody. She thought about the whole worrisome affair with confused unhappiness for a few days. Then it sank quietly into her mind and was heaped over by accumulated thousands of impressions, for nearly twenty years. One day she was picking her path among the puddles and crushed refuse of a market street in a strange city of a strange country, when without warning, plain and clear in its true colors as if she looked through a frame upon a scene that had not stirred nor changed since the moment it happened, the episode of that far-off day leaped from its burial place before her mind's eye. She was so reasonlessly horrified she halted suddenly staring, the scene before her eyes dimmed by the vision back of them. An Indian vendor had held up before her a tray of dyed sugar sweets, in the shapes of all kinds of small creatures: birds, baby chicks, baby rabbits, lambs, baby pigs. They were in gay colors and smelled of vanilla, maybe. . . . It was a very hot day and the smell in the market, with its piles of raw flesh and wilting flowers, was like the mingled sweetness and corruption she had smelled that other day in the empty cemetery at home: the day she had remembered always until now vaguely as the time she and her brother had found treasure in the opened graves. Instantly upon this thought the dreadful vision faded, and she saw clearly her brother, whose childhood face she had forgotten, standing again in the blazing sunshine, again twelve years old, a pleased sober smile in his eyes, turning the silver dove over and over in his hands.

F. SCOTT FITZGERALD

The Baby Party

WHEN JOHN ANDROS felt old he found solace in the thought of life continuing through his child. The dark trumpets of oblivion were less loud at the patter of his child's feet or at the sound of his child's voice babbling mad non sequiturs to him over the telephone. The latter incident occurred every afternoon at three when his wife called the office from the country, and he came to look forward to it as one of the vivid minutes of his day.

He was not physically old, but his life had been a series of struggles up a series of rugged hills, and here at thirty-eight having won his battles against ill-health and poverty he cherished less than the usual number of illusions. Even his feeling about his little girl was qualified. She had interrupted his rather intense love-affair with his wife, and she was the reason for their living in a suburban town, where they paid for country air with endless servant troubles and the weary merry-go-round of the commuting train.

It was little Ede as a definite piece of youth that chiefly interested him. He liked to take her on his lap and examine minutely her fragrant, downy scalp and her eyes with their irises of morning blue. Having paid this homage John was content that the nurse should take her away. After ten minutes the very vitality of the child irritated him; he was inclined to lose his temper when things were broken, and one Sunday afternoon when she had disrupted a bridge game by permanently hiding up the ace of spades, he had made a scene that had reduced his wife to tears.

This was absurd and John was ashamed of himself. It was inevitable that such things would happen, and it was impossible that little Ede should spend all her indoor hours in the nursery up-stairs when she was becoming, as her mother said, more nearly a "real person" every day.

She was two and a half, and this afternoon, for instance, she was going to a baby party. Grown-up Edith, her mother, had telephoned the information to the office, and little Ede had confirmed the business by shouting "I yam going to a *pantry!*" into John's unsuspecting left ear.

"Drop in at the Markeys' when you get home, won't you, dear?" resumed her mother. "It'll be funny. Ede's going to be all dressed up in her new pink dress——"

The conversation terminated abruptly with a squawk which indicated that the telephone had been pulled violently to the floor. John laughed and decided to get an early train out; the prospect of a baby party in some one else's house amused him.

"What a peach of a mess!" he thought humorously. "A dozen mothers, and each one looking at nothing but her own child. All the babies breaking things and grabbing at the cake, and each mama going home thinking about the subtle superiority of her own child to every other child there."

He was in a good humor to-day—all the things in his life were going better than they had ever gone before. When he got off the train at his station he shook his head at an importunate taxi man, and began to walk up the long hill toward his house through the crisp December twilight. It was only six o'clock but the moon was out, shining with proud brilliance on the thin sugary snow that lay over the lawns.

As he walked along drawing his lungs full of cold air his happiness increased, and the idea of a baby party appealed to him more and more. He began to wonder how Ede compared to other children of her own age, and if the pink dress she was to wear was something radical and mature. Increasing his gait he came in sight of his own house, where the lights of a defunct Christmas-tree still blossomed in the window, but he continued on past the walk. The party was at the Markeys' next door.

As he mounted the brick step and rang the bell he became aware of voices inside, and he was glad he was not too late. Then he raised his head and listened—the voices were not children's voices, but they were loud and pitched high with anger; there were at least three of them and one, which rose as he listened to a hysterical sob, he recognized immediately as his wife's.

"There's been some trouble," he thought quickly.

Trying the door, he found it unlocked and pushed it open.

The baby party began at half past four, but Edith Andros, calculating shrewdly that the new dress would stand out more sensationally against vestments already rumpled, planned the arrival of herself and little Ede for five. When they appeared it was already a flourishing affair. Four baby girls and nine baby boys, each one curled and washed and dressed with all the care of a proud and jealous heart, were dancing to the music of a phonograph. Never more than two or three were dancing at once, but as all were continually in motion running to and from their mothers for encouragement, the general effect was the same.

As Edith and her daughter entered, the music was temporarily drowned out by a sustained chorus, consisting largely of the word *cute* and directed toward little Ede, who stood looking timidly about and fingering the edges of her pink dress. She was not kissed—this is the sanitary age—but she was passed along a row of mamas each one of

whom said "cu-u-ute" to her and held her pink little hand before passing her on to the next. After some encouragement and a few mild pushes
she was absorbed into the dance, and became an active member of the
party.

Edith stood near the door talking to Mrs. Markey, and keeping one
eye on the tiny figure in the pink dress. She did not care for Mrs.
Markey; she considered her both snippy and common, but John and
Joe Markey were congenial and went in together on the commuting
train every morning, so the two women kept up an elaborate pretense
of warm amity. They were always reproaching each other for "not
coming to see me," and they were always planning the kind of parties
that began with "You'll have to come to dinner with us soon, and we'll
go in to the theatre," but never matured further.

"Little Ede looks perfectly darling," said Mrs. Markey, smiling and
moistening her lips in a way that Edith found particularly repulsive.
"So *grown-up*—I can't *believe* it!"

Edith wondered if "little Ede" referred to the fact that Billy
Markey, though several months younger, weighed almost five pounds
more. Accepting a cup of tea she took a seat with two other ladies on
a divan and launched into the real business of the afternoon, which of
course lay in relating the recent accomplishments and insouciances of
her child.

An hour passed. Dancing palled and the babies took to sterner
sport. They ran into the dining-room, rounded the big table, and es-
sayed the kitchen door, from which they were rescued by an expedi-
tionary force of mothers. Having been rounded up they immediately
broke loose, and rushing back to the dining-room tried the familiar
swinging door again. The word "overheated" began to be used, and
small white brows were dried with small white handkerchiefs. A general
attempt to make the babies sit down began, but the babies squirmed
off laps with peremptory cries of "Down! Down!" and the rush into the
fascinating dining-room began anew.

This phase of the party came to an end with the arrival of refreshments, a large cake with two candles, and saucers of vanilla ice-cream.
Billy Markey, a stout laughing baby with red hair and legs somewhat
bowed, blew out the candles, and placed an experimental thumb on the
white frosting. The refreshments were distributed, and the children
ate, greedily but without confusion—they had behaved remarkably well
all afternoon. They were modern babies who ate and slept at regular
hours, so their dispositions were good, and their faces healthy and pink—

such a peaceful party would not have been possible thirty years ago.

After the refreshments a gradual exodus began. Edith glanced anxiously at her watch—it was almost six, and John had not arrived. She wanted him to see Ede with the other children—to see how dignified and polite and intelligent she was, and how the only ice-cream spot on her dress was some that had dropped from her chin when she was joggled from behind.

"You're a darling," she whispered to her child, drawing her suddenly against her knee. "Do you know you're a darling? Do you *know* you're a darling?"

Ede laughed. "Bow-wow," she said suddenly.

"Bow-wow?" Edith looked around. "There isn't any bow-wow."

"Bow-wow," repeated Ede. "I want a bow-wow."

Edith followed the small pointing finger.

"That isn't a bow-wow, dearest, that's a teddy-bear."

"Bear?"

"Yes, that's a teddy-bear, and it belongs to Billy Markey. You don't want Billy Markey's teddy-bear, do you?"

Ede did want it.

She broke away from her mother and approached Billy Markey, who held the toy closely in his arms. Ede stood regarding him with inscrutable eyes, and Billy laughed.

Grown-up Edith looked at her watch again, this time impatiently.

The party had dwindled until, besides Ede and Billy, there were only two babies remaining—and one of the two remained only by virtue of having hidden himself under the dining-room table. It was selfish of John not to come. It showed so little pride in the child. Other fathers had come, half a dozen of them, to call for their wives, and they had stayed for a while and looked on.

There was a sudden wail. Ede had obtained Billy's teddy-bear by pulling it forcibly from his arms, and on Billy's attempt to recover it, she had pushed him casually to the floor.

"Why, Ede!" cried her mother, repressing an inclination to laugh.

Joe Markey, a handsome, broad-shouldered man of thirty-five, picked up his son and set him on his feet. "You're a fine fellow," he said jovially. "Let a girl knock you over! You're a fine fellow."

"Did he bump his head?" Mrs. Markey returned anxiously from bowing the next to last remaining mother out the door.

"No-o-o-o," exclaimed Markey. "He bumped something else, didn't you, Billy? He bumped something else."

Billy had so far forgotten the bump that he was already making an attempt to recover his property. He seized a leg of the bear which projected from Ede's enveloping arms and tugged at it but without success.

"No," said Ede emphatically.

Suddenly, encouraged by the success of her former half-accidental manoeuvre, Ede dropped the teddy-bear, placed her hands on Billy's shoulders and pushed him backward off his feet.

This time he landed less harmlessly; his head hit the bare floor just off the rug with a dull hollow sound, whereupon he drew in his breath and delivered an agonized yell.

Immediately the room was in confusion. With an exclamation Markey hurried to his son, but his wife was first to reach the injured baby and catch him up into her arms.

"Oh, *Billy,*" she cried, "what a terrible bump! She ought to be spanked."

Edith, who had rushed immediately to her daughter, heard this remark, and her lips came sharply together.

"Why, Ede," she whispered perfunctorily, "you bad girl!"

Ede put back her little head suddenly and laughed. It was a loud laugh, a triumphant laugh with victory in it and challenge and contempt. Unfortunately it was also an infectious laugh. Before her mother realized the delicacy of the situation, she too had laughed, an audible, distinct laugh not unlike the baby's, and partaking of the same overtones.

Then, as suddenly, she stopped.

Mrs. Markey's face had grown red with anger, and Markey, who had been feeling the back of the baby's head with one finger, looked at her, frowning.

"It's swollen already," he said with a note of reproof in his voice. "I'll get some witch-hazel."

But Mrs. Markey had lost her temper. "I don't see anything funny about a child being hurt!" she said in a trembling voice.

Little Ede meanwhile had been looking at her mother curiously. She noted that her own laugh had produced her mother's and she wondered if the same cause would always produce the same effect. So she chose this moment to throw back her head and laugh again.

To her mother the additional mirth added the final touch of hysteria to the situation. Pressing her handkerchief to her mouth she giggled irrepressibly. It was more than nervousness—she felt that in a peculiar way she was laughing with her child—they were laughing together.

It was in a way a defiance—those two against the world.

While Markey rushed up-stairs to the bathroom for ointment, his wife was walking up and down rocking the yelling boy in her arms.

"Please go home!" she broke out suddenly. "The child's badly hurt, and if you haven't the decency to be quiet, you'd better go home."

"Very well," said Edith, her own temper rising. "I've never seen any one make such a mountain out of——"

"Get out!" cried Mrs. Markey frantically. "There's the door, get out—I never want to see you in our house again. You or your brat either!"

Edith had taken her daughter's hand and was moving quickly toward the door, but at this remark she stopped and turned around, her face contracting with indignation.

"Don't you dare call her that!"

Mrs. Markey did not answer but continued walking up and down, muttering to herself and to Billy in an inaudible voice.

Edith began to cry.

"I will get out!" she sobbed, "I've never heard anybody so rude and c-common in my life. I'm glad your baby did get pushed down—he's nothing but a f-fat little fool anyhow."

Joe Markey reached the foot of the stairs just in time to hear this remark.

"Why, Mrs. Andros," he said sharply, "can't you see the child's hurt? You really ought to control yourself."

"Control m-myself!" exclaimed Edith brokenly. "You better ask her to c-control herself. I've never heard anybody so c-common in my life."

"She's insulting me!" Mrs. Markey was now livid with rage. "Did you hear what she said, Joe? I wish you'd put her out. If she won't go, just take her by the shoulders and put her out!"

"Don't you dare touch me!" cried Edith. "I'm going just as quick as I can find my c-coat!"

Blind with tears she took a step toward the hall. It was just at this moment that the door opened and John Andros walked anxiously in.

"John!" cried Edith, and fled to him wildly.

"What's the matter? Why, what's the matter?"

"They're—they're putting me out!" she wailed, collapsing against him. "He'd just started to take me by the shoulders and put me out. I want my coat!"

"That's not true," objected Markey hurriedly. "Nobody's going to put you out." He turned to John. "Nobody's going to put her out," he repeated. "She's——"

"What do you mean 'put her out'?" demanded John abruptly. "What's all this talk, anyhow?"

"Oh, let's go!" cried Edith. "I want to go. They're so *common*, John!"

"Look here!" Markey's face darkened. "You've said that about enough. You're acting sort of crazy."

"They called Ede a brat!"

For the second time that afternoon little Ede expressed emotion at an inopportune moment. Confused and frightened at the shouting voices, she began to cry, and her tears had the effect of conveying that she felt the insult in her heart.

"What's the idea of this?" broke out John. "Do you insult your guests in your own house?"

"It seems to me it's your wife that's done the insulting!" answered Markey crisply. "In fact, your baby there started all the trouble."

John gave a contemptuous snort. "Are you calling names at a little baby?" he inquired. "That's a fine manly business!"

"Don't talk to him, John," insisted Edith. "Find my coat!"

"You must be in a bad way," went on John angrily, "if you have to take out your temper on a helpless little baby."

"I never heard anything so damn twisted in my life," shouted Markey. "If that wife of yours would shut her mouth for a minute——"

"Wait a minute! You're not talking to a woman and child now——"

There was an incidental interruption. Edith had been fumbling on a chair for her coat, and Mrs. Markey had been watching her with hot, angry eyes. Suddenly she laid Billy down on the sofa, where he immediately stopped crying and pulled himself upright, and coming into the hall she quickly found Edith's coat and handed it to her without a word. Then she went back to the sofa, picked up Billy, and rocking him in her arms looked again at Edith with hot, angry eyes. The interruption had taken less than half a minute.

"Your wife comes in here and begins shouting around about how common we are!" burst out Markey violently. "Well, if we're so damn common, you'd better stay away! And, what's more, you'd better get out now!"

Again John gave a short, contemptuous laugh.

"You're not only common," he returned, "you're evidently an awful bully—when there's any helpless women and children around." He felt for the knob and swung the door open. "Come on, Edith."

Taking up her daughter in her arms, his wife stepped outside and John, still looking contemptuously at Markey, started to follow.

"Wait a minute!" Markey took a step forward; he was trembling slightly, and two large veins on his temple were suddenly full of blood. "You don't think you can get away with that, do you? With me?"

Without a word John walked out the door, leaving it open.

Edith, still weeping, had started for home. After following her with his eyes until she reached her own walk, John turned back toward the lighted doorway where Markey was slowly coming down the slippery steps. He took off his overcoat and hat, tossed them off the path onto the snow. Then, sliding a little on the iced walk, he took a step forward.

At the first blow, they both slipped and fell heavily to the sidewalk, half rising then, and again pulling each other to the ground. They found a better foothold in the thin snow to the side of the walk and rushed at each other, both swinging wildly and pressing out the snow into a pasty mud underfoot.

The street was deserted, and except for their short tired gasps and the padded sound as one or the other slipped down into the slushy mud, they fought in silence, clearly defined to each other by the full moonlight as well as by the amber glow that shone out of the open door. Several times they both slipped down together, and then for a while the conflict threshed about wildly on the lawn.

For ten, fifteen, twenty minutes they fought there senselessly in the moonlight. They had both taken off coats and vests at some silently agreed upon interval and now their shirts dripped from their backs in wet pulpy shreds. Both were torn and bleeding and so exhausted that they could stand only when by their position they mutually supported each other—the impact, the mere effort of a blow, would send them both to their hands and knees.

But it was not weariness that ended the business, and the very meaninglessness of the fight was a reason for not stopping. They stopped because once when they were straining at each other on the ground, they heard a man's footsteps coming along the sidewalk. They had rolled somehow into the shadow, and when they heard these footsteps they stopped fighting, stopped moving, stopped breathing, lay huddled together like two boys playing Indian until the footsteps had passed. Then, staggering to their feet, they looked at each other like two drunken men.

"I'll be damned if I'm going on with this thing any more," cried Markey thickly.

"I'm not going on any more either," said John Andros. "I've had enough of this thing."

Again they looked at each other, sulkily this time, as if each suspected the other of urging him to a renewal of the fight. Markey spat out a mouthful of blood from a cut lip; then he cursed softly, and picking up his coat and vest, shook off the snow from them in a surprised way, as if their comparative dampness was his only worry in the world.

"Want to come in and wash up?" he asked suddenly.

"No, thanks," said John. "I ought to be going home—my wife'll be worried."

He too picked up his coat and vest and then his overcoat and hat. Soaking wet and dripping with perspiration, it seemed absurd that less than half an hour ago he had been wearing all these clothes.

"Well—good night," he said hesitantly.

Suddenly they both walked toward each other and shook hands. It was no perfunctory hand-shake: John Andros's arm went around Markey's shoulder, and he patted him softly on the back for a little while.

"No harm done," he said brokenly.

"No—you?"

"No, no harm done."

"Well," said John Andros after a minute, "I guess I'll say good night."

Limping slightly and with his clothes over his arm, John Andros turned away. The moonlight was still bright as he left the dark patch of trampled ground and walked over the intervening lawn. Down at the station, half a mile away, he could hear the rumble of the seven o'clock train.

"But you must have been crazy," cried Edith brokenly. "I thought you were going to fix it all up there and shake hands. That's why I went away."

"Did you want us to fix it up?"

"Of course not, I never want to see them again. But I thought of course that was what you were going to do." She was touching the bruises on his neck and back with iodine as he sat placidly in a hot bath. "I'm going to get the doctor," she said insistently. "You may be hurt internally."

He shook his head. "Not a chance," he answered. "I don't want this to get all over town."

"I don't understand yet how it all happened."

"Neither do I." He smiled grimly. "I guess these baby parties are pretty rough affairs."

"Well, one thing—" suggested Edith hopefully, "I'm certainly glad we have beefsteak in the house for to-morrow's dinner."

"Why?"

"For your eye, of course. Do you know I came within an ace of ordering veal? Wasn't that the luckiest thing?"

Half an hour later, dressed except that his neck would accommodate no collar, John moved his limbs experimentally before the glass. "I believe I'll get myself in better shape," he said thoughtfully. "I must be getting old."

"You mean so that next time you can beat him?"

"I did beat him," he announced. "At least, I beat him as much as he beat me. And there isn't going to be any next time. Don't you go calling people common any more. If you get in any trouble, you just take your coat and go home. Understand?"

"Yes, dear," she said meekly. "I was very foolish and now I understand."

Out in the hall, he paused abruptly by the baby's door.

"Is she asleep?"

"Sound asleep. But you can go in and peek at her—just to say good night."

They tiptoed in and bent together over the bed. Little Ede, her cheeks flushed with health, her pink hands clasped tight together, was sleeping soundly in the cool, dark room. John reached over the railing of the bed and passed his hand lightly over the silken hair.

"She's asleep," he murmured in a puzzled way.

"Naturally, after such an afternoon."

"Miz Andros," the colored maid's stage whisper floated in from the hall, "Mr. and Miz Markey downstairs an' want to see you. Mr. Markey he's all cut up in pieces, ma'am. His face look like a roast beef. An' Miz Markey she 'pear mighty mad."

"Why, what incomparable nerve!" exclaimed Edith. "Just tell them we're not home. I wouldn't go down for anything in the world."

"You most certainly will." John's voice was hard and set.

"What?"

"You'll go down right now, and, what's more, whatever that other woman does, you'll apologize for what you said this afternoon. After that you don't ever have to see her again."

"Why—John, I can't."

"You've got to. And just remember that she probably hated to come over here just twice as much as you hate to go downstairs."

"Aren't you coming? Do I have to go alone?"

"I'll be down—in just a minute."

John Andros waited until she had closed the door behind her; then he reached over into the bed, and picking up his daughter, blankets and all, sat down in the rocking-chair holding her tightly in his arms. She moved a little, and he held his breath, but she was sleeping soundly, and in a moment she was resting quietly in the hollow of his elbow. Slowly he bent his head until his cheek was against her bright hair. "Dear little girl," he whispered. "Dear little girl, dear little girl."

John Andros knew at length what it was he had fought for so savagely that evening. He had it now, he possessed it forever, and for some time he sat there rocking very slowly to and fro in the darkness.

ROBERT PENN WARREN

~~~~~~

The Patented Gate and the
Mean Hamburger

YOU HAVE SEEN HIM a thousand times. You have seen him standing on the street corner on Saturday afternoon, in the little county-seat towns. He wears blue jean pants, or overalls washed to a pale pastel blue like the color of sky after a shower in spring, but because it is Saturday he has on a wool coat, an old one, perhaps the coat left from the suit he got married in a long time back. His long wrist bones hang out from the sleeves of the coat, the tendons showing along the bone like the dry twist of grapevine still corded on the stove-length of a hickory sapling you would find in his wood box beside his cookstove among the split chunks of gum and red oak. The big hands, with the knotted, cracked joints and the square, horn-thick nails, hang loose

off the wrist bone like clumsy, home-made tools hung on the wall
of a shed after work. If it is summer, he wears a straw hat with a
wide brim, the straw fraying loose around the edge. If it is winter, he
wears a felt hat, black once, but now weathered with streaks of dark
gray and dull purple in the sunlight. His face is long and bony, the jawbone long under the drawn-in cheeks. The flesh along the jawbone is
nicked in a couple of places where the unaccustomed razor has been
drawn over the leather-coarse skin. A tiny bit of blood crusts brown
where the nick is. The color of the face is red, a dull red like the red
clay mud or clay dust which clings to the bottom of his pants and to the
cast-iron-looking brogans on his feet, or a red like the color of a piece of
hewed cedar which has been left in the weather. The face does not
look alive. It seems to be molded from the clay or hewed from the cedar.
When the jaw moves, once, with its deliberate, massive motion on the
quid of tobacco, you are still not convinced. That motion is but the
cunning triumph of a mechanism concealed within.

But you see the eyes. You see that the eyes are alive. They are pale
blue or gray, set back under the deep brows and thorny eyebrows. They
are not wide, but are squinched up like eyes accustomed to wind or
sun or to measuring the stroke of the ax or to fixing the object over the
rifle sights. When you pass, you see that the eyes are alive and are
warily and dispassionately estimating you from the ambush of the
thorny brows. Then you pass on, and he stands there in that stillness
which is his gift.

With him may be standing two or three others like himself, but
they are still, too. They do not talk. The young men, who will be like
these men when they get to be fifty or sixty, are down at the beer parlor,
carousing and laughing with a high, whickering laugh. But the men on
the corner are long past all that. They are past many things. They have
endured and will endure in their silence and wisdom. They will stand
on the street corner and reject the world which passes under their level
gaze as a rabble passes under the guns of a rocky citadel around whose
base a slatternly town has assembled.

I had seen Jeff York a thousand times, or near, standing like that
on the street corner in town, while the people flowed past him, under
the distant and wary and dispassionate eyes in ambush. He would be
waiting for his wife and the three towheaded children who were walking around the town looking into store windows and at the people. After
a while they would come back to him, and then, wordlessly, he would
lead them to the store where they always did their trading. He would

go first, marching with a steady bent-kneed stride, setting the cast-iron brogans down deliberately on the cement; then his wife, a small woman with covert, sidewise, curious glances for the world, would follow, and behind her the towheads bunched together in a dazed, glory-struck way. In the store, when their turn came, Jeff York would move to the counter, accept the clerk's greeting, and then bend down from his height to catch the whispered directions of his wife. He would straighten up and say, "Gimme a sack of flahr, if'n you please." Then when the sack of flour had been brought, he would lean again to his wife for the next item. When the stuff had all been bought and paid for with the grease-thick, wadded dollar bills which he took from an old leather coin purse with a metal catch to it, he would heave it all together into his arms and march out, his wife and towheads behind him and his eyes fixed level over the heads of the crowd. He would march down the street and around to the hitching lot where the wagons were, and put his stuff into his wagon and cover it with an old quilt to wait till he got ready to drive out to his place.

For Jeff York had a place. That was what made him different from the other men who looked like him and with whom he stood on the street corner on Saturday afternoon. They were croppers, but he, Jeff York, had a place. But he stood with them because his father had stood with their fathers and his grandfathers with their grandfathers, or with men like their fathers and grandfathers, in other towns, in settlements in the mountains, in towns beyond the mountains. They were the great-great-great-grandsons of men who, half woodsmen and half farmers, had been shoved into the sand hills, into the limestone hills, into the barrens, two hundred, two hundred and fifty years before and had learned there the way to grabble a life out of the sand and the stone. And when the soil had leached away into the sand or burnt off the stone, they went on west, walking with the bent-kneed stride over the mountains, their eyes squinching warily in the gaunt faces, the rifle over the crooked arm, hunting a new place.

But there was a curse on them. They only knew the life they knew, and that life did not belong to the fat bottom lands, where the cane was head-tall, and to the grassy meadows and the rich swale. So they passed those places by and hunted for the place which was like home and where they could pick up the old life, with the same feel in the bones and the squirrel's bark sounding the same after first light. They had walked a long way, to the sand hills of Alabama, to the red country of North Mississippi and Louisiana, to the Barrens of Tennessee, to the Knobs of Kentucky and the scrub country of West Kentucky, to the Ozarks. Some of them had stopped in Cobb County, Tennessee, in the hilly eastern part of the county, and had built their cabins and dug up the ground for the corn patch. But the land had washed away there, too, and in the end they had come down out of the high land into the bottoms—for half of Cobb County is a rich, swelling country—where the corn was good and the tobacco unfurled a leaf like a yard of green velvet and the white houses stood among the cedars and tulip trees and maples. But they were not to live in the white houses with the limestone chimneys set strong at the end of each gable. No, they were to live in the shacks on the back of the farms, or in cabins not much different from the cabins they had once lived in two hundred years before over the mountains or, later, in the hills of Cobb County. But the shacks and the cabins now stood on somebody else's ground, and the curse which they had brought with them over the mountain trail, more precious than the bullet mold or grandma's quilt, the curse which was the very feeling in the bones and the habit in the hand, had come full circle.

Jeff York was one of those men, but he had broken the curse. It had taken him more than thirty years to do it, from the time when he was nothing but a big boy until he was fifty. It had taken him from sun to sun, year in and year out, and all the sweat in his body, and all the power of rejection he could muster, until the very act of rejection had become a kind of pleasure, a dark, secret, savage dissipation, like an obsessing vice. But those years had given him his place, sixty acres with a house and barn.

When he bought the place, it was not very good. The land was run-down from years of neglect and abuse. But Jeff York put brush in the gullies to stop the wash and planted clover on the run-down fields. He mended the fences, rod by rod. He patched the roof on the little house and propped up the porch, buying the lumber and shingles almost piece by piece and one by one as he could spare the sweat-bright and grease-slick quarters and half-dollars out of his leather purse. Then he painted the house. He painted it white, for he knew that that was the color you painted a house sitting back from the road with its couple of maples, beyond the clover field.

Last, he put up the gate. It was a patented gate, the kind you can ride up to and open by pulling on a pull rope without getting off your horse or out of your buggy or wagon. It had a high pair of posts, well braced and with a high crossbar between, and the bars for the opening mechanism extending on each side. It was painted white, too. Jeff was even prouder of the gate than he was of the place. Lewis Simmons, who lived next to Jeff's place, swore he had seen Jeff come out after dark on a mule and ride in and out of that gate, back and forth, just for the pleasure of pulling on the rope and making the mechanism work. The gate was the seal Jeff York had put on all the years of sweat and rejection. He could sit on his porch on a Sunday afternoon in summer, before milking time, and look down the rise, down the winding dirt track, to the white gate beyond the clover, and know what he needed to know about all the years passed.

Meanwhile Jeff York had married and had had the three towheads. His wife was twenty years or so younger than he, a small, dark woman, who walked with her head bowed a little and from that humble and unprovoking posture stole sidewise, secret glances at the world from eyes which were brown or black—you never could tell which because you never remembered having looked her straight in the eye—and which were surprisingly bright in that sidewise, secret flicker, like the eyes of a small, cunning bird which surprise you from the brush. When they came to town she moved along the street, with a child in her arms or later with the three trailing behind her, and stole her looks at the world. She wore a calico dress, dun-colored, which hung loose to conceal whatever shape her thin body had, and in winter over the dress a brown wool coat with a scrap of fur at the collar which looked like some tattered growth of fungus feeding on old wood. She wore black high-heeled shoes, slippers of some kind, which she kept polished and which surprised you under that dress and coat. In the slippers she moved with a slightly limping, stealthy gait, almost sliding them along the pavement, as though she had not fully mastered the complicated trick required to use them properly. You knew that she wore them only when she came to town, that she carried them wrapped up in a piece of newspaper until their wagon had reached the first house on the outskirts of town, and that, on the way back, at the same point, she would take them off and wrap them up again and hold the bundle in her lap until she got home. If the weather happened to be bad, or if it was winter, she would have a pair of old brogans under the wagon seat.

It was not that Jeff York was a hard man and kept his wife in clothes that were as bad as those worn by the poorest of the women of the croppers. In fact, some of the cropper women, poor or not, black or white, managed to buy dresses with some color in them and proper hats, and went to the moving picture show on Saturday afternoon. But Jeff still owed a little money on his place, less than two hundred dollars, which he had had to borrow to rebuild his barn after it was struck by lightning. He had, in fact, never been entirely out of debt. He had lost a mule which had got out on the highway and been hit by a truck. That had set him back. One of his towheads had been sickly for a couple of winters. He had not been in deep, but he was not a man, with all those years of rejection behind him, to forget the meaning of those years. He was good enough to his family. Nobody ever said the contrary. But he was good to them in terms of all the years he had lived through. He did what he could afford. He bought the towheads a ten-cent bag of colored candy every Saturday afternoon for them to suck on during the ride home in the wagon, and the last thing before they left town, he always took the lot of them over to the dogwagon to get hamburgers and orange pop.

The towheads were crazy about hamburgers. And so was his wife, for that matter. You could tell it, even if she didn't say anything, for she would lift her bowed-forward head a little, and her face would brighten, and she would run her tongue out to wet her lips just as the plate with the hamburger would be set on the counter before her. But all those folks, like Jeff York and his family, like hamburgers, with pickle and onions and mustard and tomato catsup, the whole works. It is something different. They stay out in the country and eat hog-meat, when they can get it, and greens and corn bread and potatoes, and nothing but a pinch of salt to brighten it on the tongue, and when they get to town and get hold of beef and wheat bread and all the stuff to jack up the flavor, they have to swallow to keep the mouth from flooding before they even take the first bite.

So the last thing every Saturday, Jeff York would take his family over to Slick Hardin's *Dew Drop Inn Diner* and give them the treat. The diner was built like a railway coach, but it was set on a concrete foundation on a lot just off the main street of town. At each end the concrete was painted to show wheels. Slick Hardin kept the grass just in front of the place pretty well mowed and one or two summers he even had a couple of flower beds in the middle of that shirttail-size lawn. Slick had a good business. For a few years he had been a prelim fighter over in Nashville and had got his name in the papers a few times. So he was a kind of hero, with the air of romance about him. He had been born, however, right in town and, as soon as he had found out he wasn't ever going to be good enough to be a real fighter, he had come back home and started the dogwagon, the first one ever in town. He was a slick-skinned fellow, about thirty-five, prematurely bald, with his head slick all over. He had big eyes, pale blue and slick looking like agates. When he said something that he thought smart, he would roll his eyes around, slick in his head like marbles, to see who was laughing. Then he'd wink. He had done very well with his business, for despite the fact that he had picked up city ways and a lot of city talk, he still remembered enough to deal with the country people, and they were the ones who brought the dimes in. People who lived right there in town, except for school kids in the afternoon and the young toughs from the pool room or men on the night shift down at the railroad, didn't often get around to the dogwagon.

Slick Hardin was perhaps trying to be smart when he said what he did to Mrs. York. Perhaps he had forgotten, just for that moment, that people like Jeff York and his wife didn't like to be kidded, at least not in that way. He said what he did, and then grinned and rolled his eyes around to see if some of the other people present were thinking it was funny.

Mrs. York was sitting on a stool in front of the counter, flanked on one side by Jeff York and on the other by the three towheads. She had just sat down to wait for the hamburger—there were several orders in ahead of the York order—and had been watching in her sidewise fashion every move of Slick Hardin's hands as he patted the pink meat onto the hot slab and wiped the split buns over the greasy iron to make them ready to receive it. She always watched him like that, and when the hamburger was set before her she would wet her lips with her tongue.

That day Slick set the hamburger down in front of Mrs. York, and said, "Anybody likes hamburger much as you, Mrs. York, ought to git him a hamburger stand."

Mrs. York flushed up, and didn't say anything, staring at her plate. Slick rolled his eyes to see how it was going, and somebody down the counter snickered. Slick looked back at the Yorks, and if he had not been so encouraged by the snicker he might, when he saw Jeff York's face, have hesitated before going on with his kidding. People like Jeff York are touchous, and they are especially touchous about the women-folks, and you do not make jokes with or about their womenfolks unless it is perfectly plain that the joke is a very special kind of friendly joke. The snicker down the counter had defined the joke as not entirely friendly. Jeff was looking at Slick, and something was growing slowly in that hewed-cedar face, and back in the gray eyes in the ambush of thorny brows.

But Slick did not notice. The snicker had encouraged him, and so he said, "Yeah, if I liked them hamburgers much as you, I'd buy me a hamburger stand. Fact, I'm selling this one. You want to buy it?"

There was another snicker, louder, and Jeff York, whose hamburger had been about half way to his mouth for another bite, laid it down deliberately on his plate. But whatever might have happened at that moment did not happen. It did not happen because Mrs. York lifted her flushed face, looked straight at Slick Hardin, swallowed hard to get down a piece of the hamburger or to master her nerve, and said in a sharp, strained voice, "You sellen this place?"

There was complete silence. Nobody had expected her to say anything. The chances were she had never said a word in that diner in the couple of hundred times she had been in it. She had come in with Jeff York and, when a stool had come vacant, had sat down, and Jeff had said, "Gimme five hamburgers, if'n you please, and make 'em well done, and five bottles of orange pop." Then, after the eating was over, he had always laid down seventy-five cents on the counter—that is, after there were five hamburger-eaters in the family—and walked out, putting his brogans down slow, and his wife and kids following without a word. But now she spoke up and asked the question, in that strained, artificial voice, and everybody, including her husband, looked at her with surprise.

As soon as he could take it in, Slick Hardin replied, "Yeah, I'm selling it."

She swallowed hard again, but this time it could not have been hamburger, and demanded, "What you asken fer hit?"

Slick looked at her in the new silence, half shrugged, a little contemptuously, and said, "Fourteen hundred and fifty dollars."

She looked back at him, while the blood ebbed from her face. "Hit's a lot of money," she said in a flat tone, and returned her gaze to the hamburger on her plate.

"Lady," Slick said defensively, "I got that much money tied up here. Look at that there stove. It is a *Heat Master* and they cost. Them coffee urns, now. Money can't buy no better. And this here lot, lady, the diner sets on. Anybody knows I got that much money tied up here. I got more. This lot cost me more'n . . ." He suddenly realized that she was not listening to him. And he must have realized, too, that she didn't have a dime in the world and couldn't buy his diner, and that he was making a fool of himself, defending his price. He stopped abruptly, shrugged his shoulders, and then swung his wide gaze down the counter to pick out somebody to wink to.

But before he got the wink off, Jeff York had said, "Mr. Hardin."

Slick looked at him and asked, "Yeah?"

"She didn't mean no harm," Jeff York said. "She didn't mean to be messen in yore business."

Slick shrugged. "Ain't no skin off my nose," he said. "Ain't no secret I'm selling out. My price ain't no secret neither."

Mrs. York bowed her head over her plate. She was chewing a mouthful of her hamburger with a slow, abstracted motion of her jaw, and you knew that it was flavorless on her tongue.

That was, of course, on a Saturday. On Thursday afternoon of the next week Slick was in the diner alone. It was the slack time, right in the middle of the afternoon. Slick, as he told it later, was wiping off the stove and wasn't noticing. He was sort of whistling to himself, he said. He had a way of whistling soft through his teeth. But he wasn't whistling loud, he said, not so loud he wouldn't have heard the door open or the steps if she hadn't come gumshoeing in on him to stand there waiting in the middle of the floor until he turned round and was so surprised he nearly had heart failure. He had thought he was there alone, and there she was, watching every move he was making, like a cat watching a goldfish swim in a bowl.

"Howdy-do," he said, when he got his breath back.

"This place still fer sale?" she asked him.

"Yeah, lady," he said.

"What you asken fer hit?"

"Lady, I done told you," Slick replied, "fourteen hundred and fifty dollars."

"Hit's a heap of money," she said.

Slick started to tell her how much money he had tied up there, but before he had got going, she had turned and slipped out of the door.

"Yeah," Slick said later to the men who came into the diner, "me like a fool starting to tell her how much money I got tied up here when I knowed she didn't have a dime. That woman's crazy. She must have walked that five or six miles in here just to ask me something she already knowed the answer to. And then turned right round and walked out. But I am selling me this place. I'm tired of slinging hash to them hicks. I got me some connections over in Nashville and I'm gonna open me a place over there. A cigar stand and about three pool tables and maybe some beer. I'll have me a sort of club in the back. You know, membership cards to get in, where the boys will play a little game. Just sociable. I got good connections over in Nashville. I'm selling this place. But that woman, she ain't got a dime. She ain't gonna buy it."

But she did.

On Saturday Jeff York led his family over to the diner. They ate hamburgers without a word and marched out. After they had gone, Slick said, "Looks like she ain't going to make the invest-mint. Gonna buy a block of bank stock instead." Then he rolled his eyes, located a brother down the counter, and winked.

It was almost the end of the next week before it happened. What had been going on inside the white house out on Jeff York's place nobody knew or was to know. Perhaps she just starved him out, just not doing the cooking or burning everything. Perhaps she just quit attending to the children properly and he had to come back tired from work and take care of them. Perhaps she just lay in bed at night and talked and talked to him, asking him to buy it, nagging him all night long, while he would fall asleep and then wake up with a start to hear her voice still going on. Or perhaps she just turned her face away from him and wouldn't let him touch her. He was a lot older than she, and she was probably the only woman he had ever had. He had been too ridden by his dream and his passion for rejection during all the years before to lay even a finger on a woman. So she had him there. Because he was a lot older and because he had never had another woman. But perhaps she used none of these methods. She was a small, dark, cunning woman, with a sidewise look from her lowered face, and she could have thought up ways of her own, no doubt.

Whatever she thought up, it worked. On Friday morning Jeff York went to the bank. He wanted to mortgage his place, he told Todd Sullivan, the president. He wanted fourteen hundred and fifty dollars, he said. Todd Sullivan would not let him have it. He already owed the bank one hundred and sixty dollars and the best he could get on a mortgage was eleven hundred dollars. That was in 1935 and then farmland wasn't worth much and half the land in the country was mortgaged anyway. Jeff York sat in the chair by Todd Sullivan's desk and didn't say anything. Eleven hundred dollars would not do him any good. Take off the hundred and sixty he owed and it wouldn't be but a little over nine hundred dollars clear to him. He sat there quietly for a minute, apparently turning that fact over in his head. Then Todd Sullivan asked him, "How much you say you need?"

Jeff York told him.

"What you want it for?" Todd Sullivan asked.

He told him that.

"I tell you," Todd Sullivan said, "I don't want to stand in the way of a man bettering himself. Never did. That diner ought to be a good proposition, all right, and I don't want to stand in your way if you want to come to town and better yourself. It will be a step up from that farm for you, and I like a man has got ambition. The bank can't lend you the money, not on that piece of property. But I tell you what I'll do. I'll buy your place. I got me some walking horses I'm keeping out on my father's place. But I could use me a little place of my own. For my horses. I'll give you seventeen hundred for it. Cash."

Jeff York did not say anything to that. He looked slow at Todd Sullivan as though he did not understand.

"Seventeen hundred," the banker repeated. "That's a good figure. For these times."

Jeff was not looking at him now. He was looking out the window, across the alleyway—Todd Sullivan's office was in the back of the bank. The banker, telling about it later when the doings of Jeff York had become for a moment a matter of interest, said, "I thought he hadn't even heard me. He looked like he was half asleep or something. I coughed to sort of wake him up. You know the way you do. I didn't want to rush him. You can't rush those people, you know. But I couldn't sit there all day. I had offered him a fair price."

It was, as a matter of fact, a fair price for the times, when the bottom was out of everything in the section.

Jeff York took it. He took the seventeen hundred dollars and bought the dogwagon with it, and rented a little house on the edge of town and moved in with his wife and the towheads. The first day after they got settled, Jeff York and his wife went over to the diner to get instructions from Slick about running the place. He showed Mrs. York all about how to work the coffee machine and the stove, and how to make up the sandwiches, and how to clean the place up after herself. She fried up hamburgers for all of them, herself, her husband, and Slick Hardin, for practice, and they ate the hamburgers while a couple of hangers-on watched them. "Lady," Slick said, for he had money in his pocket and was heading out for Nashville on the seven o'clock train that night, and was feeling expansive, "lady, you sure fling a mean hamburger."

He wiped the last crumbs and mustard off his lips, got his valise from behind the door, and said, "Lady, git in there and pitch. I hope you make a million hamburgers." Then he stepped out into the bright fall sunshine and walked away whistling up the street, whistling through his teeth and rolling his eyes as though there were somebody to wink to. That was the last anybody in town ever saw of Slick Hardin.

The next day, Jeff York worked all day down at the diner. He was scrubbing up the place inside and cleaning up the trash which had accumulated behind it. He burned all the trash. Then he gave the place a good coat of paint outside, white paint. That took him two days. Then he touched up the counter inside with varnish. He straightened up the sign out front, which had begun to sag a little. He had that place looking spick and span.

Then on the fifth day after they got settled—it was Sunday—he took a walk in the country. It was along toward sun when he started out, not late, as a matter of fact, for by October the days are shortening up. He walked out the Curtisville pike and out the cut-off leading to his farm. When he entered the cut-off, about a mile from his own place, it was still light enough for the Bowdoins, who had a filling station at the corner, to see him plain when he passed.

The next time anybody saw him was on Monday morning about six o'clock. A man taking milk into town saw him. He was hanging from the main cross bar of the white patented gate. He had jumped off the gate. But he had propped the thing open so there wouldn't be any chance of clambering back up on it if his neck didn't break when he jumped and he should happen to change his mind.

But that was an unnecessary precaution, as it developed. Dr. Stauffer said that his neck was broken very clean. "A man who can break a neck as clean as that could make a living at it," Dr. Stauffer said. And added, "If he's damned sure it ain't ever his own neck."

Mrs. York was much cut up by her husband's death. People were sympathetic and helpful, and out of a mixture of sympathy and curiosity she got a good starting trade at the diner. And the trade kept right on. She got so she didn't hang her head and look sidewise at you and the world. She would look straight at you. She got so she could walk in high heels without giving the impression that it was a trick she was learning. She wasn't a bad-looking woman, as a matter of fact, once she had caught on how to fix herself up a little. The railroad men and the pool hall gang liked to hang out there and kid with her. Also, they said, she flung a mean hamburger.

EUDORA WELTY

Lily Daw and the Three Ladies

MRS. WATTS and Mrs. Carson were both in the post office in Victory when the letter came from the Ellisville Institute for the Feeble-Minded of Mississippi. Aimee Slocum, with her hand still full of mail, ran out in front and handed it straight to Mrs. Watts, and they all three read it together. Mrs. Watts held it taut between her pink hands, and Mrs. Carson underscored each line slowly with her thimbled finger. Everybody else in the post office wondered what was up now.

"What will Lily say," beamed Mrs. Carson at last, "when we tell her we're sending her to Ellisville!"

"She'll be tickled to death," said Mrs. Watts, and added in a guttural voice to a deaf lady, "Lily Daw's getting in at Ellisville!"

"Don't you all dare go off and tell Lily without me!" called Aimee Slocum, trotting back to finish putting up the mail.

"Do you suppose they'll look after her down there?" Mrs. Carson began to carry on a conversation with a group of Baptist ladies waiting in the post office. She was the Baptist preacher's wife.

"I've always heard it was lovely down there, but crowded," said one.

"Lily lets people walk over her so," said another.

"Last night at the tent show—" said another, and then popped her hand over her mouth.

"Don't mind me, I know there are such things in the world," said Mrs. Carson, looking down and fingering the tape measure which hung over her bosom.

"Oh, Mrs. Carson. Well, anyway, last night at the tent show, why, the man was just before making Lily buy a ticket to get in."

"A ticket!"

"Till my husband went up and explained she wasn't bright, and so did everybody else."

The ladies all clucked their tongues.

"Oh, it was a very nice show," said the lady who had gone. "And Lily acted so nice. She was a perfect lady—just set in her seat and stared."

"Oh, she can be a lady—she can be," said Mrs. Carson, shaking her head and turning her eyes up. "That's just what breaks your heart."

"Yes'm, she kept her eyes on—what's that thing makes all the commotion?—the xylophone," said the lady. "Didn't turn her head to the right or to the left the whole time. Set in front of me."

"The point is, what did she do after the show?" asked Mrs. Watts practically. "Lily has gotten so she is very mature for her age."

"Oh, Etta!" protested Mrs. Carson, looking at her wildly for a moment.

"And that's how come we are sending her to Ellisville," finished Mrs. Watts.

"I'm ready, you all," said Aimee Slocum, running out with white powder all over her face. "Mail's up. I don't know how good it's up."

"Well, of course, I do hope it's for the best," said several of the other ladies. They did not go at once to take their mail out of their boxes; they felt a little left out.

The three women stood at the foot of the water tank.

"To find Lily is a different thing," said Aimee Slocum.

"Where in the wide world do you suppose she'd be?" It was Mrs. Watts who was carrying the letter.

"I don't see a sign of her either on this side of the street or on the other side," Mrs. Carson declared as they walked along.

Ed Newton was stringing Redbird school tablets on the wire across the store.

"If you're after Lily, she come in here while ago and tole me she was fixin' to git married," he said.

"Ed Newton!" cried the ladies all together, clutching one another. Mrs. Watts began to fan herself at once with the letter from Ellisville. She wore widow's black, and the least thing made her hot.

"Why she is not. She's going to Ellisville, Ed," said Mrs. Carson gently. "Mrs. Watts and I and Aimee Slocum are paying her way out of our own pockets. Besides, the boys of Victory are on their honor. Lily's not going to get married, that's just an idea she's got in her head."

"More power to you, ladies," said Ed Newton, spanking himself with a tablet.

When they came to the bridge over the railroad tracks, there was Estelle Mabers, sitting on a rail. She was slowly drinking an orange Ne-Hi.

"Have you seen Lily?" they asked her.

"I'm supposed to be out here watching for her now," said the Mabers girl, as though she weren't there yet. "But for Jewel—Jewel says Lily come in the store while ago and picked out a two-ninety-eight hat and wore it off. Jewel wants to swap her something else for it."

"Oh, Estelle, Lily says she's going to get married!" cried Aimee Slocum.

"Well, I declare," said Estelle; she never understood anything.

Loralee Adkins came riding by in her Willys-Knight, tooting the horn to find out what they were talking about.

Aimee threw up her hands and ran out into the street. "Loralee, Loralee, you got to ride us up to Lily Daw's. She's up yonder fixing to get married!"

"Hop in, my land!"

"Well, that just goes to show you right now," said Mrs. Watts, groaning as she was helped into the back seat. "What we've got to do is persuade Lily it will be nicer to go to Ellisville."

"Just to think!"

While they rode around the corner Mrs. Carson was going on in her sad voice, sad as the soft noises in the hen house at twilight. "We buried Lily's poor defenseless mother. We gave Lily all her food and kindling and every stitch she had on. Sent her to Sunday school to learn the Lord's teachings, had her baptized a Baptist. And when her old father commenced beating her and tried to cut her head off with the butcher knife, why, we went and took her away from him and gave her a place to stay."

The paintless frame house with all the weather vanes was three stories high in places and had yellow and violet stained-glass windows in front and gingerbread around the porch. It leaned steeply to one side, toward the railroad, and the front steps were gone. The car full of ladies drew up under the cedar tree.

"Now Lily's almost grown up," Mrs. Carson continued. "In fact, she's grown," she concluded, getting out.

"Talking about getting married," said Mrs. Watts disgustedly. "Thanks, Loralee, you run on home."

They climbed over the dusty zinnias onto the porch and walked through the open door without knocking.

"There certainly is always a funny smell in this house. I say it every time I come," said Aimee Slocum.

Lily was there, in the dark of the hall, kneeling on the floor by a small open trunk.

When she saw them she put a zinnia in her mouth, and held still.

"Hello, Lily," said Mrs. Carson reproachfully.

"Hello," said Lily. In a minute she gave a suck on the zinnia stem that sounded exactly like a jay bird. There she sat, wearing a petticoat for a dress, one of the things Mrs. Carson kept after her about. Her milky-yellow hair streamed freely down from under a new hat. You could see the wavy scar on her throat if you knew it was there.

Mrs. Carson and Mrs. Watts, the two fattest, sat in the double rocker. Aimee Slocum sat on the wire chair donated from the drugstore that burned.

"Well, what are you doing, Lily?" asked Mrs. Watts, who led the rocking.

Lily smiled.

The trunk was old and lined with yellow and brown paper, with an asterisk pattern showing in darker circles and rings. Mutely the ladies indicated to each other that they did not know where in the world it had come from. It was empty except for two bars of soap and a green washcloth, which Lily was now trying to arrange in the bottom.

"Go on and tell us what you're doing, Lily," said Aimee Slocum.

"Packing, silly," said Lily.

"Where are you going?"

"Going to get married, and I bet you wish you was me now," said Lily. But shyness overcame her suddenly, and she popped the zinnia back into her mouth.

"Talk to me, dear," said Mrs. Carson. "Tell old Mrs. Carson why you want to get married."

"No," said Lily, after a moment's hesitation.

"Well, we've thought of something that will be so much nicer," said Mrs. Carson. "Why don't you go to Ellisville!"

"Won't that be lovely?" said Mrs. Watts. "Goodness, yes."

"It's a lovely place," said Aimee Slocum uncertainly.

"You've got bumps on your face," said Lily.

"Aimee, dear, you stay out of this, if you don't mind," said Mrs.

Carson anxiously. "I don't know what it is comes over Lily when you come around her."

Lily stared at Aimee Slocum meditatively.

"There! Wouldn't you like to go to Ellisville now?" asked Mrs. Carson.

"No'm," said Lily.

"Why not?" All the ladies leaned down toward her in impressive astonishment.

"'Cause I'm goin' to get married," said Lily.

"Well, and who are you going to marry, dear?" asked Mrs. Watts. She knew how to pin people down and make them deny what they'd already said.

Lily bit her lip and began to smile. She reached into the trunk and held up both cakes of soap and wagged them.

"Tell us," challenged Mrs. Watts. "Who you're going to marry, now."

"A man last night."

There was a gasp from each lady. The possible reality of a lover descended suddenly like a summer hail over their heads. Mrs. Watts stood up and balanced herself.

"One of those show fellows! A musician!" she cried.

Lily looked up in admiration.

"Did he—did he do anything to you?" In the long run, it was still only Mrs. Watts who could take charge.

"Oh, yes'm," said Lily. She patted the cakes of soap fastidiously with the tips of her small fingers and tucked them in with the wash-cloth.

"What?" demanded Aimee Slocum, rising up and tottering before her scream. "What?" she called out in the hall.

"Don't ask her what," said Mrs. Carson, coming up behind. "Tell me, Lily—just yes or no—are you the same as you were?"

"He had a red coat," said Lily graciously. "He took little sticks and went *ping-pong! ding-dong!*"

"Oh, I think I'm going to faint," said Aimee Slocum, but they said, "No, you're not."

"The xylophone!" cried Mrs. Watts. "The xylophone player! Why, the coward, he ought to be run out of town on a rail!"

"Out of town? He is out of town, by now," cried Aimee. "Can't you read?—the sign in the café—Victory on the ninth, Como on the tenth? He's in Como. Como!"

"All right! We'll bring him back!" cried Mrs. Watts. "He can't get away from me!"

"Hush," said Mrs. Carson. "I don't think it's any use following that line of reasoning at all. It's better in the long run for him to be gone out of our lives for good and all. That kind of a man. He was after Lily's body alone and he wouldn't ever in this world make the poor little thing happy, even if we went out and forced him to marry her like he ought—at the point of a gun."

"Still—" began Aimee, her eyes widening.

"Shut up," said Mrs. Watts. "Mrs. Carson, you're right, I expect."

"This is my hope chest—see?" said Lily politely in the pause that followed. "You haven't even looked at it. I've already got soap and a washrag. And I have my hat—on. What are you all going to give me?"

"Lily," said Mrs. Watts, starting over, "we'll give you lots of gorgeous things if you'll only go to Ellisville instead of getting married."

"What will you give me?" asked Lily.

"I'll give you a pair of hemstitched pillowcases," said Mrs. Carson.

"I'll give you a big caramel cake," said Mrs. Watts.

"I'll give you a souvenir from Jackson—a little toy bank," said Aimee Slocum. "Now will you go?"

"No," said Lily.

"I'll give you a pretty little Bible with your name on it in real gold," said Mrs. Carson.

"What if I was to give you a pink crêpe de Chine brassière with adjustable shoulder straps?" asked Mrs. Watts grimly.

"Oh, Etta."

"Well, she needs it," said Mrs. Watts. "What would they think if she ran all over Ellisville in a petticoat looking like a Fiji?"

"I wish *I* could go to Ellisville," said Aimee Slocum luringly.

"What will they have for me down there?" asked Lily softly.

"Oh! lots of things. You'll have baskets to weave, I expect. . . ." Mrs. Carson looked vaguely at the others.

"Oh, yes indeed, they will let you make all sorts of baskets," said Mrs. Watts; then her voice too trailed off.

"No'm, I'd rather get married," said Lily.

"Lily Daw! Now that's just plain stubbornness!" cried Mrs. Watts. "You almost said you'd go and then you took it back!"

"We've all asked God, Lily," said Mrs. Carson finally, "and God seemed to tell us—Mr. Carson, too—that the place where you ought to be, so as to be happy, was Ellisville."

Lily looked reverent, but still stubborn.

"We've really just got to get her there—now!" screamed Aimee Slocum all at once. "Suppose—! She can't stay here!"

"Oh, no, no, no," said Mrs. Carson hurriedly. "We mustn't think that."

They sat sunken in despair.

"Could I take my hope chest—to go to Ellisville?" asked Lily shyly, looking at them sidewise.

"Why, yes," said Mrs. Carson blankly.

Silently they rose once more to their feet.

"Oh, if I could just take my hope chest!"

"All the time it was just her hope chest," Aimee whispered.

Mrs. Watts struck her palms together. "It's settled!"

"Praise the fathers," murmured Mrs. Carson.

Lily looked up at them, and her eyes gleamed. She cocked her head and spoke out in a proud imitation of someone—someone utterly unknown.

"O.K.—Toots!"

The ladies had been nodding and smiling and backing away toward the door.

"I think I'd better stay," said Mrs. Carson, stopping in her tracks. "Where—where could she have learned that terrible expression?"

"Pack up," said Mrs. Watts. "Lily Daw is leaving for Ellisville on Number One."

In the station the train was puffing. Nearly everyone in Victory was hanging around waiting for it to leave. The Victory Civic Band had assembled without any orders and was scattered through the crowd. Ed Newton gave false signals to start on his bass horn. A crate full of baby chickens got loose on the platform. Everybody wanted to see Lily all dressed up, but Mrs. Carson and Mrs. Watts had sneaked her into the train from the other side of the tracks.

The two ladies were going to travel as far as Jackson to help Lily change trains and be sure she went in the right direction.

Lily sat between them on the plush seat with her hair combed and pinned up into a knot under a small blue hat which was Jewel's exchange for the pretty one. She wore a traveling dress made out of part of Mrs. Watts' last summer's mourning. Pink straps glowed through. She had a purse and a Bible and a warm cake in a box, all in her lap.

Aimee Slocum had been getting the outgoing mail stamped and

bundled. She stood in the aisle of the coach now, tears shaking from her eyes.

"Good-bye, Lily," she said. She was the one who felt things.

"Good-bye, silly," said Lily.

"Oh, dear, I hope they get our telegram to meet her in Ellisville!" Aimee cried sorrowfully, as she thought how far away it was. "And it was so hard to get it all in ten words, too."

"Get off, Aimee, before the train starts and you break your neck," said Mrs. Watts, all settled and waving her dressy fan gaily. "I declare, it's so hot, as soon as we get a few miles out of town I'm going to slip my corset down."

"Oh, Lily, don't cry down there. Just be good, and do what they tell you—it's all because they love you." Aimee drew her mouth down. She was backing away, down the aisle.

Lily laughed. She pointed across Mrs. Carson's bosom out the window toward a man. He had stepped off the train and just stood there, by himself. He was a stranger and wore a cap.

"Look," she said, laughing softly through her fingers.

"Don't—look," said Mrs. Carson very distinctly, as if, out of all she had ever spoken, she would impress these two solemn words upon Lily's soft little brain. She added, "Don't look at anything till you get to Ellisville."

Outside, Aimee Slocum was crying so hard she almost ran into the stranger. He wore a cap and was short and seemed to have on perfume, if such a thing could be.

"Could you tell me, madam," he said, "where a little lady lives in this burg name of Miss Lily Daw?" He lifted his cap—and he had red hair.

"What do you want to know for?" Aimee asked before she knew it.

"Talk louder," said the stranger. He almost whispered, himself.

"She's gone away—she's gone to Ellisville!"

"Gone?"

"Gone to Ellisville!"

"Well, I like that!" The man stuck out his bottom lip and puffed till his hair jumped.

"What business did you have with Lily?" cried Aimee suddenly.

"We was only going to get married, that's all," said the man.

Aimee Slocum started to scream in front of all those people. She almost pointed to the long black box she saw lying on the ground at the man's feet. Then she jumped back in fright.

"The xylophone! The xylophone!" she cried, looking back and forth from the man to the hissing train. Which was more terrible? The bell began to ring hollowly, and the man was talking.

"Did you say Ellisville? That in the state of Mississippi?" Like lightning he had pulled out a red notebook entitled, "Permanent Facts & Data." He wrote down something. "I don't hear well."

Aimee nodded her head up and down, and circled around him.

Under "Ellis-Ville Miss" he was drawing a line; now he was flicking it with two little marks. "Maybe she didn't say she would. Maybe she said she wouldn't." He suddenly laughed very loudly, after the way he had whispered. Aimee jumped back. "Women!—Well, if we play anywheres near Ellisville, Miss., in the future I may look her up and I may not," he said.

The bass horn sounded the true signal for the band to begin. White steam rushed out of the engine. Usually the train stopped for only a minute in Victory, but the engineer knew Lily from waving at her, and he knew this was her big day.

"Wait!" Aimee Slocum did scream. "Wait, mister! I can get her for you. Wait, Mister Engineer! Don't go!"

Then there she was back on the train, screaming in Mrs. Carson's and Mrs. Watts's faces.

"The xylophone player! The xylophone player to marry her! Yonder he is!"

"Nonsense," murmured Mrs. Watts, peering over the others to look where Aimee pointed. "If he's there I don't see him. Where is he? You're looking at One-Eye Beasley."

"The little man with the cap—no, with the red hair! Hurry!"

"Is that really him?" Mrs. Carson asked Mrs. Watts in wonder. "Mercy! He's small, isn't he?"

"Never saw him before in my life!" cried Mrs. Watts. But suddenly she shut up her fan.

"Come on! This is a train we're on!" cried Aimee Slocum. Her nerves were all unstrung.

"All right, don't have a conniption fit, girl," said Mrs. Watts. "Come on," she said thickly to Mrs. Carson.

"Where are we going now?" asked Lily as they struggled down the aisle.

"We're taking you to get married," said Mrs. Watts. "Mrs. Carson, you'd better phone up your husband right there in the station."

"But I don't want to git married," said Lily, beginning to whimper. "I'm going to Ellisville."

"Hush, and we'll all have some ice-cream cones later," whispered Mrs. Carson.

Just as they climbed down the steps at the back end of the train, the band went into "Independence March."

The xylophone player was still there, patting his foot. He came up and said, "Hello, Toots. What's up—tricks?" and kissed Lily with a smack, after which she hung her head.

"So you're the young man we've heard so much about," said Mrs. Watts. Her smile was brilliant. "Here's your little Lily."

"What say?" asked the xylophone player.

"My husband happens to be the Baptist preacher of Victory," said Mrs. Carson in a loud, clear voice. "Isn't that lucky? I can get him here in five minutes: I know exactly where he is."

They were in a circle around the xylophone player, all going into the white waiting room.

"Oh, I feel just like crying, at a time like this," said Aimee Slocum. She looked back and saw the train moving slowly away, going under the bridge at Main Street. Then it disappeared around the curve.

"Oh, the hope chest!" Aimee cried in a stricken voice.

"And whom have we the pleasure of addressing?" Mrs. Watts was shouting, while Mrs. Carson was ringing up the telephone.

The band went on playing. Some of the people thought Lily was on the train, and some swore she wasn't. Everybody cheered, though, and a straw hat was thrown into the telephone wires.

EUDORA WELTY

Death of a Traveling Salesman

R. J. BOWMAN, who for fourteen years had traveled for a shoe company through Mississippi, drove his Ford along a rutted dirt path. It was a long day! The time did not seem to clear the noon hurdle and settle into soft afternoon. The sun, keeping its strength here even in winter, stayed at the top of the sky, and every time Bowman stuck his head out of the dusty car to stare up the road, it seemed to reach a long arm down and push against the top of his head, right through his hat—like the practical joke of an old drummer, long on the road. It made him feel all the more angry and helpless. He was feverish, and he was not quite sure of the way.

This was his first day back on the road after a long siege of influenza. He had had very high fever, and dreams, and had become weakened and pale, enough to tell the difference in the mirror, and he could not think clearly. . . . All afternoon, in the midst of his anger, and for no reason, he had thought of his dead grandmother. She had been a comfortable soul. Once more Bowman wished he could fall into the big feather bed that had been in her room. . . . Then he forgot her again.

This desolate hill country! And he seemed to be going the wrong way—it was as if he were going back, far back. There was not a house in sight. . . . There was no use wishing he were back in bed, though. By paying the hotel doctor his bill he had proved his recovery. He had not even been sorry when the pretty trained nurse said good-bye. He did not like illness, he distrusted it, as he distrusted the road without signposts. It angered him. He had given the nurse a really expensive bracelet, just because she was packing up her bag and leaving.

But now—what if in fourteen years on the road he had never been ill before and never had an accident? His record was broken, and he had even begun almost to question it. . . . He had gradually put up at better hotels, in the bigger towns, but weren't they all, eternally, stuffy in summer and drafty in winter? Women? He could only remember little rooms within little rooms, like a nest of Chinese paper boxes, and if he thought of one woman he saw the worn loneliness that the furniture of that room seemed built of. And he himself—he was a man who always wore rather wide-brimmed black hats, and in the wavy hotel mirrors had looked something like a bullfighter, as he paused for that inevitable instant on the landing, walking downstairs to supper. . . . He leaned out of the car again, and once more the sun pushed at his head.

Bowman had wanted to reach Beulah by dark, to go to bed and sleep off his fatigue. As he remembered, Beulah was fifty miles away from the last town, on a graveled road. This was only a cow trail. How had he ever come to such a place? One hand wiped the sweat from his face, and he drove on.

He had made the Beulah trip before. But he had never seen this hill or this petering-out path before—or that cloud, he thought shyly, looking up and then down quickly—any more than he had seen this day before. Why did he not admit he was simply lost and had been for miles? . . . He was not in the habit of asking the way of strangers, and these people never knew where the very roads they lived on went to; but then he had not even been close enough to anyone to call out. People standing in the fields now and then, or on top of the haystacks, had been too far away, looking like leaning sticks or weeds, turning a little at the solitary rattle of his car across their countryside, watching the pale sobered winter dust where it chunked out behind like big squashes down the road. The stares of these distant people had followed him solidly like a wall, impenetrable, behind which they turned back after he had passed.

The cloud floated there to one side like the bolster on his grandmother's bed. It went over a cabin on the edge of a hill, where two bare chinaberry trees clutched at the sky. He drove through a heap of dead oak leaves, his wheels stirring their weightless sides to make a silvery melancholy whistle as the car passed through their bed. No car had been along this way ahead of him. Then he saw that he was on the edge of a ravine that fell away, a red erosion, and that this was indeed the road's end.

He pulled the brake. But it did not hold, though he put all his strength into it. The car, tipped toward the edge, rolled a little. Without doubt, it was going over the bank.

He got out quietly, as though some mischief had been done him and he had his dignity to remember. He lifted his bag and sample case out, set them down, and stood back and watched the car roll over the edge. He heard something—not the crash he was listening for, but a slow, unuproarious crackle. Rather distastefully he went to look over, and he saw that his car had fallen into a tangle of immense grapevines as thick as his arm, which caught it and held it, rocked it like a grotesque child in a dark cradle, and then, as he watched, concerned somehow that he was not still inside it, released it gently to the ground.

He sighed.

Where am I? he wondered with a shock. Why didn't I do something? All his anger seemed to have drifted away from him. There was the house, back on the hill. He took a bag in each hand and with almost childlike willingness went toward it. But his breathing came with difficulty, and he had to stop to rest.

It was a shotgun house, two rooms and an open passage between, perched on the hill. The whole cabin slanted a little under the heavy heaped-up vine that covered the roof, light and green, as though forgotten from summer. A woman stood in the passage.

He stopped still. Then all of a sudden his heart began to behave strangely. Like a rocket set off, it began to leap and expand into uneven patterns of beats which showered into his brain, and he could not think. But in scattering and falling it made no noise. It shot up with great power, almost elation, and fell gently, like acrobats into nets. It began to pound profoundly, then waited irresponsibly, hitting in some sort of inward mockery first at his ribs, then against his eyes, then under his shoulder blades, and against the roof of his mouth when he tried to say, "Good afternoon, madam." But he could not hear his heart—it was as quiet as ashes falling. This was rather comforting; still, it was shocking to Bowman to feel his heart beating at all.

Stock-still in his confusion, he dropped his bags, which seemed to drift in slow bulks gracefully through the air and to cushion themselves on the gray prostrate grass near the doorstep.

As for the woman standing there, he saw at once that she was old. Since she could not possibly hear his heart, he ignored the pounding and now looked at her carefully, and yet in his distraction dreamily, with his mouth open.

She had been cleaning the lamp, and held it, half blackened, half clear, in front of her. He saw her with the dark passage behind her. She was a big woman with a weather-beaten but unwrinkled face; her lips were held tightly together, and her eyes looked with a curious dulled brightness into his. He looked at her shoes, which were like bundles. If it were summer she would be barefoot. . . . Bowman, who automatically judged a woman's age on sight, set her age at fifty. She wore a formless garment of some gray coarse material, rough-dried from a washing, from which her arms appeared pink and unexpectedly round. When she never said a word, and sustained her quiet pose of holding the lamp, he was convinced of the strength in her body.

"Good afternoon, madam," he said.

She stared on, whether at him or at the air around him he could not tell, but after a moment she lowered her eyes to show that she would listen to whatever he had to say.

"I wonder if you would be interested—" He tried once more. "An accident—my car . . ."

Her voice emerged low and remote, like a sound across a lake. "Sonny he ain't here."

"Sonny?"

"Sonny ain't here now."

Her son—a fellow able to bring my car up, he decided in blurred relief. He pointed down the hill. "My car's in the bottom of the ditch. I'll need help."

"Sonny ain't here, but he'll be here."

She was becoming clearer to him and her voice stronger, and Bowman saw that she was stupid.

He was hardly surprised at the deepening postponement and tedium of his journey. He took a breath, and heard his voice speaking over the silent blows of his heart. "I was sick. I am not strong yet. . . . May I come in?"

He stooped and laid his big black hat over the handle on his bag. It was a humble motion, almost a bow, that instantly struck him as absurd and betraying of all his weakness. He looked up at the woman, the wind blowing his hair. He might have continued for a long time in this unfamiliar attitude; he had never been a patient man, but when he was sick he had learned to sink submissively into the pillows, to wait for his medicine. He waited on the woman.

Then she, looking at him with blue eyes, turned and held open the door, and after a moment Bowman, as if convinced in his action, stood erect and followed her in.

Inside, the darkness of the house touched him like a professional hand, the doctor's. The woman set the half-cleaned lamp on a table in the center of the room and pointed, also like a professional person, a guide, to a chair with a yellow cowhide seat. She herself crouched on the hearth, drawing her knees up under the shapeless dress.

At first he felt hopefully secure. His heart was quieter. The room was enclosed in the gloom of yellow pine boards. He could see the other room, with the foot of an iron bed showing, across the passage. The bed had been made up with a red-and-yellow pieced quilt that looked like a map or a picture, a little like his grandmother's girlhood painting of Rome burning.

He had ached for coolness, but in this room it was cold. He stared at the hearth with dead coals lying on it and iron pots in the corners. The hearth and smoked chimney were of the stone he had seen ribbing the hills, mostly slate. Why is there no fire? he wondered.

And it was so still. The silence of the fields seemed to enter and move familiarly through the house. The wind used the open hall.

He felt that he was in a mysterious, quiet, cool danger. It was necessary to do what? . . . To talk.

"I have a nice line of women's low-priced shoes . . ." he said.

But the woman answered, "Sonny 'll be here. He's strong. Sonny 'll move your car."

"Where is he now?"

"Farms for Mr. Redmond."

Mr. Redmond. Mr. Redmond. That was someone he would never have to encounter, and he was glad. Somehow the name did not appeal to him. . . . In a flare of touchiness and anxiety, Bowman wished to avoid even mention of unknown men and their unknown farms.

"Do you two live here alone?" He was surprised to hear his old voice, chatty, confidential, inflected for selling shoes, asking a question like that—a thing he did not even want to know.

"Yes. We are alone."

He was surprised at the way she answered. She had taken a long time to say that. She had nodded her head in a deep way too. Had she wished to affect him with some sort of premonition? he wondered unhappily. Or was it only that she would not help him, after all, by talking with him? For he was not strong enough to receive the impact of unfamiliar things without a little talk to break their fall. He had lived a month in which nothing had happened except in his head and his body—an almost inaudible life of heartbeats and dreams that came back, a life of fever and privacy, a delicate life which had left him weak to the point of—what? Of begging. The pulse in his palm leapt like a trout in a brook.

He wondered over and over why the woman did not go ahead with cleaning the lamp. What prompted her to stay there across the room, silently bestowing her presence upon him? He saw that with her it was not a time for doing little tasks. Her face was grave; she was feeling how right she was. Perhaps it was only politeness. In docility he held his eyes stiffly wide; they fixed themselves on the woman's clasped hands as though she held the cord they were strung on.

Then, "Sonny's coming," she said.

He himself had not heard anything, but there came a man passing the window and then plunging in at the door, with two hounds beside him. Sonny was a big enough man, with his belt slung low about his hips. He looked at least thirty. He had a hot, red face that was yet full of silence. He wore muddy blue pants and an old military coat stained and patched. World War? Bowman wondered. Great God, it was a Confederate coat. On the back of his light hair he had a wide filthy black hat which seemed to insult Bowman's own. He pushed down the dogs from his chest. He was strong, with dignity and heaviness in his way of moving. . . . There was the resemblance to his mother.

They stood side by side. . . . He must account again for his presence here.

"Sonny, this man, he had his car to run off over the prec'pice an' wants to know if you will git it out for him," the woman said after a few minutes.

Bowman could not even state his case.

Sonny's eyes lay upon him.

He knew he should offer explanations and show money—at least appear either penitent or authoritative. But all he could do was to shrug slightly.

Sonny brushed by him going to the window, followed by the eager dogs, and looked out. There was effort even in the way he was looking, as if he could throw his sight out like a rope. Without turning Bowman felt that his own eyes could have seen nothing: it was too far.

"Got me a mule out there an' got me a block an' tackle," said Sonny meaningfully. "I *could* catch me my mule an' git me my ropes, an' before long I'd git your car out the ravine."

He looked completely around the room, as if in meditation, his eyes roving in their own distance. Then he pressed his lips firmly and yet shyly together, and with the dogs ahead of him this time, he lowered his head and strode out. The hard earth sounded, cupping to his powerful way of walking—almost a stagger.

Mischievously, at the suggestion of those sounds, Bowman's heart leapt again. It seemed to walk about inside him.

"Sonny's goin' to do it," the woman said. She said it again, singing it almost, like a song. She was sitting in her place by the hearth.

Without looking out, he heard some shouts and the dogs barking and the pounding of hoofs in short runs on the hill. In a few minutes Sonny passed under the window with a rope, and there was a brown mule with quivering, shining, purple-looking ears. The mule actually looked in the window. Under its eyelashes it turned targetlike eyes into his. Bowman averted his head and saw the woman looking serenely back at the mule, with only satisfaction in her face.

She sang a little more, under her breath. It occurred to him, and it seemed quite marvelous, that she was not really talking to him, but rather following the thing that came about with words that were unconscious and part of her looking.

So he said nothing, and this time when he did not reply he felt a curious and strong emotion, not fear, rise up in him.

This time, when his heart leapt, something—his soul—seemed to leap too, like a little colt invited out of a pen. He stared at the woman while the frantic nimbleness of his feeling made his head sway. He could not move; there was nothing he could do, unless perhaps he might embrace this woman who sat there growing old and shapeless before him.

But he wanted to leap up, to say to her, I have been sick and I found out then, only then, how lonely I am. Is it too late? My heart puts up a struggle inside me, and you may have heard it, protesting against emptiness. . . . It should be full, he would rush on to tell her, thinking of his heart now as a deep lake, it should be holding love like other hearts. It should be flooded with love. There would be a warm spring day . . . Come and stand in my heart, whoever you are, and a whole river would cover your feet and rise higher and take your knees in whirlpools, and draw you down to itself, your whole body, your heart too.

But he moved a trembling hand across his eyes, and looked at the placid crouching woman across the room. She was still as a statue. He felt ashamed and exhausted by the thought that he might, in one more moment, have tried by simple words and embraces to communicate some strange thing—something which seemed always to have just escaped him . . .

Sunlight touched the furthest pot on the hearth. It was late afternoon. This time tomorrow he would be somewhere on a good graveled road, driving his car past things that happened to people, quicker than their happening. Seeing ahead to the next day, he was glad, and knew that this was no time to embrace an old woman. He could feel in his pounding temples the readying of his blood for motion and for hurrying away.

"Sonny's hitched up your car by now," said the woman. "He'll git it out the ravine right shortly."

"Fine!" he cried with his customary enthusiasm.

Yet it seemed a long time that they waited. It began to get dark. Bowman was cramped in his chair. Any man should know enough to get up and walk around while he waited. There was something like guilt in such stillness and silence.

But instead of getting up, he listened. . . . His breathing restrained, his eyes powerless in the growing dark, he listened uneasily for a warning sound, forgetting in wariness what it would be. Before long he heard something—soft, continuous, insinuating.

"What's that noise?" he asked, his voice jumping into the dark. Then wildly he was afraid it would be his heart beating so plainly in the quiet room, and she would tell him so.

"You might hear the stream," she said grudgingly.

Her voice was closer. She was standing by the table. He wondered why she did not light the lamp. She stood there in the dark and did not light it.

Bowman would never speak to her now, for the time was past. I'll sleep in the dark, he thought, in his bewilderment pitying himself.

Heavily she moved on to the window. Her arm, vaguely white, rose straight from her full side and she pointed out into the darkness.

"That white speck's Sonny," she said, talking to herself.

He turned unwillingly and peered over her shoulder; he hesitated to rise and stand beside her. His eyes searched the dusky air. The white speck floated smoothly toward her finger, like a leaf on a river, growing whiter in the dark. It was as if she had shown him something secret, part of her life, but had offered no explanation. He looked away. He was moved almost to tears, feeling for no reason that she had made a silent declaration equivalent to his own. His hand waited upon his chest.

Then a step shook the house, and Sonny was in the room. Bowman felt how the woman left him there and went to the other man's side.

"I done got your car out, mister," said Sonny's voice in the dark. "She's settin' a-waitin' in the road, turned to go back where she come from."

"Fine!" said Bowman, projecting his own voice to loudness. "I'm surely much obliged—I could never have done it myself—I was sick. . . ."

"I could do it easy," said Sonny.

Bowman could feel them both waiting in the dark, and he could hear the dogs panting out in the yard, waiting to bark when he should go. He felt strangely helpless and resentful. Now that he could go, he longed to stay. From what was he being deprived? His chest was rudely shaken by the violence of his heart. These people cherished something here that he could not see, they withheld some ancient promise of food and warmth and light. Between them they had a conspiracy. He thought of the way she had moved away from him and gone to Sonny, she had flowed toward him. He was shaking with cold, he was tired, and it was not fair. Humbly and yet angrily he stuck his hand into his pocket.

"Of course I'm going to pay you for everything—"

"We don't take money for such," said Sonny's voice belligerently.

"I want to pay. But do something more . . . Let me stay—tonight. . . ." He took another step toward them. If only they could see him, they would know his sincerity, his real need! His voice went on, "I'm not very strong yet, I'm not able to walk far, even back to my car, maybe, I don't know—I don't know exactly where I am—"

He stopped. He felt as if he might burst into tears. What would they think of him!

Sonny came over and put his hands on him. Bowman felt them pass (they were professional too) across his chest, over his hips. He could feel Sonny's eyes upon him in the dark.

"You ain't no revenuer come sneakin' here, mister, ain't got no gun?"

To this end of nowhere! And yet *he* had come. He made a grave answer. "No."

"You can stay."

"Sonny," said the woman, "you'll have to borry some fire."

"I'll go git it from Redmond's," said Sonny.

"What?" Bowman strained to hear their words to each other.

"Our fire, it's out, and Sonny's got to borry some, because it's dark an' cold," she said.

"But matches—I have matches—"

"We don't have no need for 'em," she said proudly. "Sonny's goin' after his own fire."

"I'm goin' to Redmond's," said Sonny with an air of importance, and he went out.

After they had waited a while, Bowman looked out the window and saw a light moving over the hill. It spread itself out like a little fan. It zigzagged along the field, darting and swift, not like Sonny at all. . . . Soon enough, Sonny staggered in, holding a burning stick behind him in tongs, fire flowing in his wake, blazing light into the corners of the room.

"We'll make a fire now," the woman said, taking the brand.

When that was done she lit the lamp. It showed its dark and light. The whole room turned golden-yellow like some sort of flower, and the walls smelled of it and seemed to tremble with the quiet rushing of the fire and the waving of the burning lampwick in its funnel of light.

The woman moved among the iron pots. With the tongs she dropped hot coals on top of the iron lids. They made a set of soft vibrations, like the sound of a bell far away.

She looked up and over at Bowman, but he could not answer. He was trembling. . . .

"Have a drink, mister?" Sonny asked. He had brought in a chair from the other room and sat astride it with his folded arms across the back. Now we are all visible to one another, Bowman thought, and cried, "Yes sir, you bet, thanks!"

"Come after me and do just what I do," said Sonny.

It was another excursion into the dark. They went through the hall, out to the back of the house, past a shed and a hooded well. They came to a wilderness of thicket.

"Down on your knees," said Sonny.

"What?" Sweat broke out on his forehead.

He understood when Sonny began to crawl through a sort of tunnel that the bushes made over the ground. He followed, startled in spite of himself when a twig or a thorn touched him gently without making a sound, clinging to him and finally letting him go.

Sonny stopped crawling and, crouched on his knees, began to dig with both his hands into the dirt. Bowman shyly struck matches and made a light. In a few minutes Sonny pulled up a jug. He poured out some of the whisky into a bottle from his coat pocket, and buried the jug again. "You never know who's liable to knock at your door," he said, and laughed. "Start back," he said, almost formally. "Ain't no need for us to drink outdoors, like hogs."

At the table by the fire, sitting opposite each other in their chairs, Sonny and Bowman took drinks out of the bottle, passing it across. The dogs slept; one of them was having a dream.

"This is good," said Bowman. "This is what I needed." It was just as though he were drinking the fire off the hearth.

"He makes it," said the woman with quiet pride.

She was pushing the coals off the pots, and the smells of corn bread and coffee circled the room. She set everything on the table before the men, with a bone-handled knife stuck into one of the potatoes, splitting out its golden fiber. Then she stood for a minute looking at them, tall and full above them where they sat. She leaned a little toward them.

"You all can eat now," she said, and suddenly smiled.

Bowman had just happened to be looking at her. He set his cup back on the table in unbelieving protest. A pain pressed at his eyes. He saw that she was not an old woman. She was young, still young. He could think of no number of years for her. She was the same age as Sonny, and she belonged to him. She stood with the deep dark corner of the room behind her, the shifting yellow light scattering over her head and her gray formless dress, trembling over her tall body when it bent over them in its sudden communication. She was young. Her teeth were shining and her eyes glowed. She turned and walked slowly and heavily out of the room, and he heard her sit down on the cot and then lie down. The pattern on the quilt moved.

"She's goin' to have a baby," said Sonny, popping a bite into his mouth.

Bowman could not speak. He was shocked with knowing what was really in this house. A marriage, a fruitful marriage. That simple thing. Anyone could have had that.

Somehow he felt unable to be indignant or protest, although some sort of joke had certainly been played upon him. There was nothing remote or mysterious here—only something private. The only secret was the ancient communication between two people. But the memory of the woman's waiting silently by the cold hearth, of the man's stubborn journey a mile away to get fire, and how they finally brought out their food and drink and filled the room proudly with all they had to show, was suddenly too clear and too enormous within him for response. . . .

"You ain't as hungry as you look," said Sonny.

The woman came out of the bedroom as soon as the men had finished, and ate her supper while her husband stared peacefully into the fire.

Then they put the dogs out, with the food that was left.

"I think I'd better sleep here by the fire, on the floor," said Bowman.

He felt that he had been cheated, and that he could afford now to be generous. Ill though he was, he was not going to ask them for their bed. He was through with asking favors in this house, now that he understood what was there.

"Sure, mister."

But he had not known yet how slowly he understood. They had not meant to give him their bed. After a little interval they both rose and looking at him gravely went into the other room.

He lay stretched by the fire until it grew low and dying. He watched every tongue of blaze lick out and vanish. "There will be special reduced prices on all footwear during the month of January," he found himself repeating quietly, and then he lay with his lips tight shut.

How many noises the night had! He heard the stream running, the fire dying, and he was sure now that he heard his heart beating, too, the sound it made under his ribs. He heard breathing, round and deep, of the man and his wife in the room across the passage. And that was all. But emotion swelled patiently within him, and he wished that the child were his.

He must get back to where he had been before. He stood weakly before the red coals and put on his overcoat. It felt too heavy on his shoulders. As he started out he looked and saw that the woman had never got through with cleaning the lamp. On some impulse he put all the money from his billfold under its fluted glass base, almost ostentatiously.

Ashamed, shrugging a little, and then shivering, he took his bags and went out. The cold of the air seemed to lift him bodily. The moon was in the sky.

On the slope he began to run, he could not help it. Just as he reached the road, where his car seemed to sit in the moonlight like a boat, his heart began to give off tremendous explosions like a rifle, bang bang bang.

He sank in fright onto the road, his bags falling about him. He felt as if all this had happened before. He covered his heart with both hands to keep any one from hearing the noise it made.

But nobody heard it.

DYLAN THOMAS

A Story

IF YOU CAN CALL it a story. There's no real beginning or end and there's very little in the middle. It is all about a day's outing, by charabanc, to Porthcawl, which, of course, the charabanc never reached, and it happened when I was so high and much nicer.

I was staying at the time with my uncle and his wife. Although she was my aunt, I never thought of her as anything but the wife of my uncle, partly because he was so big and trumpeting and red-hairy and used to fill every inch of the hot little house like an old buffalo squeezed into an airing cupboard, and partly because she was so small and silk and quick and made no noise at all as she whisked about on padded paws, dusting the china dogs, feeding the buffalo, setting the mouse-traps that never caught her; and once she sleaked out of the room, to squeak in a nook or nibble in the hayloft, you forgot she had ever been there.

But there he was, always a steaming hulk of an uncle, his braces straining like hawsers, crammed behind the counter of the tiny shop at the front of the house, and breathing like a brass band; or guzzling and blustery in the kitchen over his gutsy supper, too big for everything except the great black boats of his boots. As he ate, the house grew smaller; he billowed out over the furniture, the loud check meadow of his waistcoat littered, as though after a picnic, with cigarette ends, peelings, cabbage stalks, birds' bones, gravy; and the forest fire of his hair crackled among the hooked hams from the ceiling. She was so small she could hit him only if she stood on a chair; and every Saturday night at half-past ten he would lift her up, under his arm, onto a chair, in the kitchen so that she could hit him on the head with whatever was handy, which was always a china dog. On Sundays, and when pickled, he sang high tenor, and had won many cups.

The first I heard of the annual outing was when I was sitting one evening on a bag of rice behind the counter, under one of my uncle's stomachs, reading an advertisement for sheep-dip, which was all there was to read. The shop was full of my uncle, and when Mr. Benjamin Franklyn, Mr. Weazley, Noah Bowen, and Will Sentry came in, I thought it would burst. It was like all being together in a drawer that smelled of cheese and turps, and twist tobacco and sweet biscuits and snuff and waistcoat. Mr. Benjamin Franklyn said that he had collected enough money for the charabanc and twenty cases of pale ale and a pound apiece over that he would distribute among the members of the outing when they first stopped for refreshment, and he was about sick and tired, he said, of being followed by Will Sentry.

"All day long, wherever I go," he said, "he's after me like a collie with one eye. I got a shadow of my own *and* a dog. I don't need no Tom, Dick or Harry pursuing me with his dirty muffler on."

Will Sentry blushed, and said, "It's only oily. I got a bicycle."

"A man has no privacy at all," Mr. Franklyn went on. "I tell you he sticks so close I'm afraid to go out the back in case I sit in his lap. It's a wonder to me," he said, "he don't follow me into bed at night."

"Wife won't let," Will Sentry said.

And that started Mr. Franklyn off again, and they tried to soothe him down by saying, "Don't you mind Will Sentry." "No harm in old Will." "He's only keeping an eye on the money, Benjie."

"Aren't I honest?" asked Mr. Franklyn in surprise. There was no answer for some time; then Noah Bowen said, "You know what the committee is. Ever since Bob the Fiddle they don't feel safe with a new treasurer."

"Do you think *I'm* going to drink the outing funds, like Bob the Fiddle did?" said Mr. Franklyn.

"You *might*," said my uncle, slowly.

"I resign," said Mr. Franklyn.

"Not with our money you won't," Will Sentry said.

"Who put the dynamite in the salmon pool?" said Mr. Weazley, but nobody took any notice of him. And, after a time, they all began to play cards in the thickening dusk of the hot, cheesy shop, and my uncle blew and bugled whenever he won, and Mr. Weazley grumbled like a dredger, and I fell to sleep on the gravy-scented mountain meadow of uncle's waistcoat.

On Sunday evening, after Bethesda, Mr. Franklyn walked into the kitchen where my uncle and I were eating sardines from the tin with spoons because it was Sunday and his wife would not let us play draughts. She was somewhere in the kitchen, too. Perhaps she was inside the grandmother clock, hanging from the weights and breathing. Then, a second later, the door opened again and Will Sentry edged into the room, twiddling his hard, round hat. He and Mr. Franklyn sat down on the settee, stiff and moth-balled and black in their chapel and funeral suits.

"I brought the list," said Mr. Franklyn. "Every member fully paid. You ask Will Sentry."

My uncle put on his spectacles, wiped his whiskery mouth with a handkerchief big as a Union Jack, laid down his spoon of sardines, took Mr. Franklyn's list of names, removed the spectacles so that he could read, and then ticked the names off one by one.

"Enoch Davies. Aye. He's good with his fists. You never know. Little Gerwain. Very melodious bass. Mr. Cadwalladwr. That's right. He can tell opening time better than my watch. Mr. Weazley. Of course. He's been to Paris. Pity he suffers so much in the charabanc. Stopped us nine times last year between the Beehive and the Red Dragon. Noah Bowen. Ah, very peaceable. He's got a tongue like a turtledove. Never a argument with Noah Bowen. Jenkins Loughor. Keep him off economics. It cost us a plate-glass window. And ten pints for the Sergeant. Mr. Jervis. Very tidy."

"He tried to put a pig in the charra," Will Sentry said.

"Live and let live," said my uncle.

Will Sentry blushed.

"Sinbad the Sailor's Arms. Got to keep in with him. Old O. Jones."

"Why old O. Jones?" said Will Sentry.

"Old O. Jones always goes," said my uncle.

I looked down at the kitchen table. The tin of sardines was gone. By Gee, I said to myself, Uncle's wife is quick as a flash.

"Cuthbert Johnny Fortnight. Now there's a card," said my uncle.

"He whistles after women," Will Sentry said.

"So do you," said Mr. Benjamin Franklyn, "in your mind."

My uncle at last approved the whole list, pausing only to say, when he came across one name, "If we weren't a Christian community, we'd chuck that Bob the Fiddle in the sea."

"We can do that in Porthcawl," said Mr. Franklyn, and soon after that he went, Will Sentry no more than an inch behind him, their Sunday-bright boots squeaking on the kitchen cobbles.

And then, suddenly, there was my uncle's wife standing in front of the dresser, with a china dog in one hand. By Gee, I said to myself again, did you ever see such a woman, if that's what she is. The lamps were not lit yet in the kitchen and she stood in a wood of shadows, with the plates on the dresser behind her shining—like pink and white eyes.

"If you go on that outing on Saturday, Mr. Thomas," she said to my uncle in her small, silk voice, "I'm going home to my mother's."

Holy Mo, I thought, she's got a mother. Now that's one old bald mouse of a hundred and five I won't be wanting to meet in a dark lane.

"It's me or the outing, Mr. Thomas."

I would have made my choice at once, but it was almost half a minute before my uncle said, "Well, then, Sarah, it's the outing, my love." He lifted her up, under his arm, onto a chair in the kitchen, and she hit him on the head with the china dog. Then he lifted her down again, and then I said good night.

For the rest of the week my uncle's wife whisked quiet and quick round the house with her darting duster, my uncle blew and bugled and swole, and I kept myself busy all the time being up to no good.

And then at breakfast time on Saturday morning, the morning of the outing, I found a note on the kitchen table. It said, "There's some eggs in the pantry. Take your boots off before you go to bed." My uncle's wife had gone, as quick as a flash.

When my uncle saw the note, he tugged out the flag of his handkerchief and blew such a hubbub of trumpets that the plates on the dresser shook. "It's the same every year," he said. And then he looked at me. "But this year it's different. *You'll* have to come on the outing, too, and what the members will say I dare not think."

The charabanc drew up outside, and when the members of the outing saw my uncle and me squeeze out of the shop together, both of us cat-licked and brushed in our Sunday best, they snarled like a zoo.

"Are you bringing a *boy?*" asked Mr. Benjamin Franklyn as we climbed into the charabanc. He looked at me with horror.

"Boys is nasty," said Mr. Weazley.

"He hasn't paid his contributions," Will Sentry said.

"No room for boys. Boys get sick in charabancs."

"So do you, Enoch Davies," said my uncle.

"Might as well bring *women.*"

The way they said it, women were worse than boys.

"Better than bringing grandfathers."

"Grandfathers is nasty, too," said Mr. Weazley.

"What can we do with him when we stop for refreshments?"

"I'm a grandfather," said Mr. Weazley.

"Twenty-six minutes to opening time," shouted an old man in a panama hat, not looking at a watch. They forgot me at once.

"Good old Mr. Cadwalladwr," they cried, and the charabanc started off down the village street.

A few cold women stood at their doorways, grimly watching us go. A very small boy waved goodbye, and his mother boxed his ears. It was a beautiful August morning.

We were out of the village, and over the bridge, and up the hill toward Steeplehat Wood when Mr. Franklyn, with his list of names in his hand, called out loud, "Where's old O. Jones?"

"Where's old O.?"

"We've left old O. behind."

"Can't go without old O."

And though Mr. Weazley hissed all the way, we turned and drove back to the village, where, outside the Prince of Wales, old O. Jones was waiting patiently and alone with a canvas bag.

"I didn't want to come at all," old O. Jones said as they hoisted him into the charabanc and clapped him on the back and pushed him on a seat and stuck a bottle in his hand, "but I always go." And over the bridge and up the hill and under the deep green wood and along the dusty road we wove, slow cows and ducks flying by, until "Stop the bus!" Mr. Weazley cried, "I left my teeth on the mantelpiece."

"Never you mind," they said, "you're not going to bite nobody," and they gave him a bottle with a straw.

"I might want to smile," he said.

"Not you," they said.

"What's the time, Mr. Cadwalladwr?"

"Twelve minutes to go," shouted back the old man in the panama, and they all began to curse him.

The charabanc pulled up outside the Mountain Sheep, a small, unhappy public house with a thatched roof like a wig with ringworm. From a flagpole by the Gents fluttered the flag of Siam. I knew it was the flag of Siam because of cigarette cards. The landlord stood at the door to welcome us, simpering like a wolf. He was a long, lean, black-fanged man with a greased love-curl and pouncing eyes. "What a beautiful August day!" he said, and touched his love-curl with a claw. That was the way he must have welcomed the Mountain Sheep before he ate it, I said to myself. The members rushed out, bleating, and into the bar.

"You keep an eye on the charra," my uncle said, "see nobody steals it now."

"There's nobody to steal it," I said, "except some cows," but my uncle was gustily blowing his bugle in the bar. I looked at the cows opposite, and they looked at me. There was nothing else for us to do. Forty-five minutes passed, like a very slow cloud. The sun shone down on the lonely road, the lost, unwanted boy, and the lake-eyed cows. In the dark bar they were so happy they were breaking glasses. A Shoni-Onion Breton man, with a beret and a necklace of onions, bicycled down the road and stopped at the door.

"*Quelle un grand matin, monsieur*," I said.

"There's French, boy bach!" he said.

I followed him down the passage, and peered into the bar. I could hardly recognize the members of the outing. They had all changed color. Beetroot, rhubarb and puce, they hollered and rollicked in that dark, damp hole like enormous ancient bad boys, and my uncle surged in the middle, all red whiskers and bellies. On the floor was broken glass and Mr. Weazley.

"Drinks all round," cried Bob the Fiddle, a small, absconding man with bright blue eyes and a plump smile.

"Who's been robbing the orphans?"

"Who sold his little babby to the gyppoes?"

"Trust old Bob, he'll let you down."

"You will have your little joke," said Bob the Fiddle, smiling like a razor, "but I forgive you, boys."

Out of the fug and babel I heard: "Where's old O. Jones?" "Where are you, old O.?" "He's in the kitchen cooking his dinner." "He never forgets his dinner time." "Good old O. Jones." "Come out and fight." "No, not now, later." "No, now when I'm in a temper." "Look at Will Sentry, he's proper snobbled." "Look at his willful feet." "Look at Mr. Weazley lording it on the floor."

Mr. Weazley got up, hissing like a gander. "That boy pushed me down deliberate," he said, pointing to me at the door, and I slunk away down the passage and out to the mild, good cows.

Time clouded over, the cows wondered, I threw a stone at them and they wandered, wondering, away. Then out blew my Uncle, ballooning, and one by one the members lumbered after him in a grizzle. They had drunk the Mountain Sheep dry. Mr. Weazley had won a string of onions that the Shoni-Onion man had raffled in the bar.

"What's the good of onions if you left your teeth on the mantelpiece?" he said. And when I looked through the back window of the thundering charabanc, I saw the pub grow smaller in the distance. And the flag of Siam, from the flagpole by the Gents, fluttered now at half mast.

The Blue Bull, the Dragon, the Star of Wales, the Twll in the Wall, the Sour Grapes, the Shepherd's Arms, the Bells of Aberdovey: I had nothing to do in the whole wild August world but remember the names where the outing stopped and keep an eye on the charabanc. And whenever it passed a public house, Mr. Weazley would cough like a billy goat and cry, "Stop the bus, I'm dying of breath." And back we would all have to go.

Closing time meant nothing to the members of that outing. Behind locked doors, they hymned and rumpused all the beautiful afternoon. And, when a policeman entered the Druid's Tap by the back door, and found them all choral with beer, "Sssh!" said Noah Bowen, "the pub is shut."

"Where do you come from?" he said in his buttoned, blue voice.

They told him.

"I got a auntie there," the policeman said. And very soon he was singing "Asleep in the Deep."

Off we drove again at last, the charabanc bouncing with tenors and flagons, and came to a river that rushed along among willows.

"Water!" they shouted.

"Porthcawl!" sang my uncle.

"Where's the donkeys?" said Mr. Weazley.

And out they lurched, to paddle and whoop in the cool, white, winding water. Mr. Franklyn, trying to polka on the slippery stones, fell in twice. "Nothing is simple," he said with dignity as he oozed up the bank.

"It's cold!" they cried.

"It's lovely!"

"It's smooth as a moth's nose!"

"It's *better* than Porthcawl!"

And dusk came down warm and gentle on thirty wild, wet, pickled, splashing men without a care in the world at the end of the world in the west of Wales. And, "Who goes there?" called Will Sentry to a wild duck flying.

They stopped at the Hermit's Nest for a rum to keep out the cold. "I played for Aberavon in 1898," said a stranger to Enoch Davies.

"Liar," said Enoch Davies.

"I can show the photos," said the stranger.

"Forged," said Enoch Davies.

"And I'll show you my cap at home."

"Stolen."

"I got friends to prove it," the stranger said in a fury.

"Bribed," said Enoch Davies.

On the way home, through the simmering moonsplashed dark, old O. Jones began to cook his supper on a primus stove in the middle of the charabanc. Mr. Weazley coughed himself blue in the smoke. "Stop the bus!" he cried, "I'm dying of breath." We all climbed down into the moonlight. There was not a public house in sight. So they carried out the remaining cases, and the primus stove, and old O. Jones himself, and took them into a field, and sat down in a circle in the field and drank and sang while old O. Jones cooked sausage and mash and the moon flew above us. And there I drifted to sleep against my uncle's mountainous waistcoat, and, as I slept, "Who goes there?" called out Will Sentry to the flying moon.

TRUMAN CAPOTE

A Christmas Memory

IMAGINE A MORNING in late November. A coming of winter morning more than twenty years ago. Consider the kitchen of a spreading old house in a country town. A great black stove is its main feature; but there is also a big round table and a fireplace with two rocking chairs placed in front of it. Just today the fireplace commenced its seasonal roar.

A woman with shorn white hair is standing at the kitchen window. She is wearing tennis shoes and a shapeless gray sweater over a summery calico dress. She is small and sprightly, like a bantam hen; but, due to a long youthful illness, her shoulders are pitifully hunched. Her face is remarkable—not unlike Lincoln's, craggy like that, and tinted by sun and wind; but it is delicate too, finely boned, and her eyes are sherry-colored and timid. "Oh my," she exclaims, her breath smoking the windowpane, "it's fruitcake weather!"

The person to whom she is speaking is myself. I am seven; she is sixty-something. We are cousins, very distant ones, and we have lived together—well, as long as I can remember. Other people inhabit the house, relatives; and though they have power over us, and frequently make us cry, we are not, on the whole, too much aware of them. We are each other's best friend. She calls me Buddy, in memory of a boy who was formerly her best friend. The other Buddy died in the 1880's, when she was still a child. She is still a child.

"I knew it before I got out of bed," she says, turning away from the window with a purposeful excitement in her eyes. "The courthouse bell sounded so cold and clear. And there were no birds singing; they've gone to warmer country, yes indeed. Oh, Buddy, stop stuffing biscuit and fetch our buggy. Help me find my hat. We've thirty cakes to bake."

It's always the same: a morning arrives in November, and my friend, as though officially inaugurating the Christmas time of year that exhilarates her imagination and fuels the blaze of her heart, announces: "It's fruitcake weather! Fetch our buggy. Help me find my hat."

The hat is found, a straw cartwheel corsaged with velvet roses out-of-doors has faded: it once belonged to a more fashionable relative. Together, we guide our buggy, a dilapidated baby carriage, out to the garden and into a grove of pecan trees. The buggy is mine; that is, it was bought for me when I was born. It is made of wicker, rather unraveled, and the wheels wobble like a drunkard's legs. But it is a faithful object; springtimes, we take it to the woods and fill it with flowers, herbs, wild fern for our porch pots; in the summer, we pile it with picnic paraphernalia and sugar-cane fishing poles and roll it down to the edge of a creek; it has its winter uses, too: as a truck for hauling firewood from the yard to the kitchen, as a warm bed for Queenie, our tough little orange and white rat terrier who has survived distemper and two rattlesnake bites. Queenie is trotting beside it now.

Three hours later we are back in the kitchen hulling a heaping buggyload of windfall pecans. Our backs hurt from gathering them: how hard they were to find (the main crop having been shaken off the trees and sold by the orchard's owners, who are not us) among the concealing leaves, the frosted, deceiving grass. Caarackle! A cheery crunch, scraps of miniature thunder sound as the shells collapse and the golden mound of sweet oily ivory meat mounts in the milk-glass bowl. Queenie begs to taste, and now and again my friend sneaks her a mite, though insisting we deprive ourselves. "We mustn't, Buddy. If we start, we won't stop. And there's scarcely enough as there is. For thirty cakes." The kitchen is growing dark. Dusk turns the window into a mirror: our reflections mingle with the rising moon as we work by the fireside in the firelight. At last, when the moon is quite high, we toss the final hull into the fire and, with joined sighs, watch it catch flame. The buggy is empty, the bowl is brimful.

We eat our supper (cold biscuits, bacon, blackberry jam) and discuss tomorrow. Tomorrow the kind of work I like best begins: buying. Cherries and citron, ginger and vanilla and canned Hawaiian pineapple, rinds and raisins and walnuts and whiskey and oh, so much flour, butter, so many eggs, spices, flavorings: why, we'll need a pony to pull the buggy home.

But before these purchases can be made, there is the question of money. Neither of us has any. Except for skinflint sums persons in the house occasionally provide (a dime is considered very big money); or what we earn ourselves from various activities: holding rummage sales, selling buckets of hand-picked blackberries, jars of homemade jam and apple jelly and peach preserves, rounding up flowers for funerals and weddings. Once we won seventy-ninth prize, five dollars, in a national football contest. Not that we know a fool thing about football. It's just that we enter any contest we hear about: at the moment our hopes are centered on the fifty-thousand-dollar Grand Prize being offered to name a new brand of coffee (we suggested "A.M."; and, after some hesitation, for my friend thought it perhaps sacrilegious, the slogan "A.M.! Amen!"). To tell the truth, our only *really* profitable enterprise was the Fun and Freak Museum we conducted in a back-yard woodshed two summers ago. The Fun was a stereopticon with slide views of Washington and New York lent us by a relative who had been to those places (she was furious when she discovered why we'd borrowed it); the Freak was a three-legged biddy chicken hatched by one of our own hens. Everybody hereabouts wanted to see that biddy: we charged grown-ups a nickel, kids two cents. And took in a good twenty dollars before the museum shut down due to the decease of the main attraction.

But one way and another we do each year accumulate Christmas savings, a Fruitcake Fund. These moneys we keep hidden in an ancient bead purse under a loose board under the floor under a chamber pot under my friend's bed. The purse is seldom removed from this safe location except to make a deposit, or, as happens every Saturday, a withdrawal; for on Saturdays I am allowed ten cents to go to the picture show. My friend has never been to a picture show, nor does she intend to: "I'd rather hear you tell the story, Buddy. That way I can imagine it more. Besides, a person my age shouldn't squander their eyes. When the Lord comes, let me see him clear." In addition to never having seen a movie, she has never: eaten in a restaurant, traveled more than five miles from home, received or sent a telegram, read anything except funny papers and the Bible, worn cosmetics, cursed, wished someone harm, told a lie on purpose, let a hungry dog go hungry. Here are a few things she has done, does do: killed with a hoe the biggest rattlesnake ever seen in this county (sixteen rattles), dip snuff (secretly), tame hummingbirds (just try it) till they balance on her finger, tell ghost stories (we both believe in ghosts) so tingling they chill you in July, talk to herself, take walks in the rain, grow the prettiest japonicas in town, know the recipe for every sort of old-time Indian cure, including a magical wart-remover.

Now, with supper finished, we retire to the room in a faraway part of the house where my friend sleeps in a scrap-quilt-covered iron bed painted rose pink, her favorite color. Silently, wallowing in the pleasures of conspiracy, we take the bead purse from its secret place and spill its contents on the scrap quilt. Dollar bills, tightly rolled and green as May buds. Somber fifty-cent pieces, heavy enough to weight a dead man's eyes. Lovely dimes, the liveliest coin, the one that really jingles. Nickels and quarters, worn smooth as creek pebbles. But mostly a hateful heap of bitter-odored pennies. Last summer others in the house contracted to pay us a penny for every twenty-five flies we killed. Oh, the carnage of August: the flies that flew to heaven! Yet it was not work in which we took pride. And, as we sit counting pennies, it is as though we were back tabulating dead flies. Neither of us has a head for figures; we count slowly, lose track, start again. According to her calculations, we have $12.73. According to mine, exactly $13. "I do hope you're wrong, Buddy. We can't mess around with thirteen. The cakes will fall. Or put somebody in the cemetery. Why, I wouldn't dream of getting out of bed on the thirteenth." This is true: she always spends thirteenths in bed. So, to be on the safe side, we subtract a penny and toss it out the window.

Of the ingredients that go into our fruitcakes, whiskey is the most expensive, as well as the hardest to obtain: State laws forbid its sale. But everybody knows you can buy a bottle from Mr. Haha Jones. And the next day, having completed our more prosaic shopping, we set out for Mr. Haha's business address, a "sinful" (to quote public opinion) fish-fry and dancing café down by the river. We've been there before, and on the same errand; but in previous years our dealings have been with Haha's wife, an iodine-dark Indian woman with brassy peroxided hair and a dead-tired disposition. Actually, we've never laid eyes on her husband, though we've heard that he's an Indian too. A giant with razor scars across his cheeks. They call him Haha because he's so gloomy, a man who never laughs. As we approach his café (a large log cabin festooned inside and out with chains of garish-gay naked light bulbs and standing by the river's muddy edge under the shade of river trees where moss drifts through the branches like gray mist) our steps slow down. Even Queenie stops prancing and sticks close by. People have been murdered in Haha's café. Cut to pieces. Hit on the head. There's a case coming up in court next month. Naturally these goings-on happen at night when the colored lights cast crazy patterns and the victrola wails. In the daytime Haha's is shabby and deserted. I knock at the door, Queenie barks, my friend calls: "Mrs. Haha, ma'am? Anyone to home?"

Footsteps. The door opens. Our hearts overturn. It's Mr. Haha Jones himself! And he *is* a giant; he *does* have scars; he *doesn't* smile. No, he glowers at us through Satan-tilted eyes and demands to know: "What you want with Haha?"

For a moment we are too paralyzed to tell. Presently my friend half-finds her voice, a whispery voice at best: "If you please, Mr. Haha, we'd like a quart of your finest whiskey."

His eyes tilt more. Would you believe it? Haha is smiling! Laughing, too. "Which one of you is a drinkin' man?"

"It's for making fruitcakes, Mr. Haha. Cooking."

This sobers him. He frowns. "That's no way to waste good whiskey." Nevertheless, he retreats into the shadowed café and seconds later appears carrying a bottle of daisy yellow unlabeled liquor. He demonstrates its sparkle in the sunlight and says: "Two dollars."

We pay him with nickels and dimes and pennies. Suddenly, jangling the coins in his hand like a fistful of dice, his face softens. "Tell you what," he proposes, pouring the money back into our bead purse, "just send me one of them fruitcakes instead."

"Well," my friend remarks on our way home, "there's a lovely man. We'll put an extra cup of raisins in *his* cake."

The black stove, stoked with coal and firewood, glows like a lighted pumpkin. Eggbeaters whirl, spoons spin round in bowls of butter and sugar, vanilla sweetens the air, ginger spices it; melting, nose-tingling odors saturate the kitchen, suffuse the house, drift out to the world on puffs of chimney smoke. In four days our work is done. Thirty-one cakes, dampened with whiskey, bask on window sills and shelves.

Who are they for?

Friends. Not necessarily neighbor friends: indeed, the larger share are intended for persons we've met maybe once, perhaps not at all. People who've struck our fancy. Like President Roosevelt. Like the Reverend and Mrs. J. C. Lucey, Baptist missionaries to Borneo who lectured here last winter. Or the little knife grinder who comes through town twice a year. Or Abner Packer, the driver of the six o'clock bus from Mobile, who exchanges waves with us every day as he passes in a dust-cloud whoosh. Or the young Wistons, a California couple whose car one afternoon broke down outside the house and who spent a pleasant hour chatting with us on the porch (young Mr. Wiston snapped our picture, the only one we've ever had taken). Is it because my friend is shy with everyone *except* strangers that these strangers, and merest acquaintances, seem to us our truest friends? I think yes. Also, the scrapbooks we keep of thank-you's on White House stationery, time-to-time communications from California and Borneo, the knife grinder's penny post cards, make us feel connected to eventful worlds beyond the kitchen with its view of a sky that stops.

Now a nude December fig branch grates against the window. The kitchen is empty, the cakes are gone; yesterday we carted the last of them to the post office, where the cost of stamps turned our purse inside out. We're broke. That rather depresses me, but my friend insists on celebrating—with two inches of whiskey left in Haha's bottle. Queenie has a spoonful in a bowl of coffee (she likes her coffee chicory-flavored and strong). The rest we divide between a pair of jelly glasses. We're both quite awed at the prospect of drinking straight whiskey; the taste of it brings screwed-up expressions and sour shudders. But by and by we begin to sing, the two of us singing different songs simultaneously. I don't know the words to mine, just: *Come on along, come on along, to the dark-town strutters' ball.* But I can dance: that's what I mean to be, a tap dancer in the movies. My dancing shadow rollicks on the walls; our voices rock the chinaware; we giggle: as if unseen hands were tickling us. Queenie rolls on her back, her paws plow the air, something like a grin stretches her black lips. Inside myself, I feel warm and sparky as those crumbling logs, carefree as the wind in the chimney. My friend waltzes round the stove, the hem of her poor calico skirt pinched between her fingers as though it were a party dress: *Show me the way to go home,* she sings, her tennis shoes squeaking on the floor. *Show me the way to go home.*

Enter: two relatives. Very angry. Potent with eyes that scold, tongues that scald. Listen to what they have to say, the words tumbling together into a wrathful tune: "A child of seven! whiskey on his breath! are you out of your mind? feeding a child of seven! must be loony! road to ruination! remember Cousin Kate? Uncle Charlie? Uncle Charlie's brother-in-law? shame! scandal! humiliation! kneel, pray, beg the Lord!"

Queenie sneaks under the stove. My friend gazes at her shoes, her chin quivers, she lifts her skirt and blows her nose and runs to her room. Long after the town has gone to sleep and the house is silent except for the chimings of clocks and the sputter of fading fires, she is weeping into a pillow already as wet as a widow's handkerchief.

"Don't cry," I say, sitting at the bottom of her bed and shivering despite my flannel nightgown that smells of last winter's cough syrup, "don't cry," I beg, teasing her toes, tickling her feet, "you're too old for that."

"It's because," she hiccups, "I *am* too old. Old and funny."

"Not funny. Fun. More fun than anybody. Listen. If you don't stop crying you'll be so tired tomorrow we can't go cut a tree."

She straightens up. Queenie jumps on the bed (where Queenie is not allowed) to lick her cheeks. "I know where we'll find real pretty trees, Buddy. And holly, too. With berries big as your eyes. It's way off in the woods. Farther than we've ever been. Papa used to bring us Christmas trees from there: carry them on his shoulder. That's fifty years ago. Well, now: I can't wait for morning."

Morning. Frozen rime lusters the grass; the sun, round as an orange and orange as hot-weather moons, balances on the horizon, burnishes the silvered winter woods. A wild turkey calls. A renegade hog grunts in the undergrowth. Soon, by the edge of knee-deep, rapid-running water, we have to abandon the buggy. Queenie wades the stream first, paddles across barking complaints at the swiftness of the current, the pneumonia-making coldness of it. We follow, holding our shoes and equipment (a hatchet, a burlap sack) above our heads. A mile more: of chastising thorns, burs and briers that catch at our clothes; of rusty pine needles brilliant with gaudy fungus and molted feathers. Here, there, a flash, a flutter, an ecstasy of shrillings remind us that not all the birds have flown south. Always, the path unwinds through lemony sun pools and pitch vine tunnels. Another creek to cross: a disturbed armada of speckled trout froths the water round us, and frogs the size of plates practice belly flops; beaver workmen are building a dam. On the farther shore, Queenie shakes herself and trembles. My friend shivers, too: not with cold but enthusiasm. One of her hat's ragged roses sheds a petal as she lifts her head and inhales the pine-heavy air. "We're almost there; can you smell it, Buddy?" she says, as though we were approaching an ocean.

And, indeed, it is a kind of ocean. Scented acres of holiday trees, prickly-leafed holly. Red berries shiny as Chinese bells: black crows swoop upon them screaming. Having stuffed our burlap sacks with enough greenery and crimson to garland a dozen windows, we set about choosing a tree. "It should be," muses my friend, "twice as tall as a boy. So a boy can't steal the star." The one we pick is twice as tall as me. A brave handsome brute that survives thirty hatchet strokes before it keels with a creaking rending cry. Lugging it like a kill, we commence the long trek out. Every few yards we abandon the struggle, sit down and pant. But we have the strength of triumphant huntsmen; that and the tree's virile, icy perfume revive us, goad us on. Many compliments accompany our sunset return along the red clay road to town; but my friend is sly and noncommittal when passers-by praise the treasure perched in our buggy: what a fine tree and where did it come from? "Yonderways," she murmurs vaguely. Once a car stops and the rich mill owner's lazy wife leans out and whines: "Giveya two-bits cash for that ol tree." Ordinarily my friend is afraid of saying no; but on this occasion she promptly shakes her head: "We wouldn't take a dollar." The mill owner's wife persists. "A dollar, my foot! Fifty cents. That's my last offer. Goodness, woman, you can get another one." In answer, my friend gently reflects: "I doubt it. There's never two of anything."

Home: Queenie slumps by the fire and sleeps till tomorrow, snoring loud as a human.

A trunk in the attic contains: a shoebox of ermine tails (off the opera cape of a curious lady who once rented a room in the house), coils of frazzled tinsel gone gold with age, one silver star, a brief rope of dilapidated, undoubtedly dangerous candy-like light bulbs. Excellent decorations, as far as they go, which isn't far enough: my friend wants our tree to blaze "like a Baptist window," droop with weighty snows of ornament. But we can't afford the made-in-Japan splendors at the five-and-dime. So we do what we've always done: sit for days at the kitchen table with scissors and crayons and stacks of colored paper. I make sketches and my friend cuts them out: lots of cats, fish too (because they're easy to draw), some apples, some watermelons, a few winged angels devised from saved-up sheets of Hershey-bar tin foil. We use safety pins to attach these creations to the tree; as a final touch, we sprinkle the branches with shredded cotton (picked in August for this purpose). My friend, surveying the effect, clasps her hands together. "Now honest, Buddy. Doesn't it look good enough to eat?" Queenie tries to eat an angel.

After weaving and ribboning holly wreaths for all the front windows, our next project is the fashioning of family gifts. Tie-dye scarves for the ladies, for the men a home-brewed lemon and licorice and aspirin syrup to be taken "at the first Symptoms of a Cold and after Hunting." But when it comes time for making each other's gift, my friend and I separate to work secretly. I would like to buy her a pearl-handled knife, a radio, a whole pound of chocolate-covered cherries (we tasted some once and she always swears: "I could live on them,

Buddy, Lord yes I could—and that's not taking His name in vain"). Instead, I am building her a kite. She would like to give me a bicycle (she's said so on several million occasions: "If only I could, Buddy. It's bad enough in life to do without something *you* want; but confound it, what gets my goat is not being able to give somebody something you want *them* to have. Only one of these days I will, Buddy. Locate you a bike. Don't ask how. Steal it, maybe"). Instead, I'm fairly certain that she is building me a kite—the same as last year, and the year before: the year before that we exchanged slingshots. All of which is fine by me. For we are champion kite-fliers who study the wind like sailors; my friend, more accomplished than I, can get a kite aloft when there isn't enough breeze to carry clouds.

Christmas Eve afternoon we scrape together a nickel and go to the butcher's to buy Queenie's traditional gift, a good gnawable beef bone. The bone, wrapped in funny paper, is placed high in the tree near the silver star. Queenie knows it's there. She squats at the foot of the tree staring up in a trance of greed: when bedtime arrives she refuses to budge. Her excitement is equaled by my own. I kick the covers and turn my pillow as though it were a scorching summer's night. Somewhere a rooster crows: falsely, for the sun is still on the other side of the world.

"Buddy, are you awake?" It is my friend, calling from her room, which is next to mine; and an instant later she is sitting on my bed holding a candle. "Well, I can't sleep a hoot," she declares. "My mind's jumping like a jack rabbit. Buddy, do you think Mrs. Roosevelt will serve our cake at dinner?" We huddle in the bed, and she squeezes my hand I-love-you. "Seems like your hand used to be so much smaller. I guess I hate to see you grow up. When you're grown up, will we still be friends?" I say always. "But I feel so bad, Buddy. I wanted so bad to give you a bike. I tried to sell my cameo Papa gave me. Buddy—" she hesitates, as though embarrassed—"I made you another kite." Then I confess that I made her one, too; and we laugh. The candle burns too short to hold. Out it goes, exposing the starlight, the stars spinning at the window like a visible caroling that slowly, slowly daybreak silences. Possibly we doze; but the beginnings of dawn splash us like cold water: we're up, wide-eyed and wandering while we wait for others to waken. Quite deliberately my friend drops a kettle on the kitchen floor. I tap-dance in front of closed doors. One by one the household emerges, looking as though they'd like to kill us both; but it's Christmas, so they can't. First, a gorgeous breakfast: just everything you can imagine—from flapjacks and fried squirrel to hominy grits and honey-in-the-comb. Which puts everyone in a good humor except my friend and I. Frankly, we're so impatient to get at the presents we can't eat a mouthful.

Well, I'm disappointed. Who wouldn't be? With socks, a Sunday school shirt, some handkerchiefs, a hand-me-down sweater and a year's subscription to a religious magazine for children. *The Little Shepherd.* It makes me boil. It really does.

My friend has a better haul. A sack of Satsumas, that's her best present. She is proudest, however, of a white wool shawl knitted by her married sister. But she *says* her favorite gift is the kite I built her. And it *is* very beautiful; though not as beautiful as the one she made me, which is blue and scattered with gold and green Good Conduct stars; moreover, my name is painted on it, "Buddy."

"Buddy, the wind is blowing."

The wind is blowing, and nothing will do till we've run to a pasture below the house where Queenie has scooted to bury her bone (and where, a winter hence, Queenie will be buried, too). There, plunging through the healthy waist-high grass, we unreel our kites, feel them twitching at the string like sky fish as they swim into the wind. Satisfied, sun-warmed, we sprawl in the grass and peel Satsumas and watch our kites cavort. Soon I forget the socks and hand-me-down sweater. I'm as happy as if we'd already won the fifty-thousand-dollar Grand Prize in that coffee-naming contest.

"My, how foolish I am!" my friend cries, suddenly alert, like a woman remembering too late she has biscuits in the oven. "You know what I've always thought?" she asks in a tone of discovery, and not smiling at me but a point beyond. "I've always thought a body would have to be sick and dying before they saw the Lord. And I imagined that when He came it would be like looking at the Baptist window: pretty as colored glass with the sun pouring through, such a shine you don't know it's getting dark. And it's been a comfort: to think of that shine taking away all the spooky feeling. But I'll wager it never happens. I'll wager at the very end a body realizes the Lord has already shown Himself. That things as they are"—her hand circles in a gesture that gathers clouds and kites and grass and Queenie pawing earth over her bone—"just what they've always seen, was seeing Him. As for me, I could leave the world with today in my eyes."

This is our last Christmas together.

Life separates us. Those who Know Best decide that I belong in a military school. And so follows a miserable succession of bugle-blowing prisons, grim reveille-ridden summer camps. I have a new home too. But it doesn't count. Home is where my friend is, and there I never go.

And there she remains, puttering around the kitchen. Alone with Queenie. Then alone. ("Buddy dear," she writes in her wild hard-to-read script, "yesterday Jim Macy's horse kicked Queenie bad. Be thankful she didn't feel much. I wrapped her in a Fine Linen sheet and rode her in the buggy down to Simpson's pasture where she can be with all her Bones . . . .") For a few Novembers she continues to bake her fruitcakes single-handed; not as many, but some: and, of course, she always sends me "the best of the batch." Also, in every letter she encloses a dime wadded in toilet paper: "See a picture show and write me the story." But gradually in her letters she tends to confuse me with her other friend, the Buddy who died in the 1880's; more and more thirteenths are not the only days she stays in bed: a morning arrives in November, a leafless birdless coming of winter morning, when she cannot rouse herself to exclaim: "Oh my, it's fruitcake weather!"

And when that happens, I know it. A message saying so merely confirms a piece of news some secret vein had already received, severing from me an irreplaceable part of myself, letting it loose like a kite on a broken string. That is why, walking across a school campus on this particular December morning, I keep searching the sky. As if I expected to see, rather like hearts, a lost pair of kites hurrying toward heaven.

POETRY

A Group of Ballads

1. BABYLON; OR, THE BONNIE BANKS O FORDIE

There were three ladies lived in a bower,
    Eh vow bonnie,
And they went out to pull a flower,
    On the bonnie banks o Fordie.

They hadna pu'ed a flower but ane,
When up started to them a banisht man.

He's ta'en the first sister by her hand,
And he's turned her round and made her stand.

"It's whether will ye be a rank robber's wife,
Or will ye die by my wee pen-knife?"

"It's I'll not be a rank robber's wife,
But I'll rather die by your wee pen-knife."

He's killed this may, and he's laid her by,
For to bear the red rose company.

He's taken the second ane by the hand,
And he's turned her round and made her stand.

"It's whether will ye be a rank robber's wife,
Or will ye die by my wee pen-knife?"

"I'll not be a rank robber's wife,
But I'll rather die by your wee pen-knife."

He's killed this may, and he's laid her by,
For to bear the red rose company.

He's taken the youngest ane by the hand,
And he's turned her round and made her stand.

Says, "Will ye be a rank robber's wife,
Or will ye die by my wee pen-knife?"

"I'll not be a rank robber's wife,
Nor will I die by your wee pen-knife.

"For I hae a brother in this wood,
And gin ye kill me, it's he'll kill thee."

"What's thy brother's name? come tell to me."
"My brother's name is Baby Lon."

"O sister, sister, what have I done!
O have I done this ill to thee!

"O since I've done this evil deed,
Good sall never be seen o me."

He's taken out his wee pen-knife,
And he's twyned himsel o his ain sweet life.

2. EDWARD

"Why dois your brand sae drap wi bluid,
        Edward, Edward,
Why dois your brand sae drap wi bluid,
  And why sae sad gang yee O?"
"O I hae killed my hauke sae guid,
        Mither, mither,
O I hae killed my hauke sae guid,
  And I had nae mair bot hee O."

"Your haukis bluid was nevir sae reid,
        Edward, Edward,
Your haukis bluid was nevir sae reid,
  My deir son I tell thee O."
"O I hae killed my reid-roan steid,
        Mither, mither,
O I hae killed my reid-roan steid,
  That erst was sae fair and frie O."

"Your steid was auld, and ye hae gat mair,
        Edward, Edward,
Your steid was auld, and ye hae gat mair,
  Sum other dule ye drie O."

"O I hae killed my fadir deir,
    Mither, mither,
O I hae killed my fadir deir,
    Alas, and wae is mee O!"

"And whatten penance wul ye drie for that,
    Edward, Edward,
And whatten penance wul ye drie for that?
    My deir son, now tell me O."
"Ile set my feit in yonder boat,
    Mither, mither,
Ile set my feit in yonder boat,
    And Ile fare ovir the sea O."

"And what wul ye doe wi your towirs and your ha,
    Edward, Edward?
And what wul ye doe wi your towirs and your ha,
    That were sae fair to see O?"
"Ile let them stand tul they down fa,
    Mither, mither,
Ile let them stand tul they down fa,
    For here nevir mair maun I bee O."

"And what wul ye leive to your bairns and your wife,
    Edward, Edward?
And what wul ye leive to your bairns and your wife,
    Whan ye gang ovir the sea O?"
"The warldis room, let them beg thrae life,
    Mither, mither,
The warldis room, let them beg thrae life,
    For them nevir mair wul I see O."

"And what wul ye leive to your ain mither deir,
    Edward, Edward?
And what wul ye leive to your ain mither deir?
    My deir son, now tell me O."
"The curse of hell frae me sall ye beir,
    Mither, mither,
The curse of hell frae me sall ye beir,
    Sic counseils ye gave to me O."

3. THE MAID FREED FROM THE GALLOWS

"O good Lord Judge, and sweet Lord Judge,
　Peace for a little while!
Methinks I see my own father,
　Come riding by the stile.

"O father, oh father, a little of your gold,
　And likewise of your fee!
To keep my body from yonder grave,
　And my neck from the gallows-tree."

"None of my gold now you shall have,
　Nor likewise of my fee;
For I am come to see you hang'd,
　And hanged you shall be."

"O good Lord Judge, and sweet Lord Judge,
　Peace for a little while!
Methinks I see my own mother,
　Come riding by the stile.

"O mother, oh mother, a little of your gold,
　And likewise of your fee,
To keep my body from yonder grave,
　And my neck from the gallows-tree!"

"None of my gold now shall you have,
　Nor likewise of my fee;
For I am come to see you hang'd,
　And hanged you shall be."

"O good Lord Judge, and sweet Lord Judge,
　Peace for a little while!
Methinks I see my own brother,
　Come riding by the stile.

"O brother, oh brother, a little of your gold,
　And likewise of your fee,
To keep my body from yonder grave,
　And my neck from the gallows-tree!"

"None of my gold now shall you have,
  Nor likewise of my fee;
For I am come to see you hang'd,
  And hanged you shall be."

"O good Lord Judge, and sweet Lord Judge,
  Peace for a little while!
Methinks I see my own sister,
  Come riding by the stile.

"O sister, oh sister, a little of your gold,
  And likewise of your fee,
To keep my body from yonder grave,
  And my neck from the gallows-tree!"

"None of my gold now shall you have,
  Nor likewise of my fee;
For I am come to see you hang'd,
  And hanged you shall be."

"O good Lord Judge, and sweet Lord Judge,
  Peace for a little while!
Methinks I see my own true-love,
  Come riding by the stile.

"O true-love, oh true-love, a little of your gold,
  And likewise of your fee,
To save my body from yonder grave,
  And my neck from the gallows-tree."

"Some of my gold now you shall have,
  And likewise of my fee,
For I am come to see you sav'd,
  And saved you shall be."

4. LORD RANDAL

"O where ha you been, Lord Randal, my son?
And where ha you been, my handsome young man?"
"I ha been at the greenwood; mother, mak my bed soon,
For I'm wearied wi' huntin, and fain wad lie down."

"And wha met ye there, Lord Randal, my son?
And wha met ye there, my handsome young man?"
"O I met wi my true-love; mother, mak my bed soon,
For I'm wearied wi' huntin, and fain wad lie down."

"And what did she give you, Lord Randal, my son?
And what did she give you, my handsome young man?"
"Eels fried in a pan; mother, mak my bed soon,
For I'm wearied wi huntin, and fain wad lie down."

"And wha gat your leavins, Lord Randal, my son?
And wha gat your leavins, my handsome young man?"
"My hawks and my hounds; mother, mak my bed soon,
For I'm wearied wi huntin, and fain wad lie down."

"And what becam of them, Lord Randal, my son?
And what becam of them, my handsome young man?"
"They stretched their legs out an died; mother, mak my bed soon,
For I'm wearied wi huntin, and fain wad lie down."

"O I fear you are poisoned, Lord Randal, my son!
I fear you are poisoned, my handsome young man!"
"O yes, I am poisoned; mother, mak my bed soon,
For I'm sick at the heart, and I fain wad lie down."

"What d'ye leave to your mother, Lord Randal, my son?
What d'ye leave to your mother, my handsome young man?"
"Four and twenty milk kye; mother, mak my bed soon,
For I'm sick at the heart, and I fain wad lie down."

"What d'ye leave to your sister, Lord Randal, my son?
What d'ye leave to your sister, my handsome young man?"
"My gold and my silver; mother, mak my bed soon,
For I'm sick at the heart, an I fain wad lie down."

"What d'ye leave to your brother, Lord Randal, my son?
What d'ye leave to your brother, my handsome young man?"
"My houses and my lands; mother, mak my bed soon,
For I'm sick at the heart, and I fain wad lie down."

"What d'ye leave to your true-love, Lord Randal, my son?
What d'ye leave to your true-love, my handsome young man?"
"I leave her hell and fire; mother, mak my bed soon,
For I'm sick at the heart, and I fain wad lie down."

5. THE DAEMON LOVER

"O where have you been, my long, long love,
  This long seven years and mair?"
"O I'm come to seek my former vows
  Ye granted me before."

"O hold your tongue of your former vows,
  For they will breed sad strife;
O hold your tongue of your former vows,
  For I am become a wife."

He turned him right and round about,
  And the tear blinded his ee:
"I wad never hae trodden on Irish ground,
  If it had not been for thee.

"I might have had a king's daughter,
  Far, far beyond the sea;
I might have had a king's daughter,
  Had it not been for love o thee."

"If ye might have had a king's daughter,
  Yersel ye had to blame!
Ye might have had taken the king's daughter,
  For ye kend that I was nane.

"If I was to leave my husband dear,
  And my two babes also,
O what have you to take me to,
  If with you I should go?"

"I hae seven ships upon the sea—
  The eighth brought me to land—
With four-and-twenty bold mariners,
  And music on every hand."

She has taken up her two little babes,
  Kissed them baith cheek and chin:
"O fair ye weel, my ain two babes,
  For I'll never see you again."

She set her foot upon the ship,
   No mariners could she behold;
But the sails were o the taffetie,
   And the masts o the beaten gold.

She had not sailed a league, a league,
   A league but barely three,
When dismal grew his countenance,
   And drumlie grew his ee.

They had not saild a league, a league,
   A league but barely three,
Until she espied his cloven foot,
   And she wept right bitterlie.

"O hold your tongue of your weeping," says he,
   "Of your weeping now let me be;
I will shew you how the lilies grow
   On the banks of Italy."

"O what hills are yon, yon pleasant hills,
   That the sun shines sweetly on?"
"O yon are the hills of heaven," he said,
   "Where you will never win."

"O whaten a mountain is yon," she said,
   "All so dreary wi frost and snow?"
"O yon is the mountain of hell," he cried,
   "Where you and I will go."

He strack the tap-mast wi his hand,
   The fore-mast wi his knee,
And he brake that gallant ship in twain,
   And sank her in the sea.

6.   SIR PATRICK SPENCE

The king sits in Dumferling toune,
   Drinking the blude-reid wine:
"O whare will I get guid sailor,
   To sail this schip of mine?"

Up and spak an eldern knicht,
   Sat at the king's richt kne:
"Sir Patrick Spence is the best sailor
   That sails upon the se."

The king had written a braid letter,
   And signd it wi his hand,
And sent it to Sir Patrick Spence,
   Was walking on the sand.

The first line that Sir Patrick red,
   A loud lauch lauched he;
The next line that Sir Patrick red,
   The teir blinded his ee.

"O wha is this has don this deid,
   This ill deid don to me,
To send me out this time o' the yeir,
   To sail upon the se?

Mak haste, mak haste, my mirry men all,
   Our guid schip sails the morne."
"O say na sae, master deir,
   For I feir a deadlie storme.

"Late late yestreen I saw the new moone
   Wi the auld moone in her arme,
And I feir, I feir, my deir master,
   That we will cum to harme."

O our Scots nobles wer richt laith
   To weet thair cork-heild schoone;
Bot lang owre a' the play wer playd,
   Thair hats they swam aboone.

O lang, lang may thair ladies sit,
   Wi thair fans into thair hand,
Or eir they se Sir Patrick Spence
   Cum sailing to the land.

O lang, lang may the ladies stand,
   Wi thair gold kems in thair hair,
Waiting for thair ain deir lords,
   For they'll se thame na mair.

Haf owre, haf owre to Aberdour,
  It's fiftie fadom deip,
And thair lies guid Sir Patrick Spence,
  Wi the Scots lords at his feit.

JOHN SKELTON

To Mistress Margaret Hussey

Merry Margaret
As midsummer flower,
Gentle as falcon
Or hawk of the tower;
With solace and gladness,
Much mirth and no madness,
All good and no badness;
So joyously,
So maidenly,
So womanly,
Her demeaning,
In every thing
Far far passing
That I can indite
Or suffice to write
Of merry Margaret,
As midsummer flower,
Gentle as falcon
Or hawk of the tower.

As patient and as still,
And as full of good will,
As the fair Isyphill,
Coriander,
Sweet pomander,
Good Cassander,

Steadfast of thought,
Well made, well wrought.
Far may be sought
Ere that ye can find
So courteous, so kind,
As merry Margaret,
This midsummer flower,
Gentle as falcon
Or hawk of the tower.

EDMUND SPENSER

Sonnets from *Amoretti*

XXII

This holy season, fit to fast and pray,
Men to devotion ought to be inclined:
Therefore, I likewise, on so holy day,
For my sweet saint some service fit will find.
Her temple fair is built within my mind,
In which her glorious image placèd is,
On which my thoughts do day and night attend,
Like sacred priests that never think amiss.
There I to her, as th' author of my bliss,
Will build an altar to appease her ire;
And on the same my heart will sacrifice,
Burning in flames of pure and chaste desire:
The which vouchsafe, O goddess, to accept,
Amongst thy dearest relics to be kept.

LXVIII

Most glorious Lord of life, that on this day
Didst make Thy triumph over death and sin,
And having harrow'd hell, didst bring away
Captivity thence captive, us to win:

This joyous day, dear Lord, with joy begin,
And grant that we, for whom Thou diddest die,
Being with Thy dear blood clean wash'd from sin,
May live for ever in felicity:
And that Thy love we weighing worthily,
May likewise love Thee for the same again;
And for Thy sake, that all like dear didst buy,
With love may one another entertain.
So let us love, dear Love, like as we ought:
Love is the lesson which the Lord us taught.

LXXIX

Men call you fair, and you do credit it,
For that yourself ye daily such do see;
But the true fair, that is the gentle wit
And virtuous mind, is much more praised of me.
For all the rest, however fair it be,
Shall turn to nought and lose that glorious hue;
But only that is permanent, and free
From frail corruption, that doth flesh ensue.
That is true beauty: that doth argue you
To be divine, and born of heavenly seed,
Deriv'd from that fair Spirit from Whom all true
And perfect beauty did at first proceed.
He only fair, and what He fair hath made;
All other fair, like flowers, untimely fade.

SIR WALTER RALEIGH

His Pilgrimage

Give me my scallop-shell of quiet,
    My staff of faith to walk upon,
My scrip of joy, immortal diet,
    My bottle of salvation,
My gown of glory, hope's true gage;
    And thus I'll take my pilgrimage.

Blood must be my body's balmer;
  No other balm will there be given;
Whilst my soul, like a quiet palmer,
  Travelleth towards the land of heaven,
Over the silver mountains,
Where spring the nectar fountains.
     There will I kiss
     The bowl of bliss,
And drink mine everlasting fill
Upon every milken hill.
My soul will be a-dry before;
But, after, it will thirst no more.

Then by that happy blissful day
  More peaceful pilgrims I shall see,
That have cast off their rags of clay,
  And walk apparelled fresh like me.
     I'll take them first
     To quench their thirst
And taste of nectar suckets
     At those clear wells
     Where sweetness dwells,
Drawn up by saints in crystal buckets.

  And when our bottles and all we
Are filled with immortality,
Then the blessèd paths we'll travel,
Strowed with rubies thick as gravel:
Ceilings of diamonds, sapphire floors,
High walls of coral, and pearly bowers.

  From thence to heaven's bribeless hall,
Where no corrupted voices brawl;
No conscience molten into gold;
No forged accuser bought or sold;
No cause deferred, no vain-spent journey;
For there Christ is the King's attorney,
Who pleads for all, without degrees,
And He hath angels but no fees.

And when the grand twelve million jury
Of our sins, with direful fury,
Against our souls black verdicts give,
Christ pleads His death; and then we live.
   Be Thou my speaker, taintless pleader!
Unblotted lawyer! true proceeder!
Thou giv'st salvation, even for alms,
Not with a bribèd lawyer's palms.

   And this is my eternal plea
To Him that made heaven and earth and sea:
That, since my flesh must die so soon,
And want a head to dine next noon,
Just at the stroke, when my veins start and spread,
Set on my soul an everlasting head!

Then am I ready, like a palmer fit,
To tread those blest paths, which before I writ.

SIR PHILIP SIDNEY

Sonnets from *Astrophel and Stella*

XXXI

With how sad steps, O Moon, thou climb'st the skies!
How silently, and with how wan a face!
What, may it be that e'en in heavenly place
That busy archer his sharp arrows tries!
Sure, if that long-with-love-acquainted eyes
Can judge of love, thou feel'st a lover's case,
I read it in thy looks; thy languish'd grace,
To me, that feel the like, thy state descries.

Then, e'en of fellowship, O Moon, tell me,
Is constant love deem'd there but want of wit?
Are beauties there as proud as here they be?
Do they above love to be loved, and yet
Those lovers scorn whom that love doth possess?
Do they call virtue, there, ungratefulness?

XXXIX

Come, Sleep, O Sleep! the certain knot of peace,
The baiting-place of wit, the balm of woe,
The poor man's wealth, the prisoner's release,
Th' indifferent judge between the high and low;
With shield of proof, shield me from out the prease
Of those fierce Darts Despair at me doth throw:
O make in me those civil wars to cease;
I will good tribute pay, if thou do so.
Take thou of me smooth pillows, sweetest bed,
A chamber deaf of noise and blind of light,
A rosy garland and a weary head;
And if these things, as being thine by right,
Move not thy heavy grace, thou shalt in me,
Livelier than elsewhere, Stella's image see.

XCV

Leave me, O Love, which reachest but to dust,
And thou, my mind, aspire to higher things!
Grow rich in that which never taketh rust;
Whatever fades, but fading pleasure brings.
Draw in thy beams, and humble all thy might
To that sweet yoke where lasting freedoms be;
Which breaks the clouds and opens forth the light
That doth both shine and give us sight to see.
O take fast hold! Let thy light be thy guide
In this small course which birth draws out to death,
And think how evil becometh him to slide
Who seeketh Heaven, and comes of heavenly breath.
Then farewell, world! thy uttermost I see.
Eternal Love, maintain thy life in me!

SAMUEL DANIEL

From *To Delia*

LI

Care-charmer Sleep, son of the sable Night,
Brother to Death, in silent darkness born,
Relieve my languish, and restore the light;
With dark forgetting of my care return.
And let the day be time enough to mourn
The shipwreck of my ill-adventured youth:
Let waking eyes suffice to wail their scorn,
Without the torment of the night's untruth.
Cease, dreams, the images of day-desires,
To model forth the passions of the morrow;
Never let rising Sun approve you liars,
To add more grief to aggravate my sorrow:
Still let me sleep, embracing clouds in vain,
And never wake to feel the day's disdain.

MICHAEL DRAYTON

From *Idea*

LXI

Since there's no help, come let us kiss and part,—
Nay, I have done, you get no more of me;
And I am glad, yea, glad with all my heart
That thus so cleanly I myself can free;
Shake hands for ever, cancel all our vows,
And when we meet at any time again,
Be it not seen in either of our brows
That we one jot of former love retain.

Now at the last gasp of love's latest breath,
When his pulse failing, passion speechless lies,
When faith is kneeling by his bed of death,
And innocence is closing up his eyes,
—Now, if thou would'st, when all have given him over,
From death to life thou might'st him yet recover!

WILLIAM SHAKESPEARE

From *Cymbeline*

DIRGE

Fear no more the heat o' the sun,
    Nor the furious winter's rages;
Thou thy worldly task hast done,
    Home art gone, and ta'en thy wages:
Golden lads and girls all must,
As chimney-sweepers, come to dust.

Fear no more the frown o' the great;
    Thou art past the tyrant's stroke;
Care no more to clothe and eat;
    To thee the reed is as the oak:
The sceptre, learning, physic, must
All follow this, and come to dust.

Fear no more the lightning-flash,
    Nor th' all-dreaded thunder-stone;
Fear not slander, censure rash;
    Thou hast finished joy and moan:
All lovers young, all lovers must
Consign to thee, and come to dust.

No exorciser harm thee!
    Nor no witchcraft charm thee!
Ghost unlaid forbear thee!
    Nothing ill come near thee!
Quiet consummation have,
And renownèd be thy grave!

From *Sonnets*

XVIII

Shall I compare thee to a summer's day?
Thou art more lovely and more temperate:
Rough winds do shake the darling buds of May.
And summer's lease hath all too short a date:
Sometime too hot the eye of heaven shines,
And often is his gold complexion dimm'd;
And every fair from fair sometimes declines,
By chance, or nature's changing course untrimm'd;
But thy eternal summer shall not fade,
Nor lose possession of that fair thou ow'st,
Nor shall death brag thou wander'st in his shade,
When in eternal lines to time thou grow'st;
   So long as men can breathe, or eyes can see,
   So long lives this, and this gives life to thee.

XXIX

When in disgrace with fortune and men's eyes
I all alone beweep my outcast state,
And trouble deaf heaven with my bootless cries,
And look upon myself, and curse my fate,
Wishing me like to one more rich in hope,
Featur'd like him, like him with friends possess'd,
Desiring this man's art, and that man's scope,
With what I most enjoy contented least;
Yet in these thoughts myself almost despising,
Haply I think on thee,—and then my state,
Like to the lark at break of day arising
From sullen earth, sings hymns at heaven's gate;
   For thy sweet love remember'd such wealth brings
   That then I scorn to change my state with kings.

LXXIII

That time of year thou mayst in me behold
When yellow leaves, or none, or few, do hang
Upon those boughs which shake against the cold,
Bare ruin'd choirs, where late the sweet birds sang.
In me thou see'st the twilight of such day
As after sunset fadeth in the West;
Which by and by black night doth take away,
Death's second self, that seals up all in rest.
In me thou see'st the glowing of such fire,
That on the ashes of his youth doth lie,
As the death-bed whereon it must expire,
Consum'd with that which it was nourish'd by.
  This thou perceiv'st, which makes thy love more strong,
  To love that well which thou must leave ere long.

CXVI

Let me not to the marriage of true minds
Admit impediments. Love is not love
Which alters when it alteration finds,
Or bends with the remover to remove:
O, no! it is an ever-fixèd mark,
That looks on tempests and is never shaken;
It is the star to every wandering bark,
Whose worth's unknown, although his height be taken.
Love's not Time's fool, though rosy lips and cheeks
Within his bending sickle's compass come;
Love alters not with his brief hours and weeks,
But bears it out even to the edge of doom.
  If this be error, and upon me prov'd,
  I never writ, nor no man ever lov'd.

CXXIX

The expense of spirit in a waste of shame
Is lust in action; and till action, lust
Is perjur'd, murderous, bloody, full of blame,
Savage, extreme, rude, cruel, not to trust;

Enjoy'd no sooner but despisèd straight;
Past reason hunted; and no sooner had,
Past reason hated, as a swallow'd bait,
On purpose laid to make the taker mad:
Mad in pursuit, and in possession so;
Had, having, and in quest to have, extreme;
A bliss in proof,—and prov'd, a very woe;
Before, a joy propos'd; behind, a dream.
    All this the world well knows; yet none knows well
    To shun the heaven that leads men to this hell.

CXXX

My mistress' eyes are nothing like the sun;
Coral is far more red than her lips' red:
If snow be white, why then her breasts are dun;
If hairs be wires, black wires grow on her head.
I have seen roses damask'd, red and white,
But no such roses see I in her cheeks;
And in some perfumes is there more delight
Than in the breath that from my mistress reeks.
I love to hear her speak, yet well I know
That music hath a far more pleasing sound:
I grant I never saw a goddess go,—
My mistress, when she walks, treads on the ground:
    And yet, by heaven, I think my love as rare
    As any she belied with false compare.

JOHN DONNE

From *Holy Sonnets*

X

Death, be not proud, though some have callèd thee
Mighty and dreadful, for thou art not so;
For those whom thou think'st thou dost overthrow
Die not, poor Death; nor yet canst thou kill me.

From rest and sleep, which but thy pictures be,
Much pleasure; then from thee much more must flow;
And soonest our best men with thee do go—
Rest of their bones and souls' delivery!
Thou'rt slave to fate, chance, kings, and desperate men,
And dost with poison, war, and sickness dwell;
And poppy or charms can make us sleep as well
And better than thy stroke. Why swell'st thou then?
One short sleep past, we wake eternally,
And Death shall be no more: Death, thou shalt die.

XIV

Batter my heart, three personed God; for you
As yet but knock, breathe, shine, and seek to mend;
That I may rise and stand, o'erthrow me and bend
Your force to break, blow, burn and make me new.
I, like an usurped town, to another due,
Labour to admit you, but Oh, to no end;
Reason, your viceroy in me, me should defend,
But is captived and proves weak or untrue.
Yet dearly I love you and would be loved fain,
But am betrothed unto your enemy:
Divorce me, untie or break that knot again,
Take me to you, imprison me, for I
Except you enthrall me, never shall be free,
Nor ever chaste, except you ravish me.

Song

Go and catch a falling star,
  Get with child a mandrake root,
Tell me where all past years are,
  Or who cleft the devil's foot,
Teach me to hear mermaids' singing,
  Or to keep off envy's stinging.
      And find
      What wind
Serves to advance an honest mind.

If thou be'st born to strange sights,
    Things invisible to see
Ride ten thousand days and nights,
    Till Age snow white hairs on thee;
Thou, when thou return'st, wilt tell me
    All strange wonders that befell thee,
        And swear
        No where
Lives a woman true, and fair.

If thou find'st one, let me know,
    Such a pilgrimage were sweet;
Yet do not, I would not go,
    Though at next door we might meet.
Though she were true, when you met her,
    And last, till you write your letter,
        Yet she
        Will be
False, ere I come, to two, or three.

The Good Morrow

I wonder, by my troth, what thou and I
Did till we loved? were we not weaned till then,
But sucked on country pleasures, childishly?
Or snorted we in the Seven Sleepers' den?
'Twas so; but this, all pleasures fancies be.
If ever any beauty I did see
Which I desired, and got, 'twas but a dream of thee.

And now good morrow to our waking souls,
Which watch not one another out of fear;
For love all love of other sights controls,
And makes one little room an everywhere.
Let sea-discoverers to new worlds have gone;
Let maps to other, worlds on worlds have shown;
Let us possess one world; each hath one, and is one.

My face in thine eye, thine in mine appears,
And true, plain hearts do in the faces rest;
Where can we find two better hemispheres
Without sharp north, without declining west?
Whatever dies, was not mixed equally;
If our two loves be one, or thou and I
Love so alike that none do slacken, none can die.

The Funeral

Whoever comes to shroud me, do not harm
    Nor question much
That subtle wreath of hair about mine arm;
The mystery, the sign you must not touch,
    For 'tis my outward soul,
Viceroy to that which, unto heav'n being gone,
    Will leave this to control
And keep these limbs, her provinces, from dissolution.

For if the sinewy thread my brain lets fall
    Through every part
Can tie those parts, and make me one of all;
These hairs, which upward grew, and strength and art
    Have from a better brain,
Can better do 't: except she meant that I
    By this should know my pain,
As prisoners then are manacled, when they're condemned to die.

Whate'er she meant by 't, bury it with me,
    For since I am
Love's martyr, it might breed idolatry
If into other hands these reliques came.
    As 't was humility
To afford to it all that a soul can do,
    So 't is some bravery
That, since you would have none of me, I bury some of you.

A Valediction Forbidding Mourning

As virtuous men pass mildly away
    And whisper to their souls to go,
Whilst some of their sad friends do say,
    "The breath goes now," and some say, "No:"

So let us melt, and make no noise,
    No tear-floods, nor sigh-tempests move;
'Twere profanation of our joys
    To tell the laity our love.

Moving of th' earth brings harms and fears;
    Men reckon what it did, and meant.
But trepidation of the spheres,
    Though greater far, is innocent.

Dull sublunary lovers' love—
    Whose soul is sense—cannot admit
Absence, because it doth remove
    Those things which elemented it.

But we by a love so much refined
    That ourselves know not what it is,
Inter-assured of the mind,
    Care less eyes, lips, and hands to miss.

Our two souls, therefore, which are one,
    Though I must go, endure not yet
A breach, but an expansion,
    Like gold to airy thinness beat.

If they be two, they are two so
    As stiff twin compasses are two;
Thy soul, the fixed foot, makes no show
    To move, but doth, if th' other do.

And though it in the center sit,
    Yet, when the other far doth roam,
It leans and harkens after it,
    And grows erect, as that comes home.

Such wilt thou be to me, who must,
    Like th' other foot, obliquely run;
Thy firmness makes my circle just,
    And makes me end where I begun.

GEORGE HERBERT

Love

Love bade me welcome; yet my soul drew back,
    Guilty of dust and sin.
But quick-ey'd Love, observing me grow slack
    From my first entrance in,
Drew nearer to me, sweetly questioning
    If I lack'd anything.

"A guest," I answer'd, "worthy to be here";
    Love said, "You shall be he."
"I, the unkind, ungrateful? Ah, my dear,
    I cannot look on Thee."
Love took my hand, and smiling did reply,
    "Who made the eyes but I?"

"Truth, Lord; but I have marr'd them; let my shame
    Go where it doth deserve."
"And know you not," says Love, "who bore the blame?"
    "My dear, then I will serve."
"You must sit down," says Love, "and taste My meat."
    So I did sit and eat.

The Pulley

When God at first made man,
Having a glass of blessings standing by—
Let us (said he) pour on him all we can;
Let the world's riches, which dispersèd lie,
    Contract into a span.

So strength first made a way,
Then beauty flow'd, then wisdom, honour, pleasure:
When almost all was out, God made a stay,
Perceiving that, alone of all His treasure,
    Rest in the bottom lay.

For if I should (said he)
Bestow this jewel also on My creature,
He would adore My gifts instead of Me,
And rest in Nature, not the God of Nature:
    So both should losers be.

Yet let him keep the rest,
But keep them with repining restlessness;
Let him be rich and weary, that at least,
If goodness lead him not, yet weariness
    May toss him to My breast.

JOHN MILTON

On His Blindness

When I consider how my light is spent
Ere half my days in this dark world and wide,
And that one talent which is death to hide
Lodged with me useless, though my soul more bent
To serve therewith my Maker, and present
My true account, lest he returning chide,

"Doth God exact day-labour, light denied?"
I fondly ask. But Patience, to prevent
That murmur, soon replies, "God doth not need
Either man's work or his own gifts. Who best
Bear his mild yoke, they serve him best. His state
Is kingly: thousands at his bidding speed,
And post o'er land and ocean without rest;
They also serve who only stand and wait."

From *Paradise Lost*

From Book VI: CHRIST VANQUISHES SATAN'S FORCES

He on his impious Foes right onward drove,
Gloomy as Night; under his burning Wheels
The steadfast Empyrean shook throughout,
All but the Throne it self of God. Full soon
Among them he arriv'd; in his right hand
Grasping ten thousand Thunders, which he sent
Before him, such as in their Souls infix'd
Plagues; they astonish'd all resistance lost,
All courage; down their idle weapons dropp'd;
O'er Shields and Helms, and helmèd heads he rode
Of Thrones and mighty Seraphim prostrate,
That wish'd the Mountains now might be again
Thrown on them as a shelter from his ire.
Nor less on either side tempestuous fell
His arrows, from the fourfold-visag'd Four,
Distinct with eyes, and from the living Wheels,
Distinct alike with multitude of eyes,
One Spirit in them rul'd, and every eye
Glar'd lightning, and shot forth pernicious fire
Among th'accurst, that wither'd all their strength,
And of their wonted vigour left them drain'd,
Exhausted, spiritless, afflicted, fall'n.
Yet half his strength he put not forth, but check'd
His Thunder in mid Volley, for he meant
Not to destroy, but root them out of Heav'n:

The overthrown he rais'd, and as a Herd
Of Goats or timorous flock together throng'd
Drove them before him Thunder-struck, pursu'd
With terrors and with furies to the bounds
And Crystal wall of Heav'n, which op'ning wide,
Roll'd inward, and a spacious Gap disclos'd
Into the wasteful Deep; the monstrous sight
Struck them with horror backward, but far worse
Urg'd them behind; headlong themselves they threw
Down from the verge of Heav'n, Eternal wrath
Burnt after them to the bottomless pit.

Hell heard th' unsufferable noise, Hell saw
Heav'n ruining from Heav'n and would have fled
Affrighted; but strict Fate had cast too deep
Her dark foundations, and too fast had bound.
Nine days they fell; confounded Chaos roar'd,
And felt tenfold confusion in their fall
Through his wild Anarchy, so huge a rout
Incumber'd him with ruin: Hell at last
Yawning receiv'd them whole, and on them clos'd,
Hell their fit habitation fraught with fire
Unquenchable, the house of woe and pain.
Disburden'd Heav'n rejoic'd, and soon repair'd
Her mural breach, returning whence it roll'd.

From Book VII: RAPHAEL RELATES TO ADAM THE SIXTH AND LAST DAY OF CREATION—THE MAKING OF MAN

Let us make now Man in our image, Man
In our similitude, and let them rule
Over the Fish and Fowl of Sea and Air,
Beast of the Field, and over all the Earth,
And every creeping thing that creeps on ground.
This said, he form'd thee, *Adam*, thee, O Man,
Dust of the ground, and in thy nostrils breath'd
The breath of Life; in his own Image hee
Created thee, in the Image of God
Express, and thou becam'st a living Soul.

Male he created thee, but thy consort
Female for Race; then bless'd Mankind, and said,
Be fruitful, multiply, and fill the Earth,
Subdue it, and throughout Dominion hold
Over Fish of the Sea, and Fowl of the Air,
And every living thing that moves on the Earth.
Wherever thus created, for no place
Is yet distinct by name, thence, as thou know'st
He brought thee into this delicious Grove,
This Garden, planted with the Trees of God,
Delectable both to behold and taste;
And freely all their pleasant fruit for food
Gave thee, all sorts are here that all th' Earth yields,
Variety without end; but of the Tree
Which tasted works knowledge of Good and Evil,
Thou may'st not; in the day thou eat'st, thou di'st;
Death is the penalty impos'd, beware,
And govern well thy appetite, lest sin
Surprise thee, and her black attendant Death.
Here finish'd he, and all that he had made
View'd, and behold all was entirely good;
So Ev'n and Morn accomplish't the Sixth day:
Yet not till the Creator from his work
Desisting, though unwearied, up return'd,
Up to the Heav'n of Heav'ns his high abode,
Thence to behold this new-created World
Th' addition of his Empire, how it shew'd
In prospect from his Throne, how good, how fair,
Answering his great Idea. Up he rode
Follow'd with acclamation and the sound
Symphonious of ten thousand Harps that tun'd
Angelic harmonies: the Earth, the Air
Resounded, (thou remember'st, for thou heard'st)
The Heav'ns and all the Constellations rung,
The Planets in their stations list'ning stood,
While the bright Pomp ascended jubilant.
Open, ye everlasting Gates, they sung,
Open, ye Heav'ns, your living doors; let in
The great Creator from his work return'd
Magnificent, his Six days work, a World;

Open, and henceforth oft; for God will deign
To visit oft the dwellings of just Men
Delighted, and with frequent intercourse
Thither will send his winged Messengers
On errands of supernal Grace. So sung
The glorious Train ascending: He through Heav'n,
That open'd wide her blazing Portals, led
To God's Eternal house direct the way,
A broad and ample road, whose dust is Gold
And pavement Stars, as Stars to thee appear,
Seen in the Galaxy, that Milky way
Which nightly as a circling Zone thou see'st
Powder'd with Stars. And now on Earth the Seventh
Ev'ning arose in *Eden*, for the Sun
Was set, and twilight from the East came on,
Forerunning Night; when at the holy mount
Of Heav'ns high-seated top, th' Imperial Throne
Of Godhead, fix'd for ever firm and sure,
The Filial Power arriv'd, and sate him down
With his great Father, for he also went
Invisible, yet staid (such privilege
Hath Omnipresence) and the work ordain'd,
Author and end of all things, and from work
Now resting, bless'd and hallow'd the Seventh day,
As resting on that day from all his work,
But not in silence holy kept; the Harp
Had work and rested not, the solemn Pipe,
And Dulcimer, all Organs of sweet stop,
All sounds on Fret by String or Golden Wire
Temper'd soft Tunings, intermix'd with Voice
Choral or Unison: of incense, Clouds
Fuming from Golden Censers hid the Mount.
Creation and the Six days acts they sung . . .

From Book X: SATAN, RETURNING TO PANDEMONIUM
FROM EDEN, HAS RECOUNTED HIS VICTORY OVER MAN

So having said, a while he stood, expecting
Their universal shout and high applause
To fill his ear, when contrary he hears
On all sides, from innumerable tongues

A dismal universal hiss, the sound
Of public scorn; he wonder'd, but not long
Had leisure, wond'ring at himself now more;
His Visage drawn he felt to sharp and spare,
His Arms clung to his Ribs, his Legs entwining
Each other, till supplanted down he fell
A monstrous Serpent, on his Belly prone,
Reluctant, but in vain; a greater power
Now rul'd him, punish'd in the shape he sinn'd,
According to his doom: he would have spoke,
But hiss for hiss return'd with forked tongue
To forked tongue, for now were all transform'd
Alike, to Serpents all as accessories
To his bold Riot: dreadful was the din
Of hissing through the Hall, thick swarming now
With complicated monsters, head and tail,
Scorpion and Asp, and *Amphisbaena* dire,
Cerastes horn'd, *Hydrus,* and *Ellops* drear,
And *Dipsas* (Not so thick swarm'd once the Soil
Bedropp'd with blood of *Gorgon,* or the Isle
Ophiusa) but still greatest hee the midst,
Now Dragon grown, larger than whom the Sun
Engender'd in the *Pythian* Vale on slime,
Huge *Python,* and his Power no less he seem'd
Above the rest still to retain; they all
Him follow'd issuing forth to th' open Field,
Where all yet left of that revolted Rout
Heav'n-fall'n, in station stood or just array,
Sublime with expectation when to see
In Triumph issuing forth their glorious Chief;
They saw, but other sight instead, a crowd
Of ugly Serpents; horror on them fell,
And horrid sympathy: for what they saw,
They felt themselves now changing; down their arms,
Down fell both Spear and Shield, down they as fast,
And the dire hiss renew'd, and the dire form
Catch'd by Contagion, like in punishment,
As in their crime. Thus was th' applause they meant,
Turn'd to exploding hiss, triumph to shame
Cast on themselves from their own mouths. There stood
A Grove hard by, sprung up with this their change,

His will who reigns above, to aggravate
Their penance, laden with fair Fruit, like that
Which grew in Paradise, the bait of *Eve*
Us'd by the Tempter: on that prospect strange
Their earnest eyes they fix'd, imagining
For one forbidden Tree a multitude
Now ris'n, to work them further woe or shame;
Yet parch'd with scalding thirst and hunger fierce,
Though to delude them sent, could not abstain,
But on they roll'd in heaps, and up the Trees
Climbing, sat thicker than the snaky locks
That curl'd *Megaera*: greedily they pluck'd
The Fruitage fair to sight, like that which grew
Near that bituminous Lake where *Sodom* flam'd;
This more delusive, not the touch, but taste
Deceiv'd; they fondly thinking to allay
Their appetite with gust, instead of Fruit
Chew'd bitter Ashes, which th' offended taste
With spattering noise rejected: oft they assay'd,
Hunger and thirst constraining, drugg'd as oft,
With hatefullest disrelish writh'd their jaws
With soot and cinders fill'd; so oft they fell
Into the same illusion, not as Man
Whom they triumph'd once laps'd. Thus were they plagu'd
And worn with Famine, long and ceaseless hiss,
Till their lost shape, permitted, they resum'd,
Yearly enjoin'd, some say, to undergo
This annual humbling certain number'd days,
To dash their pride, and joy for Man seduc'd.

SIR JOHN SUCKLING

The Constant Lover

Out upon it, I have loved
  Three whole days together!
And am like to love three more,
  If it prove fair weather.

Time shall moult away his wings
    Ere he shall discover
In the whole wide world again
    Such a constant lover.

But the spite on't is, no praise
    Is due at all to me:
Love with me had made no stays,
    Had it any been but she.

Had it any been but she,
    And that very face,
There had been at least ere this
    A dozen dozen in her place.

RICHARD LOVELACE

To Althea from Prison

When Love with unconfinèd wings
    Hovers within my gates,
And my divine Althea brings
    To whisper at the grates;
When I lie tangled in her hair
    And fetter'd to her eye,
The birds that wanton in the air
    Know no such liberty.

When flowing cups run swiftly round
    With no allaying Thames,
Our careless heads with roses bound,
    Our hearts with loyal flames;
When thirsty grief in wine we steep,
    When healths and draughts go free—
Fishes that tipple in the deep
    Know no such liberty.

When, like committed linnets, I
    With shriller throat shall sing
The sweetness, mercy, majesty,
    And glories of my King;
When I shall voice aloud how good
    He is, how great should be,
Enlargèd winds, that curl the flood,
    Know no such liberty.

Stone walls do not a prison make,
    Nor iron bars a cage;
Minds innocent and quiet take
    That for an hermitage;
If I have freedom in my love
    And in my soul am free,
Angels alone, that soar above,
    Enjoy such liberty.

ANDREW MARVELL

To His Coy Mistress

Had we but world enough, and time,
This coyness, lady, were no crime.
We would sit down, and think which way
To walk, and pass our long love's day.
Thou by the Indian Ganges' side
Should'st rubies find: I by the tide
Of Humber would complain. I would
Love you ten years before the Flood,
And you should, if you please, refuse
Till the conversion of the Jews.
My vegetable love should grow
Vaster than empires, and more slow.

An hundred years should go to praise
Thine eyes, and on thy forehead gaze:
Two hundred to adore each breast:
But thirty thousand to the rest;
An age at least to every part,
And the last age should show your heart.
For, lady, you deserve this state,
Nor would I love at lower rate.

But at my back I always hear
Time's wingèd chariot hurrying near:
And yonder all before us lie
Deserts of vast eternity.
Thy beauty shall no more be found;
Nor, in thy marble vault, shall sound
My echoing song: then worms shall try
That long-preserved virginity,
And your quaint honour turn to dust,
And into ashes all my lust.
The grave's a fine and private place,
But none, I think, do there embrace.

Now, therefore, while the youthful hue
Sits on thy skin like morning dew,
And while thy willing soul transpires
At every pore with instant fires,
Now let us sport us while we may;
And now, like amorous birds of prey,
Rather at once our Time devour,
Than languish in his slow-chapt power.
Let us roll all our strength and all
Our sweetness up into one ball,
And tear our pleasures with rough strife
Thorough the iron gates of life.
Thus, though we cannot make our sun
Stand still, yet we will make him run.

HENRY VAUGHAN

The Retreat

Happy those early days, when I
Shin'd in my Angel-infancy!
Before I understood this place
Appointed for my second race,
Or taught my soul to fancy aught
But a white celestial thought:
When yet I had not walk'd above
A mile or two from my first Love,
And looking back—at that short space—
Could see a glimpse of His bright face:
When on some gilded cloud, or flow'r,
My gazing soul would dwell an hour,
And in those weaker glories spy
Some shadows of eternity:
Before I taught my tongue to wound
My Conscience with a sinful sound,
Or had the black art to dispense
A several sin to ev'ry sense,
But felt through all this fleshly dress
Bright shoots of everlastingness.
    O how I long to travel back,
And tread again that ancient track!
That I might once more reach that plain
Where first I left my glorious train;
From whence th' enlightened spirit sees
That shady City of Palm-trees.
But ah! my soul with too much stay
Is drunk, and staggers in the way!
Some men a forward motion love,
But I by backward steps would move;
And when this dust falls to the urn,
In that state I came, return.

The World

I saw Eternity the other night
Like a great ring of pure and endless light,
  All calm, as it was bright,
And round beneath it, Time in hours, days, years
   Driv'n by the spheres
Like a vast shadow mov'd, in which the world
  And all her train were hurl'd;
The doting Lover in his quaintest strain
   Did there complain,
Near him, his lute, his fancy, and his flights,
   Wit's sour delights,
With gloves and knots, the silly snares of pleasure,
   Yet his dear treasure,
All scatter'd lay, while he his eyes did pour
   Upon a flow'r.

The darksome Statesman hung with weights and woe
Like a thick midnight-fog mov'd there so slow
   He did nor stay, nor go;
Condemning thoughts (like sad eclipses) scowl
   Upon his soul,
And clouds of crying witnesses without
   Pursued him with one shout.
Yet digg'd the Mole, and lest his ways be found
   Workt under ground,
Where he did clutch his prey, but One did see
   That policy,
Churches and altars fed him, perjuries
   Were gnats and flies,
It rain'd about him blood and tears, but he
   Drank them as free.

The fearful Miser on a heap of rust
Sat pining all his life there, did scarce trust
    His own hands with the dust,
Yet would not place one piece above, but lives
      In fear of thieves.
Thousands there were as frantic as himself
    And hugg'd each one his pelf,
The downright Epicure plac'd heav'n in sense
    And scorn'd pretense
While others slipt into a wide excess
    Said little less;
The weaker sort slight, trivial wares enslave
    Who think them brave,
And poor, despisèd Truth sat counting by
    Their victory.

Yet some, who all this while did weep and sing,
And sing, and weep, soar'd up into the ring,
    But most would use no wing.
O fools (said I), thus to prefer dark night
    Before true light,
To live in grots, and caves, and hate the day
    Because it shows the way,
The way which from this dead and dark abode
    Leads up to God,
A way where you might tread the sun, and be
    More bright than he.
But as I did their madness so discuss
    One whisper'd thus,
This ring the Bridegroom did for none provide
    But for his Bride.

WILLIAM BLAKE

The Lamb

Little Lamb, who made thee?
Dost thou know who made thee?
Gave thee life, and bid thee feed,
By the stream and o'er the mead;

Gave thee clothing of delight,
Softest clothing, woolly, bright;
Gave thee such a tender voice,
Making all the vales rejoice?
   Little Lamb, who made thee?
   Dost thou know who made thee?

Little Lamb, I'll tell thee,
Little Lamb, I'll tell thee:
He is callèd by thy name,
For he calls himself a Lamb.
He is meek, and he is mild;
He became a little child.
I a child, and thou a lamb,
We are callèd by his name.
   Little Lamb, God bless thee!
   Little Lamb, God bless thee!

The Tiger

Tiger! Tiger! burning bright
In the forests of the night,
What immortal hand or eye
Could frame thy fearful symmetry?

In what distant deeps or skies
Burnt the fire of thine eyes?
On what wings dare he aspire?
What the hand dare seize the fire?

And what shoulder and what art
Could twist the sinews of thy heart?
And, when thy heart began to beat,
What dread hand and what dread feet?

What the hammer? What the chain?
In what furnace was thy brain?
What the anvil? What dread grasp
Dare its deadly terrors clasp?

When the stars threw down their spears,
And water'd heaven with their tears,
Did he smile his work to see?
Did he who made the lamb make thee?

Tiger! Tiger! burning bright
In the forests of the night,
What immortal hand or eye
Dare frame thy fearful symmetry?

WILLIAM WORDSWORTH

The Solitary Reaper

Behold her, single in the field,
Yon solitary highland lass!
Reaping and singing by herself;
Stop here, or gently pass!
Alone she cuts and binds the grain,
And sings a melancholy strain;
O listen! for the vale profound
Is overflowing with the sound.

No nightingale did ever chaunt
More welcome notes to weary bands
Of travelers in some shady haunt,
Among Arabian sands:
A voice so thrilling ne'er was heard
In spring-time from the cuckoo-bird,
Breaking the silence of the seas
Among the farthest Hebrides.

Will no one tell me what she sings?—
Perhaps the plaintive numbers flow
For old, unhappy, far-off things,
And battles long ago:
Or is it some more humble lay,
Familiar matter of today?
Some natural sorrow, loss, or pain,
That has been, and may be again?

Whate'er the theme, the maiden sang
As if her song could have no ending;
I saw her singing at her work,
And o'er the sickle bending;—
I listened, motionless and still;
And, as I mounted up the hill
The music in my heart I bore,
Long after it was heard no more.

Composed upon Westminster Bridge

Earth has not anything to show more fair:
Dull would he be of soul who could pass by
A sight so touching in its majesty:
This city now doth like a garment wear
The beauty of the morning; silent, bare,
Ships, towers, domes, theaters, and temples lie
Open unto the fields, and to the sky;
All bright and glittering in the smokeless air.

Never did sun more beautifully steep
In his first splendor valley, rock, or hill;
Ne'er saw I, never felt, a calm so deep!
The river glideth at his own sweet will:
Dear God! the very houses seem asleep;
And all that mighty heart is lying still!

It Is a Beauteous Evening

It is a beauteous evening, calm and free,
The holy time is quiet as a Nun
Breathless with adoration: the broad sun
Is sinking down in its tranquillity;
The gentleness of heaven broods o'er the Sea:
Listen! the mighty Being is awake,
And doth with his eternal motion make
A sound like thunder—everlastingly.

Dear Child! dear Girl! that walkest with me here,
If thou appear untouched by solemn thought,
Thy nature is not therefore less divine:
Thou liest in Abraham's bosom all the year,
And worship'st at the Temple's inner shrine,
God being with thee when we know it not.

GEORGE GORDON, LORD BYRON

From *Childe Harold's Pilgrimage*

THE OCEAN

There is a pleasure in the pathless woods,
There is a rapture on the lonely shore,
There is society where none intrudes
By the deep sea, and music in its roar:
I love not man the less, but nature more,
From these our interviews, in which I steal
From all I may be, or have been before,
To mingle with the universe, and feel
What I can ne'er express, yet cannot all conceal.

Roll on, thou deep and dark blue Ocean,—roll!
Ten thousand fleets sweep over thee in vain;
Man marks the earth with ruin,—his control
Stops with the shore;—upon the watery plain
The wrecks are all thy deed, nor doth remain
A shadow of man's ravage, save his own,
When, for a moment, like a drop of rain,
He sinks into thy depths with bubbling groan,
Without a grave, unknelled, uncoffined, and unknown.

His steps are not upon thy paths,—thy fields
Are not a spoil for him,—thou dost arise
And shake him from thee; the vile strength he wields
For earth's destruction thou dost all despise,
Spurning him from thy bosom to the skies,
And send'st him, shivering in thy playful spray
And howling, to his gods, where haply lies
His petty hope in some near port or bay,
And dashest him again to earth:—there let him lay.

The armaments which thunderstrike the walls
Of rock-built cities, bidding nations quake
And monarchs tremble in their capitals,
The oak leviathans, whose huge ribs make
Their clay creator the vain title take
Of lord of thee and arbiter of war,—
These are thy toys, and, as the snowy flake,
They melt into thy yeast of waves, which mar
Alike the Armada's pride or spoils of Trafalgar.

Thy shores are empires, changed in all save thee;
Assyria, Greece, Rome, Carthage, what are they?
Thy waters wasted them while they were free,
And many a tyrant since; their shores obey
The stranger, slave, or savage; their decay
Has dried up realms to deserts: not so thou;
Unchangeable save to thy wild waves' play,
Time writes no wrinkles on thine azure brow;
Such as creation's dawn beheld, thou rollest now.

Thou glorious mirror, where the Almighty's form
Glasses itself in tempests; in all time,
Calm or convulsed,—in breeze, or gale, or storm,
Icing the pole, or in the torrid clime
Dark-heaving; boundless, endless, and sublime,
The image of Eternity,—the throne
Of the Invisible! even from out thy slime
The monsters of the deep are made; each zone
Obeys thee; thou goest forth, dread, fathomless, alone.

And I have loved thee, Ocean! and my joy
Of youthful sports was on thy breast to be
Borne, like thy bubbles, onward; from a boy
I wantoned with thy breakers,—they to me
Were a delight; and if the freshening sea
Made them a terror, 'twas a pleasing fear;
For I was as it were a child of thee,
And trusted to thy billows far and near,
And laid my hand upon thy mane,—as I do here.

She Walks in Beauty

She walks in beauty, like the night,
    Of cloudless climes and starry skies;
And all that's best of dark and bright
    Meet in her aspect and her eyes:
Thus mellowed to that tender light
    Which heaven to gaudy day denies.

One shade the more, one ray the less,
    Had half impaired the nameless grace
Which waves in every raven tress,
    Or softly lightens o'er her face;
Where thoughts serenely sweet express
    How pure, how dear their dwelling-place.

And on that cheek, and o'er that brow,
    So soft, so calm, yet eloquent,
The smiles that win, the tints that glow,
    But tell of days in goodness spent,
A mind at peace with all below,
    A heart whose love is innocent!

PERCY BYSSHE SHELLEY

Ode to the West Wind

O wild West Wind, thou breath of Autumn's being,
Thou, from whose unseen presence the leaves dead
Are driven, like ghosts from an enchanter fleeing,
Yellow, and black, and pale, and hectic red,
Pestilence-stricken multitudes: O thou
Who chariotest to their dark wintry bed
The wingèd seeds, where they lie cold and low,
Each like a corpse within its grave, until
Thine azure sister of the Spring shall blow
Her clarion o'er the dreaming earth, and fill
(Driving sweet buds like flocks to feed in air)
With living hues and odours plain and hill:
Wild Spirit, which art moving everywhere;
Destroyer and Preserver; Hear, oh, hear!

Thou on whose stream, mid the steep sky's commotion,
Loose clouds like earth's decaying leaves are shed,
Shook from the tangled boughs of Heaven and Ocean,
Angels of rain and lightning: there are spread
On the blue surface of thine aëry surge,
Like the bright hair uplifted from the head
Of some fierce Maenad, even from the dim verge
Of the horizon to the zenith's height,
The locks of the approaching storm. Thou dirge
Of the dying year, to which this closing night
Will be the dome of a vast sepulchre,

Vaulted with all thy congregated might
Of vapours, from whose solid atmosphere
Black rain, and fire, and hail, will burst: O hear!

Thou who didst waken from his summer dreams
The blue Mediterranean, where he lay,
Lull'd by the coil of his crystàlline streams,
Beside a pumice isle in Baiæ's bay,
And saw in sleep old palaces and towers
Quivering within the wave's intenser day,
All overgrown with azure moss, and flowers
So sweet, the sense faints picturing them! Thou
For whose path the Atlantic's level powers
Cleave themselves into chasms, while far below
The sea-blooms and the oozy woods which wear
The sapless foliage of the ocean, know
Thy voice, and suddenly grow gray with fear,
And tremble and despoil themselves: O hear!

If I were a dead leaf thou mightest bear;
If I were a swift cloud to fly with thee;
A wave to pant beneath thy power, and share
The impulse of thy strength, only less free
Than thou, O uncontrollable! if even
I were as in my boyhood, and could be
The comrade of thy wanderings over heaven,
As then, when to outstrip thy skiey speed
Scarce seem'd a vision—I would ne'er have striven
As thus with thee in prayer in my sore need.
Oh, lift me as a wave, a leaf, a cloud!
I fall upon the thorns of life! I bleed!
A heavy weight of hours has chained and bowed
One too like thee: tameless, and swift, and proud.

Make me thy lyre, even as the forest is;
What if my leaves are falling like its own!
The tumult of thy mighty harmonies
Will take from both a deep, autumnal tone,
Sweet though in sadness. Be thou, spirit fierce,
My spirit! Be thou me, impetuous one!

Drive my dead thoughts over the universe
Like withered leaves to quicken a new birth!
And, by the incantation of this verse,
Scatter, as from an unextinguished hearth
Ashes and sparks, my words among mankind!
Be through my lips to unawakened earth
The trumpet of a prophecy! O Wind,
If Winter comes, can Spring be far behind?

Ozymandias

I met a traveler from an antique land
Who said: Two vast and trunkless legs of stone
Stand in the desert. Near them, on the sand,
Half sunk, a shattered visage lies, whose frown,
And wrinkled lip, and sneer of cold command,
Tell that its sculptor well those passions read
Which yet survive, stamped on these lifeless things,
The hand that mocked them and the heart that fed;
And on the pedestal these words appear:
"My name is Ozymandias, king of kings:
Look on my works, ye Mighty, and despair!"
Nothing beside remains. Round the decay
Of that colossal wreck, boundless and bare
The lone and level sands stretch far away.

WILLIAM CULLEN BRYANT

Thanatopsis

To him who in the love of Nature holds
Communion with her visible forms, she speaks
A various language; for his gayer hours

She has a voice of gladness, and a smile
And eloquence of beauty, and she glides
Into his darker musings, with a mild
And healing sympathy, that steals away
Their sharpness, ere he is aware. When thoughts
Of the last bitter hour come like a blight
Over thy spirit, and sad images
Of the stern agony, and shroud, and pall,
And breathless darkness, and the narrow house,
Make thee to shudder and grow sick at heart;—
Go forth, under the open sky, and list
To Nature's teachings, while from all around—
Earth and her waters, and the depths of air—
Comes a still voice—

             Yet a few days, and thee
The all-beholding sun shall see no more
In all his course; nor yet in the cold ground,
Where thy pale form was laid with many tears,
Nor in the embrace of ocean, shall exist
Thy image. Earth, that nourished thee, shall claim
Thy growth, to be resolved to earth again,
And, lost each human trace, surrendering up
Thine individual being, shalt thou go
To mix forever with the elements,
To be a brother to the insensible rock
And to the sluggish clod, which the rude swain
Turns with his share, and treads upon. The oak
Shall send his roots abroad, and pierce thy mold.

    Yet not to thine eternal resting-place
Shalt thou retire alone, nor couldst thou wish
Couch more magnificent. Thou shalt lie down
With patriarchs of the infant world—with kings,
The powerful of the earth—the wise, the good,
Fair forms, and hoary seers of ages past,
All in one mighty sepulcher. The hills
Rock-ribbed and ancient as the sun,—the vales
Stretching in pensive quietness between;
The venerable woods—rivers that move
In majesty, and the complaining brooks
That make the meadows green; and, poured round all,

Old Ocean's gray and melancholy waste,—
Are but the solemn decorations all
Of the great tomb of man. The golden sun,
The planets, all the infinite host of heaven,
Are shining on the sad abodes of death
Through the still lapse of ages. All that tread
The globe are but a handful to the tribes
That slumber in its bosom.—Take the wings
Of morning, pierce the Barcan wilderness,
Or lose thyself in the continuous woods
Where rolls the Oregon, and hears no sound,
Save his own dashings—yet the dead are there;
And millions in those solitudes, since first
The flight of years began, have laid them down
In their last sleep—the dead reign there alone.
So shalt thou rest, and what if thou withdraw
In silence from the living, and no friend
Take note of thy departure? All that breathe
Will share thy destiny. The gay will laugh
When thou art gone, the solemn brood of care
Plod on, and each one as before will chase
His favorite phantom; yet all these shall leave
Their mirth and their employments, and shall come
And make their bed with thee. As the long train
Of ages glides away, the sons of men,
The youth in life's green spring, and he who goes
In the full strength of years, matron and maid,
The speechless babe, and the gray-headed man—
Shall one by one be gathered to thy side,
By those, who in their turn shall follow them.

So live, that when thy summons comes to join
The innumerable caravan, which moves
To that mysterious realm, where each shall take
His chamber in the silent halls of death,
Thou go not, like the quarry-slave at night,
Scourged to his dungeon, but, sustained and soothed
By an unfaltering trust, approach thy grave,
Like one who wraps the drapery of his couch
About him, and lies down to pleasant dreams.

To a Waterfowl

Whither, midst falling dew,
While glow the heavens with the last steps of day,
Far, through their rosy depths, dost thou pursue
Thy solitary way?

Vainly the fowler's eye
Might mark thy distant flight to do thee wrong,
As, darkly seen against the crimson sky,
Thy figure floats along.

Seek'st thou the plashy brink
Of weedy lake, or marge of river wide,
Or where the rocking billows rise and sink
On the chafed ocean-side?

There is a Power whose care
Teaches thy way along that pathless coast—
The desert and illimitable air—
Lone wandering, but not lost.

All day thy wings have fanned,
At that far height, the cold, thin atmosphere,
Yet stoop not, weary, to the welcome land,
Though the dark night is near.

And soon that toil shall end;
Soon shalt thou find a summer home, and rest,
And scream among thy fellows; reeds shall bend,
Soon, o'er thy sheltered nest.

Thou'rt gone, the abyss of heaven
Hath swallowed up thy form; yet, on my heart
Deeply hath sunk the lesson thou hast given,
    And shall not soon depart.

He who, from zone to zone,
Guides through the boundless sky thy certain flight,
In the long way that I must tread alone
    Will lead my steps aright.

JOHN KEATS

When I Have Fears That I May Cease to Be

When I have fears that I may cease to be
Before my pen has gleaned my teeming brain,
Before high-pilèd books, in charact'ry,
Hold like rich garners the full-ripened grain;
When I behold, upon the night's starred face,
Huge cloudy symbols of a high romance,
And think that I may never live to trace
Their shadows, with the magic hand of chance;
And when I feel, fair creature of an hour!
That I shall never look upon thee more,
Never have relish in the faery power
Of unreflecting love;—then on the shore
Of the wide world I stand alone, and think,
Till Love and Fame to nothingness do sink.

Bright Star! Would I Were Steadfast as Thou Art

Bright star! would I were steadfast as thou art—
Not in lone splendour hung aloft the night,
And watching, with eternal lids apart,
Like Nature's patient sleepless Eremite,
The moving waters at their priestlike task
Of pure ablution round earth's human shores,
Or gazing on the new soft-fallen mask
Of snow upon the mountains and the moors—
No—yet still steadfast, still unchangeable,
Pillowed upon my fair love's ripening breast,
To feel for ever its soft fall and swell,
Awake for ever in a sweet unrest,
Still, still to hear her tender-taken breath,
And so live ever—or else swoon to death.

Ode to a Nightingale

My heart aches, and a drowsy numbness pains
    My sense, as though of hemlock I had drunk,
Or emptied some dull opiate to the drains
    One minute past, and Lethe-wards had sunk:
'Tis not through envy of thy happy lot,
    But being too happy in thine happiness—
        That thou, light-wingèd Dryad of the trees,
            In some melodious plot
    Of beechen green, and shadows numberless,
        Singest of summer in full-throated ease.

O for a draught of vintage! that hath been
  Cooled a long age in the deep delvèd earth,
Tasting of Flora and the country green,
  Dance, and Provençal song, and sunburnt mirth!
O for a beaker full of the warm South,
  Full of the true, the blushful Hippocrene,
    With beaded bubbles winking at the brim,
      And purple-stainèd mouth;
  That I might drink, and leave the world unseen,
    And with thee fade away into the forest dim:

Fade away, dissolve, and quite forget
  What thou among the leaves hast never known,
The weariness, the fever, and the fret
  Here, where men sit and hear each other groan;
Where palsy shakes a few, sad, last gray hairs,
  Where youth grows pale, and specter-thin, and dies;
    Where but to think is to be full of sorrow
      And leaden-eyed despairs,
  Where Beauty cannot keep her lustrous eyes,
    Or new Love pine at them beyond to-morrow.

Away! away! for I will fly to thee,
  Not charioted by Bacchus and his pards,
But on the viewless wings of Poesy,
  Though the dull brain perplexes and retards:
Already with thee! tender is the night,
  And haply the Queen-Moon is on her throne,
    Clustered around by all her starry Fays;
      But here there is no light,
  Save what from heaven is with the breezes blown
    Through verdurous glooms and winding mossy ways.

I cannot see what flowers are at my feet,
  Nor what soft incense hangs upon the boughs,
But, in embalmèd darkness, guess each sweet
  Wherewith the seasonable month endows
The grass, the thicket, and the fruit-tree wild;

White hawthorn, and the pastoral eglantine;
  Fast-fading violets covered up in leaves;
    And mid-May's eldest child,
The coming musk-rose, full of dewy wine,
  The murmurous haunt of flies on summer eves.

Darkling I listen; and for many a time
  I have been half in love with easeful Death,
Called him soft names in many a musèd rhyme,
  To take into the air my quiet breath;
Now more than ever seems it rich to die,
  To cease upon the midnight with no pain,
    While thou art pouring forth thy soul abroad
      In such an ecstasy!
  Still wouldst thou sing, and I have ears in vain—
  To thy high requiem become a sod.

Thou wast not born for death, immortal Bird!
  No hungry generations tread thee down;
The voice I hear this passing night was heard
  In ancient days by emperor and clown:
Perhaps the self-same song that found a path
  Through the sad heart of Ruth, when, sick for home,
    She stood in tears amid the alien corn;
      The same that oft-times hath
  Charmed magic casements, opening on the foam
  Of perilous seas, in faery lands forlorn.

Forlorn! the very word is like a bell
  To toll me back from thee to my sole self!
Adieu! the fancy cannot cheat so well
  As she is famed to do, deceiving elf.
Adieu! adieu! thy plaintive anthem fades
  Past the near meadows, over the still stream,
    Up the hill-side; and now 'tis buried deep
      In the next valley-glades:
  Was it a vision, or a waking dream?
    Fled is that music:—Do I wake or sleep?

To Autumn

Season of mists and mellow fruitfulness,
    Close bosom-friend of the maturing sun;
Conspiring with him how to load and bless
    With fruit the vines that round the thatch-eaves run;
To bend with apples the moss'd cottage-trees,
    And fill all fruit with ripeness to the core;
        To swell the gourd, and plump the hazel shells
    With a sweet kernel; to set budding more,
And still more, later flowers for the bees,
Until they think warm days will never cease,
        For Summer has o'er-brimm'd their clammy cells.

Who hath not seen thee oft amid thy store?
    Sometimes whoever seeks abroad may find
Thee sitting careless on a granary floor,
    Thy hair soft-lifted by the winnowing wind;
Or on a half-reap'd furrow sound asleep,
    Drows'd with the fume of poppies, while thy hook
        Spares the next swath and all its twinèd flowers:
And sometimes like a gleaner thou dost keep
    Steady thy laden head across a brook;
    Or by a cider-press, with patient look,
        Thou watchest the last oozings hours by hours.

Where are the songs of Spring? Ay, where are they?
    Think not of them, thou hast thy music too,—
While barrèd clouds bloom the soft-dying day,
    And touch the stubble-plains with rosy hue;
Then in a wailful choir the small gnats mourn
    Among the river sallows, borne aloft
        Or sinking as the light wind lives or dies;

And full-grown lambs loud bleat from hilly bourn;
Hedge-crickets sing; and now with treble soft
The redbreast whistles from a garden-croft;
    And gathering swallows twitter in the skies.

On First Looking into Chapman's Homer

Much have I travelled in the realms of gold,
    And many goodly states and kingdoms seen;
    Round many western islands have I been
Which bards in fealty to Apollo hold.
Oft of one wide expanse had I been told
    That deep-browed Homer ruled as his demesne:
    Yet never did I breathe its pure serene
Till I heard Chapman speak out loud and bold.
Then felt I like some watcher of the skies
    When a new planet swims into his ken;
Or like stout Cortez when with eagle eyes
    He stared at the Pacific—and all his men
Looked at each other with a wild surmise—
    Silent, upon a peak in Darien.

Ode on a Grecian Urn

Thou still unravished bride of quietness,
    Thou foster-child of silence and slow time,
Sylvan historian, who canst thus express
    A flowery tale more sweetly than our rhyme:

What leaf-fringed legend haunts about thy shape
　　Of deities or mortals, or of both,
　　　　In Tempe or the dales of Arcady?
　　What men or gods are these? What maidens loth?
What mad pursuit? What struggle to escape?
　　　　What pipes and timbrels? What wild ecstasy?

Heard melodies are sweet, but those unheard
　　Are sweeter; therefore, ye soft pipes, play on;
Not to the sensual ear, but, more endeared,
　　Pipe to the spirit ditties of no tone:
Fair youth, beneath the trees, thou canst not leave
　　Thy song, nor ever can those trees be bare;
　　　　Bold Lover, never, never canst thou kiss,
Though winning near the goal—yet, do not grieve;
　　She cannot fade, though thou hast not thy bliss.
　　　　For ever wilt thou love, and she be fair!

Ah, happy, happy boughs! that cannot shed
　　Your leaves, nor ever bid the Spring adieu;
And, happy melodist, unwearièd,
　　For ever piping songs forever new;
More happy love! more happy, happy love!
　　For ever warm and still to be enjoyed,
　　　　For ever panting, and for ever young;
All breathing human passion far above,
　　That leaves a heart high-sorrowful and cloyed,
　　　　A burning forehead, and a parching tongue.

Who are these coming to the sacrifice?
　　To what green altar, O mysterious priest,
Lead'st thou that heifer lowing at the skies,
　　And all her silken flanks with garlands drest?
What little town by river or sea shore,
　　Or mountain-built with peaceful citadel,
　　　　Is emptied of its folk, this pious morn?
And, little town, thy streets for evermore
　　Will silent be; and not a soul to tell
　　　　Why thou art desolate, can e'er return.

O Attic shape! Fair attitude, with brede
   Of marble men and maidens overwrought,
With forest branches and the trodden weed;
   Thou, silent form, dost tease us out of thought
As doth eternity: Cold Pastoral!
   When old age shall this generation waste,
    Thou shalt remain, in midst of other woe
Than ours, a friend to man, to whom thou say'st,
   "Beauty is truth, truth beauty,"—that is all
    Ye know on earth and all ye need to know.

La Belle Dame sans Merci

"O what can ail thee, knight-at-arms,
   Alone and palely loitering?
The sedge is wither'd from the lake,
   And no birds sing.

"O what can ail thee, knight-at-arms,
   So haggard and so woe-begone?
The squirrel's granary is full,
   And the harvest's done.

"I see a lily on thy brow
   With anguish moist and fever dew;
And on thy cheek a fading rose
   Fast withereth too."

"I met a lady in the meads,
   Full beautiful—a faery's child,
Her hair was long, her foot was light,
   And her eyes were wild.

"I made a garland for her head,
  And bracelets too, and fragrant zone;
She look'd at me as she did love,
    And made sweet moan.

"I set her on my pacing steed
  And nothing else saw all day long,
For sideways would she lean, and sing
    A faery's song.

"She found me roots of relish sweet,
  And honey wild and manna dew,
And sure in language strange she said,
    'I love thee true!'

"She took me to her elfin grot,
  And there she wept and sigh'd full sore;
And there I shut her wild, wild eyes
    With kisses four.

"And there she lullèd me asleep,
  And there I dream'd—Ah! woe betide!
The latest dream I ever dream'd
    On the cold hill's side.

"I saw pale kings and princes too,
  Pale warriors, death-pale were they all;
Who cried—'La belle Dame sans Merci
    Hath thee in thrall!'

"I saw their starved lips in the gloam
  With horrid warning gapèd wide,
And I awoke and found me here
    On the cold hill's side.

"And this is why I sojourn here
  Alone and palely loitering,
Though the sedge is wither'd from the lake,
    And no birds sing."

RALPH WALDO EMERSON

The Rhodora

ON BEING ASKED, WHENCE IS THE FLOWER?

In May, when sea-winds pierced our solitudes,
I found the fresh Rhodora in the woods,
Spreading its leafless blooms in a damp nook,
To please the desert and the sluggish brook.
The purple petals, fallen in the pool,
Made the black water with their beauty gay;
Here might the red-bird come his plumes to cool,
And court the flower that cheapens his array.
Rhodora! if the sages ask thee why
This charm is wasted on the earth and sky,
Tell them, dear, that if eyes were made for seeing,
Then Beauty is its own excuse for being:
Why thou wert there, O rival of the rose!
I never thought to ask, I never knew;
But, in my simple ignorance, suppose
The self-same Power that brought me there brought you.

The Snow-Storm

Announced by all the trumpets of the sky
Arrives the snow, and, driving o'er the fields,
Seems nowhere to alight: the whited air
Hides hills and woods, the river, and the heaven,
And veils the farm-house at the garden's end.

The sled and traveler stopped, the courier's feet
Delayed, all friends shut out, the house-mates sit
Around the radiant fireplace, enclosed
In a tumultuous privacy of storm.

Come see the north wind's masonry.
Out of an unseen quarry evermore
Furnished with tile, the fierce artificer
Curves his white bastions with projected roof
Round every windward stake, or tree, or door.
Speeding, the myriad-handed, his wild work
So fanciful, so savage, naught cares he
For number or proportion. Mockingly
On coop or kennel he hangs Parian wreaths;
A swan-like form invests the hidden thorn;
Fills up the farmer's lane from wall to wall,
Maugre the farmer's sighs; and, at the gate
A tapering turret overtops the work.
And when his hours are numbered, and the world
Is all his own, retiring, as he were not,
Leaves, when the sun appears, astonished Art
To mimic in slow structures, stone by stone,
Built in an age, the mad wind's night-work,
The frolic architecture of the snow.

HENRY WADSWORTH LONGFELLOW

Mezzo Cammin

Half of my life is gone, and I have let
The years slip from me and have not fulfilled
The aspiration of my youth to build
Some tower of song with lofty parapet.

Not indolence, nor pleasure, nor the fret
Of restless passions that would not be stilled,
But sorrow, and a care that almost killed,
Kept me from what I may accomplish yet;
Though, half-way up the hill, I see the Past
Lying beneath me with its sounds and sights,—
A city in the twilight dim and vast,
With smoking roofs, soft bells, and gleaming lights,—
And here above me on the autumnal blast
The cataract of Death far thundering from the heights.

Divina Commedia

I

Oft have I seen at some cathedral door
A laborer, pausing in the dust and heat,
Lay down his burden, and with reverent feet
Enter, and cross himself, and on the floor
Kneel to repeat his paternoster o'er;
Far off the noises of the world retreat;
The loud vociferations of the street
Become an undistinguishable roar.
So, as I enter here from day to day,
And leave my burden at this minster gate,
Kneeling in prayer, and not ashamed to pray,
The tumult of the time disconsolate
To inarticulate murmurs dies away,
While the eternal ages watch and wait.

II

How strange the sculptures that adorn these towers!
This crowd of statues, in whose folded sleeves
Birds build their nests; while canopied with leaves
Parvis and portal bloom like trellised bowers,
And the vast minster seems a cross of flowers!

But fiends and dragons on the gargoyled eaves
Watch the dead Christ between the living thieves,
And, underneath, the traitor Judas lowers!
Ah! from what agonies of heart and brain,
What exultations trampling on despair,
What tenderness, what tears, what hate of wrong,
What passionate outcry of a soul in pain,
Uprose this poem of the earth and air,
This mediaeval miracle of song!

III

I enter, and I see thee in the gloom
Of the long aisles, O poet saturnine!
And strive to make my steps keep pace with thine.
The air is filled with some unknown perfume;
The congregation of the dead make room
For thee to pass; the votive tapers shine;
Like rooks that haunt Ravenna's groves of pine
The hovering echoes fly from tomb to tomb.
From the confessionals I hear arise
Rehearsals of forgotten tragedies,
And lamentations from the crypts below;
And then a voice celestial that begins
With the pathetic words, "Although your sins
As scarlet be," and ends with "as the snow."

IV

With snow-white veil and garments as of flame,
She stands before thee, who so long ago
Filled thy young heart with passion and the woe
From which thy song and all its splendors came;
And while with stern rebuke she speaks thy name,
The ice about thy heart melts as the snow
On mountain heights, and in swift overflow
Comes gushing from thy lips in sobs of shame.
Thou makest full confession; and a gleam,
As of the dawn on some dark forest cast,
Seems on thy lifted forehead to increase;

Lethe and Eunoë—the remembered dream
And the forgotten sorrow—bring at last
That perfect pardon which is perfect peace.

V

I lift mine eyes, and all the windows blaze
With forms of Saints and holy men who died,
Here martyred and hereafter glorified;
And the great Rose upon its leaves displays
Christ's Triumph, and the angelic roundelays,
With splendor upon splendor multiplied;
And Beatrice again at Dante's side
No more rebukes, but smiles her words of praise.
And then the organ sounds, and unseen choirs
Sing the old Latin hymns of peace and love
And benedictions of the Holy Ghost;
And the melodious bells among the spires
O'er all the house-tops and through heaven above
Proclaim the elevation of the Host!

VI

O star of morning and of liberty!
O bringer of the light, whose splendor shines
Above the darkness of the Apennines,
Forerunner of the day that is to be!
The voices of the city and the sea,
The voices of the mountains and the pines,
Repeat thy song, till the familiar lines
Are footpaths for the thought of Italy!
Thy flame is blown abroad from all the heights,
Through all the nations, and a sound is heard,
As of a mighty wind, and men devout,
Strangers of Rome, and the new proselytes,
In their own language hear the wondrous word,
And many are amazed and many doubt.

The Tide Rises, the Tide Falls

The tide rises, the tide falls,
The twilight darkens, the curlew calls;
Along the sea-sands damp and brown
The traveller hastens toward the town,
    And the tide rises, the tide falls.

Darkness settles on roofs and walls,
But the sea, the sea in the darkness calls;
The little waves, with their soft, white hands,
Efface the footprints in the sands,
    And the tide rises, the tide falls.

The morning breaks; the steeds in their stalls
Stamp and neigh, as the hostler calls;
The day returns, but nevermore
Returns the traveller to the shore,
    And the tide rises, the tide falls.

ALFRED, LORD TENNYSON

Ulysses

It little profits that an idle king,
By this still hearth, among these barren crags,
Matched with an aged wife, I mete and dole
Unequal laws unto a savage race,
That hoard, and sleep, and feed, and know not me.

I cannot rest from travel: I will drink
Life to the lees: all times I have enjoyed
Greatly, have suffered greatly, both with those
That loved me, and alone; on shore, and when
Through scudding drifts the rainy Hyades
Vext the dim sea. I am become a name;
For always roaming with a hungry heart
Much have I seen and known: cities of men
And manners, climates, councils, governments,
Myself not least, but honored of them all,—
And drunk delight of battle with my peers,
Far on the ringing plains of windy Troy.
I am a part of all that I have met;
Yet all experience is an arch wherethrough
Gleams that untraveled world, whose margin fades
For ever and for ever when I move.
How dull it is to pause, to make an end,
To rust unburnished, not to shine in use!
As though to breathe were life! Life piled on life
Were all too little, and of one to me
Little remains: but every hour is saved
From that eternal silence, something more,
A bringer of new things; and vile it were
For some three suns to store and hoard myself,
And this gray spirit yearning in desire
To follow knowledge, like a sinking star,
Beyond the utmost bound of human thought.
    This is my son, mine own Telemachus,
To whom I leave the scepter and the isle—
Well-loved of me, discerning to fulfill
This labor, by slow prudence to make mild
A rugged people, and through soft degrees
Subdue them to the useful and the good.
Most blameless is he, centered in the sphere
Of common duties, decent not to fail
In offices of tenderness, and pay
Meet adoration to my household gods,
When I am gone. He works his work, I mine.
    There lies the port: the vessel puffs her sail:
There gloom the dark broad seas. My mariners,
Souls that have toil'd, and wrought, and thought with me—

That ever with a frolic welcome took
The thunder and the sunshine, and opposed
Free hearts, free foreheads—you and I are old;
Old age hath yet his honor and his toil.
Death closes all: but something ere the end,
Some work of noble note, may yet be done,
Not unbecoming men that strove with Gods.
The lights begin to twinkle from the rocks:
The long day wanes: the slow moon climbs: the deep
Moans round with many voices. Come, my friends,
'Tis not too late to seek a newer world.
Push off, and sitting well in order smite
The sounding furrows; for my purpose holds
To sail beyond the sunset, and the baths
Of all the western stars, until I die.
It may be that the gulfs will wash us down:
It may be we shall touch the Happy Isles,
And see the great Achilles, whom we knew.
Though much is taken, much abides; and though
We are not now that strength which in old days
Moved earth and heaven, that which we are, we are;—
One equal temper of heroic hearts,
Made weak by time and fate, but strong in will
To strive, to seek, to find, and not to yield.

OLIVER WENDELL HOLMES

The Chambered Nautilus

This is the ship of pearl, which, poets feign,
   Sails the unshadowed main,—
   The venturous bark that flings
On the sweet summer wind its purpled wings
In gulfs enchanted, where the Siren sings,
   And coral reefs lie bare,
Where the cold sea-maids rise to sun their streaming hair.

Its webs of living gauze no more unfurl!
   Wrecked is the ship of pearl!
    And every chambered cell,
Where its dim dreaming life was wont to dwell,
As the frail tenant shaped his growing shell,
   Before thee lies revealed,—
Its irised ceiling rent, its sunless crypt unsealed!

Year after year beheld the silent toil
   That spread his lustrous coil;
    Still, as the spiral grew,
He left the past year's dwelling for the new,
Stole with soft step its shining archway through,
   Built up its idle door,
Stretched in his last-found home, and knew the old no more.

Thanks for the heavenly message brought by thee,
   Child of the wandering sea,
    Cast from her lap forlorn!
From thy dead lips a clearer note is born
Than ever Triton blew from wreathèd horn!
   While on mine ear it rings,
Through the deep caves of thought I hear a voice that sings:—

Build thee more stately mansions, O my soul,
   As the swift seasons roll!
    Leave thy low-vaulted past!
Let each new temple, nobler than the last,
Shut thee from heaven with a dome more vast,
   Till thou at length art free,
Leaving thine outgrown shell by life's unresting sea!

The Last Leaf

    I saw him once before,
    As he passed by the door,
       And again
    The pavement stones resound
    As he totters o'er the ground
       With his cane.

They say that in his prime,
Ere the pruning-knife of Time
    Cut him down,
Not a better man was found
By the Crier on his round
    Through the town.

But now he walks the streets,
And he looks at all he meets
    Sad and wan,
And he shakes his feeble head,
That it seems as if he said,
    "They are gone."

The mossy marbles rest
On the lips that he has prest
    In their bloom,
And the names he loved to hear
Have been carved for many a year
    On the tomb.

My grandmamma has said—
Poor old lady, she is dead
    Long ago—
That he had a Roman nose,
And his cheek was like a rose
    In the snow.

But now his nose is thin,
And it rests upon his chin
    Like a staff,
And a crook is in his back,
And a melancholy crack
    In his laugh.

I know it is a sin
For me to sit and grin
    At him here;
But the old three-cornered hat,
And the breeches, and all that,
    Are so queer!

And if I should live to be
The last leaf upon the tree
    In the spring,
Let them smile as I do now,
At the old forsaken bough
    Where I cling.

ROBERT BROWNING

My Last Duchess

That's my last Duchess painted on the wall,
Looking as if she were alive. I call
That piece a wonder, now: Frà Pandolf's hands
Worked busily a day, and there she stands.
Will't please you sit and look at her? I said
"Frà Pandolf" by design, for never read
Strangers like you that pictured countenance,
The depth and passion of its earnest glance,
But to myself they turned (since none puts by
The curtain I have drawn for you, but I)
And seemed as they would ask me, if they durst,
How such a glance came there; so, not the first
Are you to turn and ask thus. Sir, 'twas not
Her husband's presence only, called that spot
Of joy into the Duchess' cheek: perhaps
Frà Pandolf chanced to say, "Her mantle laps
Over my Lady's wrist too much," or "Paint
Must never hope to reproduce the faint
Half-flush that dies along her throat"; such stuff
Was courtesy, she thought, and cause enough
For calling up that spot of joy. She had
A heart—how shall I say?—too soon made glad,
Too easily impressed; she liked whate'er
She looked on, and her looks went everywhere.
Sir, 'twas all one! My favor at her breast,
The dropping of the daylight in the West,

The bough of cherries some officious fool
Broke in the orchard for her, the white mule
She rode with round the terrace—all and each
Would draw from her alike the approving speech,
Or blush, at least. She thanked men,—good; but thanked
Somehow—I know not how—as if she ranked
My gift of a nine-hundred-years'-old name
With anybody's gift. Who'd stoop to blame
This sort of trifling? Even had you skill
In speech—(which I have not)—to make your will
Quite clear to such an one, and say, "Just this
Or that in you disgusts me; here you miss,
Or there exceed the mark"—and if she let
Herself be lessoned so, nor plainly set
Her wits to yours, forsooth, and made excuse,
—E'en then would be some stooping, and I choose
Never to stoop. Oh, sir, she smiled, no doubt,
Whene'er I passed her; but who passed without
Much the same smile? This grew; I gave commands;
Then all smiles stopped together. There she stands
As if alive. Will 't please you rise? We'll meet
The company below, then. I repeat,
The Count your master's known munificence
Is ample warrant that no just pretence
Of mine for dowry will be disallowed;
Though his fair daughter's self, as I avowed
At starting, is my object. Nay, we'll go
Together down, sir! Notice Neptune, though,
Taming a sea-horse, thought a rarity,
Which Claus of Innsbruck cast in bronze for me!

Home-Thoughts from Abroad

Oh, to be in England
Now that April's there,
And whoever wakes in England
Sees, some morning, unaware,

That the lowest boughs and the brush-wood sheaf
Round the elm-tree bole are in tiny leaf,
While the chaffinch sings on the orchard bough
In England—now!

And after April, when May follows,
And the whitethroat builds, and all the swallows—
Hark! where my blossomed pear-tree in the hedge
Leans to the field and scatters on the clover
Blossoms and dewdrops—at the bent-spray's edge—
That's the wise thrush; he sings each song twice over,
Lest you should think he never could recapture
The first fine careless rapture!
And though the fields look rough with hoary dew,
All will be gay when noontide wakes anew
The buttercups, the little children's dower,
—Far brighter than this gaudy melon-flower!

WALT WHITMAN

When Lilacs Last in the Dooryard Bloom'd

1

When lilacs last in the dooryard bloom'd,
And the great star early droop'd in the western sky in the night,
I mourn'd, and yet shall mourn with ever-returning spring.

Ever-returning spring, trinity sure to me you bring,
Lilac blooming perennial and drooping star in the west,
And thought of him I love.

2

O powerful western fallen star!
O shades of night—O moody, tearful night!
O great star disappear'd—O the black murk that hides the star!
O cruel hands that hold me powerless—O helpless soul of me!
O harsh surrounding cloud that will not free my soul.

3

In the dooryard fronting an old farm-house near the white-wash'd
    palings,
Stands the lilac-bush tall-growing with heart-shaped leaves of rich
    green,
With many a pointed blossom rising delicate, with the perfume strong
    I love,
With every leaf a miracle—and from this bush in the dooryard,
With delicate-color'd blossoms and heart-shaped leaves of rich green,
A sprig with its flower I break.

4

In the swamp in secluded recesses,
A shy and hidden bird is warbling a song.

Solitary the thrush,
The hermit withdrawn to himself, avoiding the settlements,
Sings by himself a song.

Song of the bleeding throat,
Death's outlet song of life, (for well dear brother I know,
If thou wast not granted to sing thou would'st surely die.)

5

Over the breast of the spring, the land, amid cities,
Amid lanes and through old woods, where lately the violets peep'd from
    the ground, spotting the gray debris,
Amid the grass in the fields each side of the lanes, passing the endless
    grass,
Passing the yellow-spear'd wheat, every grain from its shroud in the
    dark-brown fields uprisen,
Passing the apple-tree blows of white and pink in the orchards,
Carrying a corpse to where it shall rest in the grave,
Night and day journeys a coffin.

6

Coffin that passes through lanes and streets,
Through day and night with the great cloud darkening the land,
With the pomp of the inloop'd flags with the cities draped in black,

With the show of the States themselves as of crape-veil'd women
    standing,
With processions long and winding and the flambeaus of the night,
With the countless torches lit, with the silent sea of faces and the
    unbared heads,
With the waiting depot, the arriving coffin, and the sombre faces,
With dirges through the night, with the thousand voices rising strong
    and solemn,
With all the mournful voices of the dirges pour'd around the coffin,
The dim-lit churches and the shuddering organs—where amid these you
    journey,
With the tolling tolling bells' perpetual clang,
Here, coffin that slowly passes,
I give you my sprig of lilac.

7

(Nor for you, for one alone,
Blossoms and branches green to coffins all I bring,
For fresh as the morning, thus would I chant a song for you O sane and
    sacred death.

All over bouquets of roses,
O death, I cover you over with roses and early lilies,
But mostly and now the lilac that blooms the first,
Copious I break, I break the sprigs from the bushes,
With loaded arms I come, pouring for you,
For you and the coffins all of you O death.)

8

O western orb sailing the heaven,
Now I know what you must have meant as a month since I walk'd,
As I walk'd in silence the transparent shadowy night,
As I saw you had something to tell as you bent to me night after night,
As you droop'd from the sky low down as if to my side, (while the other
    stars all look'd on,)
As we wander'd together the solemn night, (for something I know not
    what kept me from sleep,)
As the night advanced, and I saw on the rim of the west how full you
    were of woe,

As I stood on the rising ground in the breeze in the cool transparent
    night,
As I watch'd where you pass'd and was lost in the netherward black
    of the night,
As my soul in its trouble dissatisfied sank, as where you sad orb,
Concluded, dropt in the night, and was gone.

9

Sing on there in the swamp,
O singer bashful and tender, I hear your notes, I hear your call,
I hear, I come presently, I understand you,
But a moment I linger, for the lustrous star has detain'd me,
The star my departing comrade holds and detains me.

10

O how shall I warble myself for the dead one there I loved?
And how shall I deck my song for the large sweet soul that has gone?
And what shall my perfume be for the grave of him I love?

Sea-winds blown from east and west,
Blown from the Eastern sea and blown from the Western sea, till there
    on the prairies meeting,
These and with these and the breath of my chant,
I'll perfume the grave of him I love.

11

O what shall I hang on the chamber walls?
And what shall the pictures be that I hang on the walls,
To adorn the burial-house of him I love?

Pictures of growing spring and farms and homes,
With the Fourth-month eve at sundown, and the gray smoke lucid and
    bright,
With floods of the yellow gold of the gorgeous, indolent, sinking sun,
    burning, expanding the air,
With the fresh sweet herbage under foot, and the pale green leaves
    of the trees prolific,

In the distance the flowing glaze, the breast of the river, with a wind-
dapple here and there,
With ranging hills on the banks, with many a line against the sky, and
shadows,
And the city at hand with dwellings so dense, and stacks of chimneys,
And all the scenes of life and the workshops, and the workmen
homeward returning.

12

Lo, body and soul—this land,
My own Manhattan with spires, and the sparkling and hurrying tides,
and the ships,
The varied and ample land, the South and the North in the light, Ohio's
shores and flashing Missouri,
And ever the far-spreading prairies cover'd with grass and corn.

Lo, the most excellent sun so calm and haughty,
The violet and purple morn with just-felt breezes,
The gentle soft-born measureless light,
The miracle spreading bathing all, the fulfill'd noon,
The coming eve delicious, the welcome night and the stars,
Over my cities shining all, enveloping man and land.

13

Sing on, sing on you gray-brown bird,
Sing from the swamps, the recesses, pour your chant from the bushes,
Limitless out of the dusk, out of the cedars and pines.

Sing on dearest brother, warble your reedy song,
Loud human song, with voice of uttermost woe.
O liquid and free and tender!
O wild and loose to my soul—O wondrous singer!
You only I hear—yet the star holds me, (but will soon depart,)
Yet the lilac with mastering odor holds me.

14

Now while I sat in the day and look'd forth,
In the close of the day with its light and the fields of spring, and the
farmers preparing their crops,

In the large unconscious scenery of my land with its lakes and forests,
In the heavenly aerial beauty, (after the perturb'd winds and the
    storms,)
Under the arching heavens of the afternoon swift passing, and the
    voices of children and women,
The many-moving sea-tides, and I saw the ships how they sail'd,
And the summer approaching with richness, and the fields all busy
    with labor,
And the infinite separate houses, how they all went on, each with its
    meals and minutia of daily usages,
And the streets how their throbbings throbb'd, and the cities pent—
    lo, then and there,
Falling upon them all and among them all, enveloping me with the rest,
Appear'd the cloud, appear'd the long black trail,
And I knew death, its thought, and the sacred knowledge of death.

Then with the knowledge of death as walking one side of me,
And the thought of death close-walking the other side of me,
And I in the middle as with companions, and as holding the hands of
    companions,
I fled forth to the hiding receiving night that talks not,
Down to the shores of the water, the path by the swamp in the dimness,
To the solemn shadowy cedars and ghostly pines so still.

And the singer so shy to the rest receiv'd me,
The gray-brown bird I know receiv'd us comrades three,
And he sang the carol of death, and a verse for him I love.

From deep secluded recesses,
From the fragrant cedars and the ghostly pines so still,
Came the carol of the bird.

And the charm of the carol rapt me,
As I held as if by their hands my comrades in the night,
And the voice of my spirit tallied the song of the bird.

Come lovely and soothing death,
Undulate round the world, serenely arriving, arriving,
In the day, in the night, to all, to each,
Sooner or later delicate death.

Prais'd be the fathomless universe,
For life and joy, and for objects and knowledge curious,
And for love, sweet love—but praise! praise! praise!
For the sure-enwinding arms of cool-enfolding death.

Dark mother always gliding near with soft feet,
Have none chanted for thee a chant of fullest welcome?
Then I chant it for thee, I glorify thee above all,
I bring thee a song that when thou must indeed come, come
unfalteringly.

Approach strong deliveress,
When it is so, when thou hast taken them I joyously sing the dead,
Lost in the loving floating ocean of thee,
Laved in the flood of thy bliss O death.
From me to thee glad serenades,
Dances for thee I propose saluting thee, adornments and feastings for
thee,
And the sights of the open landscape and the high-spread sky are fitting,
And life and the fields, and the huge and thoughtful night.

The night in silence under many a star,
The ocean shore and the husky whispering wave whose voice I know,
And the soul turning to thee O vast and well-veil'd death,
And the body gratefully nestling close to thee.

Over the tree-tops I float thee a song,
Over the rising and sinking waves, over the myriad fields and the
prairies wide,
Over the dense-pack'd cities all and the teeming wharves and ways,
I float this carol with joy, with joy to thee O death.

15

To the tally of my soul,
Loud and strong kept up the gray-brown bird,
With pure deliberate notes spreading filling the night.
Loud in the pines and cedars dim,
Clear in the freshness moist and the swamp-perfume,
And I with my comrades there in the night.

While my sight that was bound in my eyes unclosed,
As to long panoramas of visions.

And I saw askant the armies,
I saw as in noiseless dreams hundreds of battle-flags,
Borne through the smoke of the battles and pierc'd with missiles I
     saw them,
And carried hither and yon through the smoke, and torn and bloody,
And at last but a few shreds left on the staffs, (and all in silence,)
And the staffs all splinter'd and broken.

I saw battle-corpses, myriads of them,
And the white skeletons of young men, I saw them,
I saw the debris and debris of all the slain soldiers of the war,
But I saw they were not as was thought,
They themselves were fully at rest, they suffer'd not,
The living remain'd and suffer'd, the mother suffer'd,
And the wife and the child and the musing comrade suffer'd,
And the armies that remain'd suffer'd.

16

Passing the visions, passing the night,
Passing, unloosing the hold of my comrades' hands,
Passing the song of the hermit bird and the tallying song of my soul,
Victorious song, death's outlet song, yet varying ever-altering song,
As low and wailing, yet clear the notes, rising and falling, flooding the
     night,
Sadly sinking and fainting, as warning and warning, and yet again
     bursting with joy,
Covering the earth and filling the spread of the heaven,
As that powerful psalm in the night I heard from recesses,
Passing, I leave thee lilac with heart-shaped leaves,
I leave thee there in the dooryard, blooming, returning with spring.

I cease from my song for thee,
From my gaze on thee in the west, fronting the west, communing with
     thee,
O comrade lustrous with silver face in the night.

Yet each to keep and all, retrievements out of the night,
The song, the wondrous chant of the gray-brown bird,
And the tallying chant, the echo arous'd in my soul,
With the lustrous and drooping star with the countenance full of woe,
With the holders holding my hand nearing the call of the bird,
Comrades mine and I in the midst, and their memory ever to keep,
    for the dead I loved so well,
For the sweetest, wisest soul of all my days and lands—and this for
    his dear sake,
Lilac and star and bird twined with the chant of my soul,
There in the fragrant pines and the cedars dusk and dim.

Out of the Cradle Endlessly Rocking

Out of the cradle endlessly rocking,
Out of the mocking-bird's throat, the musical shuttle,
Out of the Ninth-month midnight,
Over the sterile sands and the fields beyond, where the child leaving his
    bed wander'd alone, bareheaded, barefoot,
Down from the shower'd halo,
Up from the mystic play of shadows twining and twisting as if they
    were alive,
Out from the patches of briers and blackberries,
From the memories of the bird that chanted to me,
From your memories sad brother, from the fitful risings and fallings I
    heard,
From under that yellow half-moon late-risen and swollen as if with
    tears,
From those beginning notes of yearning and love there in the mist,
From the thousand responses of my heart never to cease,
From the myriad thence-arous'd words,
From the word stronger and more delicious than any,
From such as now they start the scene revisiting,
As a flock, twittering, rising, or overhead passing,

Borne hither, ere all eludes me, hurriedly,
A man, yet by these tears a little boy again,
Throwing myself on the sand, confronting the waves,
I, chanter of pains and joys, uniter of here and hereafter,
Taking all hints to use them, but swiftly leaping beyond them,
A reminiscence sing.

Once Paumanok,
When the lilac-scent was in the air and Fifth-month grass was growing,
Up this seashore in some briers,
Two feather'd guests from Alabama, two together,
And their nest, and four light-green eggs spotted with brown,
And every day the he-bird to and fro near at hand,
And every day the she-bird crouch'd on her nest, silent, with bright eyes,
And every day I, a curious boy, never too close, never disturbing them,
Cautiously peering, absorbing, translating.

Shine! shine! shine!
Pour down your warmth, great sun!
While we bask, we two together.

Two together!
Winds blow south, or winds blow north,
Day come white, or day come black,
Home, or rivers and mountains from home,
Singing all time, minding no time,
While we two keep together.

Till of a sudden,
May-be kill'd, unknown to her mate,
One forenoon that she-bird crouch'd not on the nest,
Nor return'd that afternoon, nor the next,
Nor ever appear'd again.

And thenceforward all summer in the sound of the sea,
And at night under the full of the moon in calmer weather,
Over the hoarse surging of the sea,
Or flitting from brier to brier by day,
I saw, I heard at intervals the remaining one, the he-bird,
The solitary guest from Alabama.

Blow! blow! blow!
Blow up sea-winds along Paumanok's shore;
I wait and I wait till you blow my mate to me.

Yes, when the stars glisten'd,
All night long on the prong of a moss-scallop'd stake,
Down almost amid the slapping waves,
Sat the lone singer wonderful causing tears.

He call'd on his mate,
He pour'd forth the meanings which I of all men know.

Yes my brother I know,
The rest might not, but I have treasur'd every note,
For more than once dimly down to the beach gliding,
Silent, avoiding the moonbeams, blending myself with the shadows,
Recalling now the obscure shapes, the echoes, the sounds and sights
     after their sorts,
The white arms out in the breakers tirelessly tossing,
I, with bare feet, a child, the wind wafting my hair,
Listen'd long and long.

Listen'd to keep, to sing, now translating the notes,
Following you my brother.

Soothe! soothe! soothe!
Close on its wave soothes the wave behind,
And again another behind embracing and lapping, every one close,
But my love soothes not me, not me.

Low hangs the moon, it rose late,
It is lagging—O I think it is heavy with love, with love.

O madly the sea pushes upon the land,
With love, with love.

O night! do I not see my love fluttering out among the breakers?
What is that little black thing I see there in the white?

Loud! loud! loud!
Loud I call to you, my love!

High and clear I shoot my voice over the waves,
Surely you must know who is here, is here,
You must know who I am, my love.

Low-hanging moon!
What is that dusky spot in your brown yellow?
O it is the shape, the shape of my mate!
O moon do not keep her from me any longer.

Land! land! O land!
Whichever way I turn, O I think you could give me my mate back
  again if you only would,
For I am almost sure I see her dimly whichever way I look.

O rising stars!
Perhaps the one I want so much will rise, will rise with one of you.

O throat! O trembling throat!
Sound clearer through the atmosphere!
Pierce the woods, the earth,
Somewhere listening to catch you must be the one I want.

Shake out carols!
Solitary here, the night's carols!
Carols of lonesome love! death's carols!
Carols under that lagging, yellow, waning moon!
O under that moon where she droops almost down into the sea!
O reckless despairing carols.

But soft! sink low!
Soft! let me just murmur,
And do you wait a moment you husky-nois'd sea,
For somewhere I believe I heard my mate responding to me,
So faint, I must be still, be still to listen,
But not altogether still, for then she might not come immediately to
  me.

Hither my love!
Here I am! here!
With this just-sustain'd note I announce myself to you,
This gentle call is for you my love, for you.

Do not be decoy'd elsewhere,
That is the whistle of the wind, it is not my voice,
That is the fluttering, the fluttering of the spray,
Those are the shadows of leaves.

O darkness! O in vain!
O I am very sick and sorrowful.

O brown halo in the sky near the moon, drooping upon the sea!
O troubled reflection in the sea!
O throat! O throbbing heart!
And I singing uselessly, uselessly all the night.

O past! O happy life! O songs of joy!
In the air, in the woods, over fields,
Loved! loved! loved! loved! loved!
But my mate no more, no more with me!
We two together no more.

The aria sinking,
All else continuing, the stars shining,
The winds blowing, the notes of the bird continuous echoing,
With angry moans the fierce old mother incessantly moaning,
On the sands of Paumanok's shore gray and rustling,
The yellow half-moon enlarged, sagging down, drooping, the face of
    the sea almost touching,
The boy ecstatic, with his bare feet the waves, with his hair the at-
    mosphere dallying,
The love in the heart long pent, now loose, now at last tumultuously
    bursting,
The aria's meaning, the ears, the soul, swiftly depositing,
The strange tears down the cheeks coursing,
The colloquy there, the trio, each uttering,
The undertone, the savage old mother incessantly crying,
To the boy's soul's questions sullenly timing, some drown'd secret
    hissing,
To the outsetting bard.

Demon or bird! (said the boy's soul,)
Is it indeed toward your mate you sing? or is it really to me?

For I, that was a child, my tongue's use sleeping, now I have heard
    you,
Now in a moment I know what I am for, I awake,
And already a thousand singers, a thousand songs, clearer, louder and
    more sorrowful than yours,
A thousand warbling echoes have started to life within me, never to
    die.

O you singer solitary, singing by yourself, projecting me,
O solitary me listening, never more shall I cease perpetuating you,
Never more shall I escape, never more the reverberations,
Never more the cries of unsatisfied love be absent from me,
Never again leave me to be the peaceful child I was before what there
    in the night,
By the sea under the yellow and sagging moon,
The messenger there arous'd, the fire, the sweet hell within,
The unknown want, the destiny of me.

O give me the clew! (it lurks in the night here somewhere,)
O if I am to have so much, let me have more!

A word then, (for I will conquer it,)
The word final, superior to all,
Subtle, sent up—what is it?—I listen;
Are you whispering it, and have been all the time, you sea-waves?
Is that it from your liquid rims and wet sands?

Whereto answering, the sea,
Delaying not, hurrying not,
Whisper'd me through the night, and very plainly before daybreak,
List'd to me the low and delicious word death,
And again death, death, death, death,
Hissing melodious, neither like the bird nor like my arous'd child's
    heart,
But edging near as privately for me rustling at my feet,
Creeping thence steadily up to my ears and laving me softly all over,
Death, death, death, death, death.

Which I do not forget,
But fuse the song of my dusky demon and brother,

That he sang to me in the moonlight on Paumanok's gray beach,
With the thousand responsive songs at random,
My own songs awaked from that hour,
And with them the key, the word up from the waves,
The word of the sweetest song and all songs,
That strong and delicious word which, creeping to my feet,
(Or like some old crone rocking the cradle, swathed in sweet garments,
    bending aside,)
The sea whisper'd me.

MATTHEW ARNOLD

Dover Beach

The sea is calm to-night.
The tide is full, the moon lies fair
Upon the straits;—on the French coast the light
Gleams and is gone; the cliffs of England stand,
Glimmering and vast, out in the tranquil bay.
Come to the window, sweet is the night-air!
Only, from the long line of spray
Where the sea meets the moon-blanched land,
Listen! you hear the grating roar
Of pebbles which the waves draw back, and fling,
At their return, up the high strand,
Begin, and cease, and then again begin,
With tremulous cadence slow, and bring
The eternal note of sadness in.

Sophocles long ago
Heard it on the Aegean, and it brought
Into his mind the turbid ebb and flow
Of human misery; we
Find also in the sound a thought,
Hearing it by this distant northern sea.

The Sea of Faith
Was once, too, at the full, and round earth's shore
Lay like the folds of a bright girdle furled.
But now I only hear
Its melancholy, long, withdrawing roar,
Retreating, to the breath
Of the night-wind, down the vast edges drear
And naked shingles of the world.

Ah, love, let us be true
To one another! for the world, which seems
To lie before us like a land of dreams,
So various, so beautiful, so new,
Hath really neither joy, nor love, nor light,
Nor certitude, nor peace, nor help for pain;
And we are here as on a darkling plain
Swept with confused alarms of struggle and flight,
Where ignorant armies clash by night.

GEORGE MEREDITH

Lucifer in Starlight

On a starr'd night Prince Lucifer uprose.
  Tired of his dark dominion swung the fiend
Above the rolling ball in cloud part screen'd,
Where sinners hugg'd their spectre of repose.
Poor prey to his hot fit of pride were those.
  And now upon his western wing he lean'd,
  Now his huge bulk o'er Afric's sands careen'd,
Now the black planet shadow'd Arctic snows.
Soaring through wider zones that prick'd his scars
  With memory of the old revolt from Awe,
He reach'd a middle height, and at the stars,
Which are the brain of heaven, he look'd, and sank.
Around the ancient track march'd, rank on rank,
  The army of unalterable law.

From *Modern Love*

1

By this he knew she wept with waking eyes:
That, at his hand's light quiver by her head,
The strange low sobs that shook their common bed
Were called into her with a sharp surprise,
And strangled mute, like little gaping snakes,
Dreadfully venomous to him. She lay
Stone-still, and the long darkness flowed away
With muffled pulses. Then, as midnight makes
Her giant heart of Memory and Tears
Drink the pale drug of silence, and so beat
Sleep's heavy measure, they from head to feet
Were moveless, looking through their dead black years,
By vain regret scrawled over the blank wall.
Like sculptured effigies they might be seen
Upon their marriage-tomb, the sword between;
Each wishing for the sword that severs all.

16

In our old shipwrecked days there was an hour,
When in the firelight steadily aglow,
Joined slackly, we beheld the red chasm grow
Among the clicking coals. Our library-bower
That eve was left to us; and hushed we sat
As lovers to whom Time is whispering.
From sudden-opened doors we heard them sing;
The nodding elders mixed good wine with chat.
Well knew we that Life's greatest treasure lay
With us, and of it was our talk. "Ah, yes!
Love dies!" I said (I never thought it less).
She yearned to me that sentence to unsay.

Then when the fire domed blackening, I found
Her cheek was salt against my kiss, and swift
Up the sharp scale of sobs her breast did lift.—
Now am I haunted by that taste! that sound!

43

Mark where the pressing wind shoots javelin-like
Its skeleton shadow on the broad-backed wave!
Here is a fitting spot to dig Love's grave—
Here where the ponderous breakers plunge and strike,
And dart their hissing tongues high up the sand;
In hearing of the ocean, and in sight
Of those ribbed wind-streaks running into white.
If I the death of Love had deeply planned,
I never could have made it half so sure,
As by the unblest kisses which upbraid
The full-waked sense; or failing that, degrade!
'Tis morning; but no morning can restore
What we have forfeited. I see no sin;
The wrong is mixed. In tragic life, God wot,
No villain need be! Passions spin the plot;
We are betrayed by what is false within.

EMILY DICKINSON

A Narrow Fellow in the Grass

A narrow fellow in the grass
Occasionally rides;
You may have met him—did you not?
His notice sudden is.

The grass divides as with a comb,
A spotted shaft is seen;
And then it closes at your feet
And opens further on.

He likes a boggy acre,
A floor too cool for corn.
Yet when a boy, and barefoot,
I more than once, at morn,

Have passed, I thought, a whip lash
Unbraiding in the sun,—
When, stooping to secure it,
It wrinkled, and was gone.

Several of nature's people
I know, and they know me;
I feel for them a transport
Of cordiality;

But never met this fellow,
Attended or alone,
Without a tighter breathing,
And Zero at the Bone.

I Never Saw a Moor

I never saw a moor,
I never saw the sea;
Yet know I how the heather looks,
And what a wave must be.

I never spoke with God,
Nor visited in heaven;
Yet certain am I of the spot
As if the chart were given.

Parting

My life closed twice before its close;
   It yet remains to see
If Immortality unveil
   A third event to me,

So huge, so hopeless to conceive,
   As these that twice befell.
Parting is all we know of heaven,
   And all we need of hell.

The Soul Selects Her Own Society

The soul selects her own society,
Then shuts the door;
On her divine majority
Obtrude no more.

Unmoved, she notes the chariot's pausing
At her low gate;
Unmoved, an emperor is kneeling
Upon her mat.

I've known her from an ample nation
Choose one;
Then close the valves of her attention
Like stone.

They Say That Time Assuages

They say that "time assuages,"—
Time never did assuage;
An actual suffering strengthens,
As sinews do, with age.

Time is a test of trouble,
But not a remedy.
If such it prove, it prove too
There was no malady.

I Had Been Hungry All the Years

I had been hungry all the years;
My noon had come to dine;
I, trembling, drew the table near,
And touched the curious wine.

'Twas this on tables I had seen,
When turning, hungry, lone,
I looked in windows, for the wealth
I could not hope to own.

I did not know the ample bread,
'Twas so unlike the crumb
The birds and I had often shared
In Nature's dining-room.

The plenty hurt me, 'twas so new,—
Myself felt ill and odd,
Like berry of a mountain bush
Transplanted to the road.

Nor was I hungry; so I found
That hunger was a way
Of persons outside windows,
The entering takes away.

Because I Could Not Stop for Death

Because I could not stop for Death,
He kindly stopped for me;
The carriage held but just ourselves
And Immortality.

We slowly drove, he knew no haste,
And I had put away
My labor, and my leisure too,
For his civility.

We passed the school where children played
At wrestling in a ring;
We passed the fields of gazing grain,
We passed the setting sun.

We paused before a house that seemed
A swelling of the ground;
The roof was scarcely visible,
The cornice but a mound.

Since then 't is centuries; but each
Feels shorter than the day
I first surmised the horses' heads
Were toward eternity.

LEWIS CARROLL (Charles L. Dodgson)

Father William

"You are old, Father William," the young man said,
  "And your hair has become very white,
And yet you incessantly stand on your head—
  Do you think, at your age, it is right?"

"In my youth," Father William replied to his son,
  "I feared it might injure the brain;
But now that I'm perfectly sure I have none,
  Why, I do it again and again."

"You are old," said the youth, "as I mentioned before,
  And have grown most uncommonly fat;
Yet you turned a back-somersault in at the door—
  Pray, what is the reason of that?"

"In my youth," said the sage, as he shook his gray locks,
  "I kept all my limbs very supple
By the use of this ointment—one shilling the box—
  Allow me to sell you a couple?"

"You are old," said the youth, "and your jaws are too weak
  For anything tougher than suet;
Yet you finished the goose, with the bones and the beak—
  Pray, how did you manage to do it?"

"In my youth," said his father, "I took to the law,
  And argued each case with my wife;
And the muscular strength which it gave to my jaw
  Has lasted the rest of my life."

"You are old," said the youth, "one would hardly suppose
  That your eye was as steady as ever;
Yet you balanced an eel on the end of your nose—
  What made you so awfully clever?"

"I have answered three questions, and that is enough,"
  Said his father; "don't give yourself airs!
Do you think I can listen all day to such stuff?
  Be off, or I'll kick you downstairs!"

THOMAS HARDY

Channel Firing

That night your great guns, unawares,
Shook all our coffins as we lay,
And broke the chancel window-squares,
We thought it was the Judgment-day

And sat upright. While drearisome
Arose the howl of wakened hounds:
The mouse let fall the altar-crumb,
The worms drew back into the mounds,

The glebe cow drooled. Till God called, "No;
It's gunnery practice out at sea
Just as before you went below;
The world is as it used to be:

"All nations striving strong to make
Red war yet redder. Mad as hatters
They do no more for Christès sake
Than you who are helpless in such matters.

"That this is not the judgment-hour
For some of them's a blessed thing,
For if it were they'd have to scour
Hell's floor for so much threatening . . .

"Ha, ha. It will be warmer when
I blow the trumpet (if indeed
I ever do; for you are men,
And rest eternal sorely need)."

So down we lay again. "I wonder,
Will the world ever saner be,"
Said one, "than when He sent us under
In our indifferent century!"

And many a skeleton shook his head.
"Instead of preaching forty year,"
My neighbor Parson Thirdly said,
"I wish I had stuck to pipes and beer."

Again the guns disturbed the hour,
Roaring their readiness to avenge,
As far inland as Stourton Tower,
And Camelot, and starlit Stonehenge.

"Ah, Are You Digging on My Grave?"

"Ah, are you digging on my grave,
    My loved one?—planting rue?"
—"No: yesterday he went to wed
One of the brightest wealth has bred.
'It cannot hurt her now,' he said,
    'That I should not be true.'"

"Then who is digging on my grave?
    My nearest dearest kin?"
—"Ah, no: they sit and think, 'What use!
What good will planting flowers produce?
No tendance of her mound can loose
    Her spirits from Death's gin.'"

"But some one digs upon my grave?
   My enemy?—prodding sly?"
—"Nay: when she heard you had passed the Gate
That shuts on all flesh soon or late,
She thought you no more worth her hate,
   And cares not where you lie."

"Then who is digging on my grave?
   Say—since I have not guessed!"
—"O it is I, my mistress dear,
Your little dog, who still lives near,
And much I hope my movements here
   Have not disturbed your rest?"

"Ah, yes! *You* dig upon my grave . . .
   Why flashed it not on me
That one true heart was left behind!
What feeling do we ever find
To equal among human kind
   A dog's fidelity!"

"Mistress, I dug upon your grave
   To bury a bone, in case
I should be hungry near this spot
When passing on my daily trot.
I am sorry, but I quite forgot
   It was your resting-place."

The Oxen

   Christmas Eve, and twelve of the clock.
     "Now they are all on their knees,"
   An elder said as we sat in a flock
     By the embers in hearthside ease.

We pictured the meek mild creatures where
  They dwelt in their strawy pen,
Nor did it occur to one of us there
  To doubt they were kneeling then.

So fair a fancy few would weave
  In these years! Yet, I feel,
If someone said on Christmas Eve,
  "Come; see the oxen kneel,

"In the lonely barton by yonder coomb
  Our childhood used to know,"
I should go with him in the gloom,
  Hoping it might be so.

SIDNEY LANIER

A Ballad of Trees and the Master

Into the woods my Master went,*
Clean forspent, forspent.
Into the woods my Master came,
Forspent with love and shame.
But the olives they were not blind to Him,
The little gray leaves were kind to Him:
The thorn-tree had a mind to Him
When into the woods He came.

Out of the woods my Master went,
And He was well content.
Out of the woods my Master came,
Content with death and shame.
When Death and Shame would woo Him last,
From under the trees they drew Him last:
'Twas on a tree they slew Him—last
When out of the woods He came.

---

* *Matthew* 26: 36 ff.

GERARD MANLEY HOPKINS

God's Grandeur

The world is charged with the grandeur of God.
It will flame out, like shining from shook foil;
It gathers to a greatness, like the ooze of oil
Crushed. Why do men then now not reck his rod?

Generations have trod, have trod, have trod;
And all is seared with trade; bleared, smeared with toil;
And wears man's smudge and shares man's smell: the soil
Is bare now, nor can foot feel, being shod.

And for all this, nature is never spent;
There lives the dearest freshness deep down things;
And though the last lights off the black West went
Oh, morning, at the brown brink eastward, springs—
Because the Holy Ghost over the bent
World broods with warm breast and with ah! bright wings.

Pied Beauty

Glory be to God for dappled things—
  For skies of couple-color as a brinded cow;
    For rose-moles all in stipple upon trout that swim;
Fresh-firecoal chestnut-falls; finches' wings;
  Landscape plotted and pieced—fold, fallow, and plough;
    And áll trádes, their gear and tackle and trim.

All things counter, original, spare, strange;
  Whatever is fickle, freckled (who knows how?)
    With swift, slow; sweet, sour; adazzle, dim;
He fathers-forth whose beauty is past change:
          Praise Him.

Inversnaid

This darksome burn, horseback brown,
His rollrock highroad roaring down,
In coop and in comb the fleece of his foam
Flutes and low to the lake falls home.

A windpuff-bonnet of fawn-froth
Turns and twindles over the broth
Of a pool so pitchblack, fell-frowning,
It rounds and rounds Despair to drowning.

Degged with dew, dappled with dew
Are the groins of the braes that the brook treads through,
Wiry heathpacks, flitches of fern,
And the beadbonny ash that sits over the burn.

What would the world be, once bereft
Of wet and of wildness? Let them be left,
O let them be left, wildness and wet;
Long live the weeds and the wilderness yet.

A. E. HOUSMAN

When I Was One-and-Twenty

When I was one-and-twenty
    I heard a wise man say,
"Give crowns and pounds and guineas
    But not your heart away;
Give pearls away and rubies
    But keep your fancy free."
But I was one-and-twenty,
    No use to talk to me.

When I was one-and-twenty
    I heard him say again,
"The heart out of the bosom
    Was never given in vain;
'Tis paid with sighs aplenty
    And sold for endless rue."
And I am two-and-twenty,
    And oh, 'tis true, 'tis true.

Reveille

Wake: the silver dusk returning
    Up the beach of darkness brims,
And the ship of sunrise burning
    Strands upon the eastern rims.

Wake: the vaulted shadow shatters,
    Trampled to the floor it spanned,
And the tent of night in tatters
    Straws the sky-pavilioned land.

Up, lad, up, 'tis late for lying:
    Hear the drums of morning play;
Hark, the empty highways crying
    "Who'll beyond the hills away?"

Towns and countries woo together,
    Forelands beacon, belfries call;
Never lad that trod on leather
    Lived to feast his heart with all.

Up, lad: thews that lie and cumber
    Sunlit pallets never thrive;
Morns abed and daylight slumber
    Were not meant for man alive.

Clay lies still, but blood's a rover;
    Breath's a ware that will not keep
Up, lad: when the journey's over
    There'll be time enough to sleep.

Loveliest of Trees, the Cherry Now

Loveliest of trees, the cherry now
Is hung with bloom along the bough,
And stands about the woodland ride
Wearing white for Eastertide.

Now, of my threescore years and ten,
Twenty will not come again,
And take from seventy springs a score
It only leaves me fifty more.

And since to look at things in bloom
Fifty springs are little room,
About the woodlands I will go
To see the cherry hung with snow.

With Rue My Heart Is Laden

With rue my heart is laden
For laughing friends I had,
For many a rose-lipt maiden
And many a light-foot lad.

By brooks too broad for leaping
The light-foot lads are laid.
And rose-lipt girls are sleeping
In fields where roses fade.

To an Athlete Dying Young

The time you won your town the race
We chaired you through the market-place;
Man and boy stood cheering by,
And home we brought you shoulder-high.

To-day, the road all runners come,
Shoulder-high we bring you home,
And set you at your threshold down,
Townsman of a stiller town.

Smart lad, to slip betimes away
From fields where glory does not stay,
And early though the laurel grows
It withers quicker than the rose.

Eyes the shady night has shut
Cannot see the record cut,
And silence sounds no worse than cheers
After earth has stopped the ears:

Now you will not swell the rout
Of lads that wore their honours out,
Runners whom renown outran
And the name died before the man.

So set, before its echoes fade,
The fleet foot on the sill of shade,
And hold to the low lintel up
The still-defended challenge-cup.

And round that early-laurelled head
Will flock to gaze the strengthless dead,
And find unwithered on its curls
The garland briefer than a girl's.

WILLIAM BUTLER YEATS

Leda and the Swan

A sudden blow: the great wings beating still
Above the staggering girl, her thighs caressed
By the dark webs, her nape caught in his bill,
He holds her helpless breast upon his breast.

How can those terrified vague fingers push
The feathered glory from her loosening thighs?
And how can body, laid in that white rush,
But feel the strange heart beating where it lies?

A shudder in the loins engenders there
The broken wall, the burning roof and tower
And Agamemnon dead.
                    Being so caught up,
So mastered by the brute blood of the air,
Did she put on his knowledge with his power
Before the indifferent beak could let her drop?

Sailing to Byzantium

That is no country for old men. The young
In one another's arms, birds in the trees,
—Those dying generations—at their song,
The salmon-falls, the mackerel-crowded seas,
Fish, flesh, or fowl, commend all summer long
Whatever is begotten, born, and dies.
Caught in that sensual music all neglect
Monuments of unageing intellect.

II

An aged man is but a paltry thing,
A tattered coat upon a stick, unless
Soul clap its hands and sing, and louder sing
For every tatter in its mortal dress,
Nor is there singing school but studying
Monuments of its own magnificence;
And therefore I have sailed the seas and come
To the holy city of Byzantium.

III

O sages standing in God's holy fire
As in the gold mosaic of a wall,
Come from the holy fire, perne in a gyre,
And be the singing-masters of my soul.
Consume my heart away; sick with desire
And fastened to a dying animal
It knows not what it is; and gather me
Into the artifice of eternity.

IV

Once out of nature I shall never take
My bodily form from any natural thing,
But such a form as Grecian goldsmiths make
Of hammered gold and gold enamelling
To keep a drowsy Emperor awake;
Or set upon a golden bough to sing
To lords and ladies of Byzantium
Of what is past, or passing, or to come.

The Second Coming

Turning and turning in the widening gyre
The falcon cannot hear the falconer;
Things fall apart; the centre cannot hold;
Mere anarchy is loosed upon the world,

The blood-dimmed tide is loosed, and everywhere
The ceremony of innocence is drowned;
The best lack all conviction, while the worst
Are full of passionate intensity.

Surely some revelation is at hand;
Surely the Second Coming is at hand.
The Second Coming! Hardly are those words out
When a vast image out of *Spiritus Mundi*
Troubles my sight: somewhere in sands of the desert
A shape with lion body and the head of a man,
A gaze blank and pitiless as the sun,
Is moving its slow thighs, while all about it
Reel shadows of the indignant desert birds.
The darkness drops again; but now I know
That twenty centuries of stony sleep
Were vexed to nightmare by a rocking cradle,
And what rough beast, its hour come round at last,
Slouches towards Bethlehem to be born?

EDWIN ARLINGTON ROBINSON

Mr. Flood's Party

Old Eben Flood, climbing alone one night
Over the hill between the town below
And the forsaken upland hermitage
That held as much as he should ever know
On earth again of home, paused warily.
The road was his with not a native near;
And Eben, having leisure, said aloud,
For no man else in Tilbury Town to hear:

"Well, Mr. Flood, we have the harvest moon
Again, and we may not have many more;
The bird is on the wing, the poet says,
And you and I have said it here before.

Drink to the bird." He raised up to the light
The jug that he had gone so far to fill,
And answered huskily: "Well, Mr. Flood,
Since you propose it, I believe I will."

Alone, as if enduring to the end
A valiant armor of scarred hopes outworn,
He stood there in the middle of the road
Like Roland's ghost winding a silent horn.
Below him, in the town among the trees,
Where friends of other days had honored him,
A phantom salutation of the dead
Rang thinly till old Eben's eyes were dim.

Then, as a mother lays her sleeping child
Down tenderly, fearing it may awake,
He set the jug down slowly at his feet
With trembling care, knowing that most things break;
And only when assured that on firm earth
It stood, as the uncertain lives of men
Assuredly did not, he paced away,
And with his hand extended paused again:

"Well, Mr. Flood, we have not met like this
In a long time; and many a change has come
To both of us, I fear, since last it was
We had a drop together. Welcome home!"
Convivially returning with himself,
Again he raised the jug up to the light;
And with an acquiescent quaver said:
"Well, Mr. Flood, if you insist, I might.

"Only a very little, Mr. Flood—
For auld lang syne. No more, sir; that will do."
So, for the time, apparently it did,
And Eben evidently thought so too;
For soon amid the silver loneliness
Of night he lifted up his voice and sang,
Secure, with only two moons listening,
Until the whole harmonious landscape rang—

"For auld lang syne." The weary throat gave out,
The last word wavered; and the song being done,
He raised again the jug regretfully
And shook his head, and was again alone.
There was not much that was ahead of him,
And there was nothing in the town below—
Where strangers would have shut the many doors
That many friends had opened long ago.

Miniver Cheevy

Miniver Cheevy, child of scorn,
    Grew lean while he assailed the seasons;
He wept that he was ever born,
    And he had reasons.

Miniver loved the days of old
    When swords were bright and steeds were prancing;
The vision of a warrior bold
    Would set him dancing.

Miniver sighed for what was not,
    And dreamed, and rested from his labors;
He dreamed of Thebes and Camelot,
    And Priam's neighbors.

Miniver mourned the ripe renown
    That made so many a name so fragrant;
He mourned Romance, now on the town,
    And Art, a vagrant.

Miniver loved the Medici,
    Albeit he had never seen one;
He would have sinned incessantly
    Could he have been one.

Miniver cursed the commonplace
  And eyed a khaki suit with loathing;
He missed the medieval grace
  Of iron clothing.

Miniver scorned the gold he sought,
  But sore annoyed was he without it;
Miniver thought, and thought, and thought,
  And thought about it.

Miniver Cheevy, born too late,
  Scratched his head and kept on thinking;
Miniver coughed, and called it fate,
  And kept on drinking.

Richard Cory

Whenever Richard Cory went down town,
  We people on the pavement looked at him:
He was a gentleman from sole to crown,
  Clean favored, and imperially slim.

And he was always quietly arrayed,
  And he was always human when he talked;
But still he fluttered pulses when he said,
  "Good-morning," and he glittered when he walked.

And he was rich—yes; richer than a king,
  And admirably schooled in every grace:
In fine, we thought that he was everything
  To make us wish that we were in his place.

So on we worked, and waited for the light,
  And went without the meat, and cursed the bread;
And Richard Cory, one calm summer night,
  Went home and put a bullet through his head.

Charles Carville's Eyes

A melancholy face Charles Carville had,
But not so melancholy as it seemed,
When once you knew him, for his mouth redeemed
His insufficient eyes, forever sad:
In them there was no life-glimpse, good or bad,
Nor joy nor passion in them ever gleamed;
His mouth was all of him that ever beamed,
His eyes were sorry, but his mouth was glad.

He never was a fellow that said much,
And half of what he did say was not heard
By many of us: we were out of touch
With all his whims and all his theories
Till he was dead, so those blank eyes of his
Might speak them. Then we heard them, every word.

Reuben Bright

Because he was a butcher and thereby
Did earn an honest living (and did right),
I would not have you think that Reuben Bright
Was any more a brute than you or I;
For when they told him that his wife must die,
He stared at them, and shook with grief and fright,
And cried like a great baby half that night,
And made the women cry to see him cry.

And after she was dead, and he had paid
The singers and the sexton and the rest,
He packed a lot of things that she had made
Most mournfully away in an old chest
Of hers, and put some chopped-up cedar boughs
In with them, and tore down the slaughter-house.

Cliff Klingenhagen

Cliff Klingenhagen had me in to dine
With him one day; and after soup and meat,
And all the other things that were to eat,
Cliff took two glasses and filled one with wine
And one with wormwood. Then, without a sign
For me to choose at all, he took the draught
Of bitterness himself, and lightly quaffed
It off, and said the other one was mine.

And when I asked him what the deuce he meant
By doing that, he only looked at me
And smiled, and said it was a way of his.
And though I know the fellow, I have spent
Long time a-wondering when I shall be
As happy as Cliff Klingenhagen is.

STEPHEN CRANE

I Saw a Man

I saw a man pursuing the horizon;
Round and round they sped.
I was disturbed at this;
I accosted the man.
"It is futile," I said,
"You can never—"
"You lie," he cried.
And ran on.

The Book of Wisdom

I met a seer.
He held a book in his hands,
The book of wisdom.
"Sir," I addressed him,
"Let me read."
"Child—" he began.
"Sir," I said,
"Think not that I am a child,
For already I know much
Of that which you hold;
Aye, much."

He smiled.
Then he opened the book
And held it before me.
Strange that I should have grown
so suddenly blind.

The Heart

In the desert
I saw a creature, naked, bestial,
Who, squatting upon the ground,
Held his heart in his hands,
And ate of it.
I said, "Is it good, friend?"
"It is bitter—bitter," he answered;
"But I like it
Because it is bitter,
And because it is my heart."

GUY WETMORE CARRYL

How Jack Found That Beans May Go Back on a Chap

Without the slightest basis
For hypochondriasis
   A widow had forebodings which a cloud around her flung,
And with expression cynical
For half the day a clinical
   Thermometer she held beneath her tongue.

Whene'er she read the papers
She suffered from the vapors,
   At every tale of malady or accident she'd groan;
In every new and smart disease,
From housemaid's knee to heart disease,
   She recognized the symptoms as her own!

She had a yearning chronic
To try each novel tonic,
   Elixir, panacea, lotion, opiate, and balm;
And from a homeopathist
Would change to an hydropathist,
   And back again, with stupefying calm!

She was nervous, cataleptic,
And anemic, and dyspeptic:
   Though not convinced of apoplexy, yet she had her fears.
She dwelt with force fanatical
Upon a twinge rheumatical,
   And said she had a buzzing in her ears!

Now all of this bemoaning
And this grumbling and this groaning
   The mind of Jack, her son and heir, unconscionably bored.
His heart completely hardening,
He gave his time to gardening,
   For raising beans was something he adored.

Each hour in accents morbid
This limp maternal bore bid
   Her callous son affectionate and lachrymose good-bys.
She never granted Jack a day
Without some long "Alackaday!"
   Accompanied by rolling of the eyes.

But Jack, no panic showing,
Just watched his beanstalk growing,
   And twined with tender fingers the tendrils up the pole.
At all her words funereal
He smiled a smile ethereal,
   Or sighed an absent-minded "Bless my soul!"

That hollow-hearted creature
Would never change a feature:
   No tear bedimmed his eye, however touching was her talk.
She never fussed or flurried him,
The only thing that worried him
   Was when no bean-pods grew upon the stalk!

But then he wabbled loosely
His head, and wept profusely,
   And, taking out his handkerchief to mop away his tears,
Exclaimed: "It hasn't got any!"
He found this blow to botany
   Was sadder than were all his mother's fears.

The Moral is that gardeners pine
Whene'er no pods adorn the vine.
Of all sad words experience gleans
The saddest are: "It *might* have beans."
(I did not make this up myself:
'Twas in a book upon my shelf.
It's witty, but I don't deny
It's rather Whittier than I!)

WALTER DE LA MARE

The Listeners

"Is there anybody there?" said the Traveler,
  Knocking on the moonlit door;
And his horse in the silence champed the grasses
  Of the forest's ferny floor.
And a bird flew up out of the turret,
  Above the Traveler's head:
And he smote upon the door again a second time;
  "Is there anybody there?" he said.
But no one descended to the Traveler;
  No head from the leaf-fringed sill
Leaned over and looked into his gray eyes,
  Where he stood perplexed and still.
But only a host of phantom listeners
  That dwelt in the lone house then
Stood listening in the quiet of the moonlight
  To that voice from the world of men:
Stood thronging the faint moonbeams on the dark stair
  That goes down to the empty hall,
Hearkening in an air stirred and shaken
  By the lonely Traveler's call.
And he felt in his heart their strangeness,
  Their stillness answering his cry,
While his horse moved, cropping the dark turf,
  'Neath the starred and leafy sky;
For he suddenly smote on the door, even
  Louder, and lifted his head:—
"Tell them I came, and no one answered,
  That I kept my word," he said.
Never the least stir made the listeners,
  Though every word he spake
Fell echoing through the shadowiness of the still house
  From the one man left awake:

Aye, they heard his foot upon the stirrup,
  And the sound of iron on stone,
And how the silence surged softly backward,
  When the plunging hoofs were gone.

ROBERT FROST

Mowing

There was never a sound beside the wood but one,
And that was my long scythe whispering to the ground.
What was it it whispered? I knew not well myself;
Perhaps it was something about the heat of the sun,
Something, perhaps, about the lack of sound—
And that was why it whispered and did not speak.
It was no dream of the gift of idle hours,
Or easy gold at the hand of fay or elf:
Anything more than the truth would have seemed too weak
To the earnest love that laid the swale in rows,
Not without feeble-pointed spikes of flowers
(Pale orchises), and scared a bright green snake.
The fact is the sweetest dream the labor knows.
My long scythe whispered and left the hay to make.

The Road Not Taken

  Two roads diverged in a yellow wood,
  And sorry I could not travel both
  And be one traveler, long I stood
  And looked down one as far as I could
  To where it bent in the undergrowth;

Then took the other, as just as fair,
And having perhaps the better claim,
Because it was grassy and wanted wear;
Though as for that the passing there
Had worn them really about the same,

And both that morning equally lay
In leaves no step had trodden black.
Oh, I kept the first for another day!
Yet knowing how way leads on to way,
I doubted if I should ever come back.

I shall be telling this with a sigh
Somewhere ages and ages hence:
Two roads diverged in a wood, and I—
I took the one less traveled by,
And that has made all the difference.

The Silken Tent

She is as in a field a silken tent
At midday when a sunny summer breeze
Has dried the dew and all its ropes relent,
So that in guys it gently sways at ease,
And its supporting central cedar pole,
That is its pinnacle to heavenward
And signifies the sureness of the soul,
Seems to owe naught to any single cord,
But strictly held by none, is loosely bound
By countless silken ties of love and thought
To everything on earth the compass round,
And only by one's going slightly taut
In the capriciousness of summer air
Is of the slightest bondage made aware.

Desert Places

Snow falling and night falling fast, oh, fast
In a field I looked into going past,
And the ground almost covered smooth in snow,
But a few weeds and stubble showing last.

The woods around it have it—it is theirs.
All animals are smothered in their lairs.
I am too absent-spirited to count;
The loneliness includes me unawares.

And lonely as it is that loneliness
Will be more lonely ere it will be less—
A blanker whiteness of benighted snow
With no expression, nothing to express.

They cannot scare me with their empty spaces
Between stars—on stars where no human race is.
I have it in me so much nearer home
To scare myself with my own desert places.

Wild Grapes

What tree may not the fig be gathered from?
The grape may not be gathered from the birch?
It's all you know the grape, or know the birch.

As a girl gathered from the birch myself
Equally with my weight in grapes, one autumn,
I ought to know what tree the grape is fruit of.
I was born, I suppose, like anyone,
And grew to be a little boyish girl
My brother could not always leave at home.
But that beginning was wiped out in fear
The day I swung suspended with the grapes,
And was come after like Eurydice
And brought down safely from the upper regions;
And the life I live now's an extra life
I can waste as I please on whom I please.
So if you see me celebrate two birthdays,
And give myself out as two different ages,
One of them five years younger than I look—

One day my brother led me to a glade
Where a white birch he knew of stood alone,
Wearing a thin head-dress of pointed leaves,
And heavy on her heavy hair behind,
Against her neck, an ornament of grapes.
Grapes, I knew grapes from having seen them last year.
One bunch of them, and there began to be
Bunches all around me growing in white birches,
The way they grew round Leif the Lucky's German;
Mostly as much beyond my lifted hands, though,
As the moon used to seem when I was younger,
And only freely to be had for climbing.
My brother did the climbing; and at first
Threw me down grapes to miss and scatter
And have to hunt for in sweet fern and hardhack;
Which gave him some time to himself to eat,
But not so much, perhaps, as a boy needed.
So then, to make me wholly self-supporting,
He climbed still higher and bent the tree to earth
And put it in my hands to pick my own grapes.
'Here, take a tree-top, I'll get down another.
Hold on with all your might when I let go.'
I said I had the tree. It wasn't true.
The opposite was true. The tree had me.

The minute it was left with me alone
It caught me up as if I were the fish
And it the fishpole. So I was translated
To loud cries from my brother of 'Let go!
Don't you know anything, you girl? Let go!'
But I, with something of the baby grip
Acquired ancestrally in just such trees
When wilder mothers than our wildest now
Hung babies out on branches by the hands
To dry or wash or tan, I don't know which,
(You'll have to ask an evolutionist)—
I held on uncomplainingly for life.
My brother tried to make me laugh to help me.
'What are you doing up there in those grapes?
Don't be afraid. A few of them won't hurt you.
I mean, they won't pick you if you don't them.'
Much danger of my picking anything!
By that time I was pretty well reduced
To a philosophy of hang-and-let-hang.
'Now you know how it feels,' my brother said,
'To be a bunch of fox-grapes, as they call them,
That when it thinks it has escaped the fox
By growing where it shouldn't—on a birch,
Where a fox wouldn't think to look for it—
And if he looked and found it, couldn't reach it—
Just then come you and I to gather it.
Only you have the advantage of the grapes
In one way: you have one more stem to cling by,
And promise more resistance to the picker.'

One by one I lost off my hat and shoes,
And still I clung. I let my head fall back,
And shut my eyes against the sun, my ears
Against my brother's nonsense; 'Drop,' he said,
'I'll catch you in my arms. It isn't far.'
(Stated in lengths of him it might not be.)
'Drop or I'll shake the tree and shake you down.'
Grim silence on my part as I sank lower,
My small wrists stretching till they showed the banjo strings.
'Why, if she isn't serious about it!
Hold tight awhile till I think what to do.

I'll bend the tree down and let you down by it.'
I don't know much about the letting down;
But once I felt ground with my stocking feet
And the world came revolving back to me,
I know I looked long at my curled-up fingers,
Before I straightened them and brushed the bark off.
My brother said: 'Don't you weigh anything?
Try to weigh something next time, so you won't
Be run off with by birch trees into space.'

It wasn't my not weighing anything
So much as my not knowing anything—
My brother had been nearer right before.
I had not taken the first step in knowledge;
I had not learned to let go with the hands,
As still I have not learned to with the heart,
And have no wish to with the heart—nor need,
That I can see. The mind—is not the heart.
I may yet live, as I know others live,
To wish in vain to let go with the mind—
Of cares, at night, to sleep; but nothing tells me
That I need learn to let go with the heart.

Birches

When I see birches bend to left and right
Across the lines of straighter darker trees,
I like to think some boy's been swinging them.
But swinging doesn't bend them down to stay
As ice-storms do. Often you must have seen them
Loaded with ice a sunny winter morning
After a rain. They click upon themselves
As the breeze rises, and turn many-colored
As the stir cracks and crazes their enamel.

Soon the sun's warmth makes them shed crystal shells
Shattering and avalanching on the snow-crust—
Such heaps of broken glass to sweep away
You'd think the inner dome of heaven had fallen.
They are dragged to the withered bracken by the load,
And they seem not to break; though once they are bowed
So low for long, they never right themselves:
You may see their trunks arching in the woods
Years afterwards, trailing their leaves on the ground
Like girls on hands and knees that throw their hair
Before them over their heads to dry in the sun.
But I was going to say when Truth broke in
With all her matter-of-fact about the ice-storm
I should prefer to have some boy bend them
As he went out and in to fetch the cows—
Some boy too far from town to learn baseball,
Whose only play was what he found himself,
Summer or winter, and could play alone.
One by one he subdued his father's trees
By riding them down over and over again
Until he took the stiffness out of them,
And not one but hung limp, not one was left
For him to conquer. He learned all there was
To learn about not launching out too soon
And so not carrying the tree away
Clear to the ground. He always kept his poise
To the top branches, climbing carefully
With the same pains you use to fill a cup
Up to the brim, and even above the brim.
Then he flung outward, feet first, with a swish,
Kicking his way down through the air to the ground.
So was I once myself a swinger of birches.
And so I dream of going back to be.
It's when I'm weary of considerations,
And life is too much like a pathless wood
Where your face burns and tickles with the cobwebs
Broken across it, and one eye is weeping
From a twig's having lashed across it open.
I'd like to get away from earth awhile
And then come back to it and begin over.

May no fate willfully misunderstand me
And half grant what I wish and snatch me away
Not to return. Earth's the right place for love:
I don't know where it's likely to go better.
I'd like to go by climbing a birch tree,
And climb black branches up a snow-white trunk
Toward heaven, till the tree could bear no more,
But dipped its top and set me down again.
That would be good both going and coming back.
One could do worse than be a swinger of birches.

CARL SANDBURG

Four Preludes on Playthings of the Wind

"The Past Is a Bucket of Ashes"

1

The woman named Tomorrow
sits with a hairpin in her teeth
and takes her time
and does her hair the the way she wants it
and fastens at last the last braid and coil
and puts the hairpin where it belongs
and turns and drawls: Well, what of it?
My grandmother, Yesterday, is gone.
What of it? Let the dead be dead.

2

The doors were cedar
and the panel strips of gold
and the girls were golden girls
and the panels read and the girls chanted:
    We are the greatest city,
    and the greatest nation:
    nothing like us ever was.

The doors are twisted on broken hinges,
Sheets of rain swish through on the wind
    where the golden girls ran and the panels read:
      We are the greatest city,
      the greatest nation,
      nothing like us ever was.

3

It has happened before.
Strong men put up a city and got
    a nation together,
And paid singers to sing and women
    to warble: We are the greatest city,
      the greatest nation,
      nothing like us ever was.

And while the singers sang
and the strong men listened
and paid the singers well,
    there were rats and lizards who listened
    . . . and the only listeners left now
    . . . are . . . the rats . . . and the lizards.
    And there are black crows
    crying, "Caw, caw,"
    bringing mud and sticks
    building a nest
    over the words carved
    on the doors where the panels were cedar
    and the strips on the panels were gold
    and the golden girls came singing:
      We are the greatest city,
      the greatest nation:
      nothing like us ever was.

The only singers now are crows crying, "Caw, caw,"
And the sheets of rain whine in the wind and doorways.
And the only listeners now are . . . the rats . . . and the lizards.

4

The feet of the rats
scribble on the doorsills;
the hieroglyphs of the rat footprints
chatter the pedigrees of the rats
and babble of the blood
and gabble of the breed
of the grandfathers and the great-grandfathers
of the rats.

And the wind shifts
and the dust on a doorsill shifts
and even the writing of the rat footprints
tells us nothing, nothing at all
about the greatest city, the greatest nation
where the strong men listened
and the women warbled: Nothing like us ever was.

ROBINSON JEFFERS

Hurt Hawks

I

The broken pillar of the wing jags from the clotted shoulder,
The wing trails like a banner in defeat,
No more to use the sky forever but live with famine
And pain a few days: cat nor coyote
Will shorten the week of waiting for death, there is game without talons.
He stands under the oak-bush and waits
The lame feet of salvation; at night he remembers freedom
And flies in a dream, the dawns ruin it.
He is strong and pain is worse to the strong, incapacity is worse.
The curs of the day come and torment him
At distance, no one but death the redeemer will humble that head,
The intrepid readiness, the terrible eyes.

The wild God of the world is sometimes merciful to those
That ask mercy, not often to the arrogant.
You do not know him, you communal people, or you have forgotten
    him;
Intemperate and savage, the hawk remembers him;
Beautiful and wild, the hawks, and men that are dying, remember him.

II

I'd sooner, except the penalties, kill a man than a hawk; but the great
    redtail
Had nothing left but unable misery
From the bones too shattered for mending, the wing that trailed under
    his talons when he moved.
We had fed him six weeks, I gave him freedom,
He wandered over the foreland hill and returned in the evening, asking
    for death,
Not like a beggar, still eyed with the old
Implacable arrogance. I gave him the lead gift in the twilight. What
    fell was relaxed,
Owl-downy, soft feminine feathers; but what
Soared: the fierce rush: the night-herons by the flooded river cried
    fear at its rising
Before it was quite unsheathed from reality.

JOHN CROWE RANSOM

Blue Girls

Twirling your blue skirts, traveling the sward
Under the towers of your seminary,
Go listen to your teachers old and contrary
Without believing a word.

Tie the white fillets then about your lustrous hair
And think no more of what will come to pass
Than bluebirds that go walking on the grass
And chattering on the air.

Practice your beauty, blue girls, before it fail;
And I will cry with my loud lips and publish
Beauty which all our power shall never establish,
It is so frail.

For I could tell you a story which is true:
I know a lady with a terrible tongue,
Blear eyes fallen from blue,
All her perfections tarnished—and yet it is not long
Since she was lovelier than any of you.

Bells for John Whiteside's Daughter

There was such speed in her little body,
And such lightness in her footfall,
It is no wonder that her brown study
Astonishes us all.

Her wars were bruited in our high window.
We looked among orchard trees and beyond,
Where she took arms against her shadow,
Or harried unto the pond

The lazy geese, like a snow cloud
Dripping their snow on the green grass,
Tricking and stopping, sleepy and proud,
Who cried in goose, Alas,

For the tireless heart within the little
Lady with rod that made them rise
From their noon apple-dreams, and scuttle
Goose-fashion under the skies!

But now go the bells, and we are ready;
In one house we are sternly stopped
To say we are vexed at her brown study,
Lying so primly propped.

T. S. ELIOT

The Love Song of J. Alfred Prufrock

> *S'io credesse che mia risposta fosse*
> *A persona che mai tornasse al mondo,*
> *Questa fiamma staria senza piu scosse.*
> *Ma perciocche giammai di questo fondo*
> *Non torno vivo alcun, s'i'odo il vero,*
> *Senza tema d'infamia ti rispondo.**

Let us go then, you and I,
When the evening is spread out against the sky
Like a patient etherised upon a table;
Let us go, through certain half-deserted streets,
The muttering retreats
Of restless nights in one-night cheap hotels
And sawdust restaurants with oyster-shells:
Streets that follow like a tedious argument
Of insidious intent
To lead you to an overwhelming question . . .
Oh, do not ask, "What is it?"
Let us go and make our visit.

In the room the women come and go
Talking of Michelangelo.

The yellow fog that rubs its back upon the window-panes,
The yellow smoke that rubs its muzzle on the window-panes
Licked its tongue into the corners of the evening,
Lingered upon the pools that stand in drains,

---

*If I thought my answer were to one who ever could return to the world, this flame should shake no more. But since none ever did return alive from this depth, if what I hear be true, without fear of infamy I answer thee.

Let fall upon its back the soot that falls from chimneys,
Slipped by the terrace, made a sudden leap,
And seeing that it was a soft October night,
Curled once about the house, and fell asleep.

And indeed there will be time
For the yellow smoke that slides along the street,
Rubbing its back upon the window-panes;
There will be time, there will be time
To prepare a face to meet the faces that you meet;
There will be time to murder and create,
And time for all the works and days of hands
That lift and drop a question on your plate;
Time for you and time for me,
And time yet for a hundred indecisions,
And for a hundred visions and revisions,
Before the taking of a toast and tea.

In the room the women come and go
Talking of Michelangelo.

And indeed there will be time
To wonder, "Do I dare?" and, "Do I dare?"
Time to turn back and descend the stair,
With a bald spot in the middle of my hair—
[They will say: "How his hair is growing thin!"]
My morning coat, my collar mounting firmly to the chin,
My necktie rich and modest, but asserted by a simple pin—
[They will say: "But how his arms and legs are thin!"]
Do I dare
Disturb the universe?
In a minute there is time
For decisions and revisions which a minute will reverse.

For I have known them all already, known them all:—
Have known the evenings, mornings, afternoons,
I have measured out my life with coffee spoons;
I know the voices dying with a dying fall
Beneath the music from a farther room.
    So how should I presume?

And I have known the eyes already, known them all—
The eyes that fix you in a formulated phrase,
And when I am formulated, sprawling on a pin,
When I am pinned and wriggling on the wall,
Then how should I begin
To spit out all the butt-ends of my days and ways?
  And how should I presume?

And I have known the arms already, known them all—
Arms that are braceleted and white and bare
[But in the lamplight, downed with light brown hair!]
Is it perfume from a dress
That makes me so digress?
Arms that lie along a table, or wrap about a shawl.
  And should I then presume?
  And how should I begin?

                    . . . . .

Shall I say, I have gone at dusk through narrow streets
And watched the smoke that rises from the pipes
Of lonely men in shirt-sleeves, leaning out of windows? . . .

I should have been a pair of ragged claws
Scuttling across the floors of silent seas.

                    . . . . . .

And the afternoon, the evening, sleeps so peacefully!
Smoothed by long fingers,
Asleep . . . tired . . . or it malingers,
Stretched on the floor, here beside you and me.
Should I, after tea and cakes and ices,
Have the strength to force the moment to its crisis?
But though I have wept and fasted, wept and prayed,
Though I have seen my head [grown slightly bald] brought in upon a
    platter,
I am no prophet—and here's no great matter;
I have seen the moment of my greatness flicker,
And I have seen the eternal Footman hold my coat, and snicker,
And in short, I was afraid.

And would it have been worth it, after all,
After the cups, the marmalade, the tea,
Among the porcelain, among some talk of you and me,
Would it have been worth while,
To have bitten off the matter with a smile,
To have squeezed the universe into a ball
To roll it toward some overwhelming question,
To say: "I am Lazarus, come from the dead,
Come back to tell you all, I shall tell you all"—
If one, settling a pillow by her head,
  Should say: "That is not what I meant at all.
  That is not it, at all."

And would it have been worth it, after all,
Would it have been worth while,
After the sunsets and the dooryards and the sprinkled streets,
After the novels, after the teacups, after the skirts that trail along the
    floor—
And this, and so much more?—
It is impossible to say just what I mean!
But as if a magic lantern threw the nerves in patterns on a screen:
Would it have been worth while
If one, settling a pillow or throwing off a shawl,
And turning toward the window, should say:
  "That is not it at all,
  That is not what I meant, at all."

. . . . . .

No! I am not Prince Hamlet, nor was meant to be;
Am an attendant lord, one that will do
To swell a progress, start a scene or two,
Advise the prince; no doubt, an easy tool,
Deferential, glad to be of use,
Politic, cautious, and meticulous;
Full of high sentence, but a bit obtuse;
At times, indeed, almost ridiculous—
Almost, at times, the Fool.

I grow old . . . I grow old . . .
I shall wear the bottoms of my trousers rolled.

Shall I part my hair behind? Do I dare to eat a peach?
I shall wear white flannel trousers, and walk upon the beach.
I have heard the mermaids singing, each to each.

I do not think that they will sing to me.

I have seen them riding seaward on the waves
Combing the white hair of the waves blown back
When the wind blows the water white and black.

We have lingered in the chambers of the sea
By sea-girls wreathed with seaweed red and brown
Till human voices wake us, and we drown.

Portrait of a Lady

> *Thou hast committed—*
> *Fornication: but that was in another country,*
> *And besides, the wench is dead.*
>   —THE JEW OF MALTA

I

Among the smoke and fog of a December afternoon
You have the scene arrange itself—as it will seem to do—
With "I have saved this afternoon for you";
And four wax candles in the darkened room,
Four rings of light upon the ceiling overhead,
An atmosphere of Juliet's tomb
Prepared for all the things to be said, or left unsaid.
We have been, let us say, to hear the latest Pole
Transmit the Preludes, through his hair and finger-tips.
"So intimate, this Chopin, that I think his soul
Should be resurrected only among friends
Some two or three, who will not touch the bloom
That is rubbed and questioned in the concert room."

—And so the conversation slips
Among velleities and carefully caught regrets
Through attenuated tones of violins
Mingled with remote cornets
And begins.
"You do not know how much they mean to me, my friends,
And how, how rare and strange it is, to find
In a life composed so much, so much of odds and ends,
[For indeed I do not love it . . . you knew? you are not blind!
How keen you are!]
To find a friend who has these qualities,
Who has, and gives
Those qualities upon which friendship lives.
How much it means that I say this to you—
Without these friendships—life, what *cauchemar!*"

Among the windings of the violins
And the ariettes
Of cracked cornets
Inside my brain a dull tom-tom begins
Absurdly hammering a prelude of its own,
Capricious monotone
That is at least one definite "false note."
—Let us take the air, in a tobacco trance,
Admire the monuments,
Discuss the late events,
Correct our watches by the public clocks.
Then sit for half an hour and drink our bocks.

II

Now that lilacs are in bloom
She has a bowl of lilacs in her room
And twists one in her fingers while she talks.
"Ah, my friend, you do not know, you do not know
What life is, you who hold it in your hands";
(Slowly twisting the lilac stalks)
"You let it flow from you, you let it flow,
And youth is cruel, and has no remorse
And smiles at situations which it cannot see."

I smile, of course,
And go on drinking tea.
"Yet with these April sunsets, that somehow recall
My buried life, and Paris in the Spring,
I feel immeasurably at peace, and find the world
To be wonderful and youthful, after all."

The voice returns like the insistent out-of-tune
Of a broken violin on an August afternoon:
"I am always sure that you understand
My feelings, always sure that you feel,
Sure that across the gulf you reach your hand.

You are invulnerable, you have no Achilles' heel.
You will go on, and when you have prevailed
You can say: at this point many a one has failed.
But what have I, but what have I, my friend,
To give you, what can you receive from me?
Only the friendship and the sympathy
Of one about to reach her journey's end.

I shall sit here, serving tea to friends. . . ."

I take my hat: how can I make a cowardly amends
For what she has said to me?
You will see me any morning in the park
Reading the comics and the sporting page.
Particularly I remark
An English countess goes upon the stage.
A Greek was murdered at a Polish dance,
Another bank defaulter has confessed.
I keep my countenance,
I remain self-possessed
Except when a street piano, mechanical and tired
Reiterates some worn-out common song
With the smell of hyacinths across the garden
Recalling things that other people have desired.
Are these ideas right or wrong?

III

The October night comes down; returning as before
Except for a slight sensation of being ill at ease
I mount the stairs and turn the handle of the door
And feel as if I had mounted on my hands and knees.
"And so you are going abroad; and when do you return?
But that's a useless question.
You hardly know when you are coming back,
You will find so much to learn."
My smile falls heavily among the bric-à-brac.

"Perhaps you can write to me."
My self-possession flares up for a second;
This is as I had reckoned.
"I have been wondering frequently of late
(But our beginnings never know our ends!)
Why we have not developed into friends."
I feel like one who smiles, and turning shall remark
Suddenly, his expression in a glass.
My self-possession gutters; we are really in the dark.

"For everybody said so, all our friends,
They all were sure our feelings would relate
So closely! I myself can hardly understand.
We must leave it now to fate.
You will write, at any rate.
Perhaps it is not too late.
I shall sit here, serving tea to friends."

And I must borrow every changing shape
To find expression . . . dance, dance
Like a dancing bear,
Cry like a parrot, chatter like an ape.
Let us take the air, in a tobacco trance—

Well! and what if she should die some afternoon,
Afternoon grey and smoky, evening yellow and rose;
Should die and leave me sitting pen in hand
With the smoke coming down above the housetops;

Doubtful, for a while
Not knowing what to feel or if I understand
Or whether wise or foolish, tardy or too soon . . .
Would she not have the advantage, after all?
This music is successful with a "dying fall"
Now that we talk of dying—
And should I have the right to smile?

CONRAD AIKEN

King Borborigmi

You say you heard King Borborigmi laugh?
Say how it was. Some heavenly body moved him?
The moon laughed first? Dark earth put up a finger
Of honeysuckle, through his moonlit window,
And tickled him?

        —King Borborigmi laughed
Alone, walking alone in an empty room,
Thinking, and yet not thinking, seeing, yet blind.
One hand was on his chin, feeling the beard
That razors could not stay; the other groped;
For it was dark, and in the dark were chairs;
Midnight, or almost midnight; Aldebaran
Hanging among the dews.

        —King Borborigmi
Laughed once or twice at nothing, just as midnight
Released a flock of bells?

        —Not this alone;
Not bells in flight toward Aldebaran;
Nor the immitigable beard; nor dews
Heavily pattering on the pent-house roof;
Nor chairs in shadow which his foot disturbed.

Yet it was all of these, and more: the air
Twirling the curtain where a red moth hung:
The one bell flying later than the others
Into the starstrung silence: the garden breaking
To let a thousand seedlings have their way:
An eye-tooth aching, and the pendulum
That heavily ticked upon the leftward swing.

—These trifles woke the laughter of a king?

—Much less than these, and more! He softly stepped
Among the webby world, and felt it shudder.
Under the earth—a strand or two of web—
He saw his father's bones, fallen apart,
The jawbone sunken and the skull caved in.
Among his mother's bones a cactus rooted,
And two moles crept, and ants held carnival.
Above the obscene tomb an aloe blossomed;
Dew glistened on the marble. This he saw,
And at the selfsame moment heard the cook
Wind the alarm-clock in her bedroom, yawn,
And creak the bed. And it was then, surprised,
He touched a chair, and laughed, and twitched the curtain,—
And the moth flew out.

                              —Alas, poor Borborigmi,
That it should be so little, and so sorry
A thing to make him laugh!

                              —Young Borborigmi
Saw more than this. The infinite octopus
With eyes of chaos and long arms of stars,
And belly of void and darkness, became clear
About him, and he saw himself embraced
And swept along a vein, with chairs and teeth,
Houses and bones and gardens, cooks and clocks;
The midnight bell, a snoring cook, and he,
Mingled and flowed like atoms.

—It was this
That made him laugh—to see himself as one
Corpuscle in the infinite octopus? . . .
And was this all, old fool, old turner of leaves? . . .

—Alone, thinking alone in an empty room
Where moonlight and the mouse were met together,
And pulse and clock together ticked, and dew
Made contrapuntal patter, Borborigmi
Fathomed in his own viscera the world,
Went downward, sounding like a diver, holding
His peakèd nose; and when he came up, laughed.
These things and others saw. But last of all,
Ultimate or penultimate, he saw
The one thing that undid him!

—What was this?
The one grotesquer thing among grotesques?
Carrion, offal, or the toothbrush ready
For carnal fangs? Cancer, that grasps the heart,
Or fungus, whitely swelling in the brain?
Some gargoyle of the thought?

—King Borborigmi,
Twitching the curtain as the last bell flew
Melodious to Aldebaran, beheld
The moth fly also. Downward dropped it softly
Among dropped petals, white. And there one rose
Was open in the moonlight! Dew was on it;
The bat, with ragged wing, cavorting, sidling,
Snapped there a sleeping bee—

—And crunched the moth? . . .

—It was the rose in moonlight, crimson, yet
Blanched by the moon; the bee asleep; the bat
And fallen moth—but most the guileless rose.
Guileless! . . . King Borborigmi struck his foot
Against a chair, and saw the guileless rose
Joining himself (King Bubblegut), and all
Those others—the immitigable beard;

Razors and teeth; his mother's bones; the tomb;
The yawning cook; the clock; the dew; the bells
Bursting upward like bubbles—; all so swept
Along one vein of the infinite octopus
With eyes of chaos and long arms of stars
And belly of void and darkness. It was then
He laughed; as he would never laugh again.
For he saw everything; and, in the centre
Of corrupt change, one guileless rose; and laughed
For puzzlement and sorrow

                —Ah, poor man,
Poor Borborigmi, young, to be so wise!

—Wise? No. For what he laughed at was just this:
That to see all, to know all, is to rot.
So went to bed; and slept; is sleeping still,
If none has waked him.

              —Dead? King Borborigmi
Is dead? Died laughing? Sleeps a dreamless sleep
Till cook's alarm clock wakes him?

              —Sleeps Like Hamlet,
King of infinite space in a walnut shell—
But has bad dreams; I fear he has bad dreams.

ARCHIBALD MacLEISH

~~~~~~

Ars Poetica

A poem should be palpable and mute
As a globed fruit,

Dumb
As old medallions to the thumb,

Silent as the sleeve-worn stone
Of casement ledges where the moss has grown—

A poem should be wordless
As the flight of birds.

        ✻   ✻   ✻

A poem should be motionless in time
As the moon climbs,

Leaving, as the moon releases
Twig by twig the night-entangled trees,

Leaving, as the moon behind the winter leaves,
Memory by memory the mind—

A poem should be motionless in time
As the moon climbs.

        ✻   ✻   ✻

A poem should be equal to:
Not true.

For all the history of grief
An empty doorway and a maple leaf.

For love
The leaning grasses and two lights above the sea—

A poem should not mean
But be.

You, Andrew Marvell

And here face down beneath the sun
And here upon earth's noonward height
To feel the always coming on
The always rising of the night

To feel creep up the curving east
The earthy chill of dusk and slow
Upon those under lands the vast
And ever climbing shadow grow

And strange at Ecbatan the trees
Take leaf by leaf the evening strange
The flooding dark about their knees
The mountains over Persia change

And now at Kermanshah the gate
Dark empty and the withered grass
And through the twilight now the late
Few travelers in the westward pass

And Baghdad darken and the bridge
Across the silent river gone
And through Arabia the edge
Of evening widen and steal on

And deepen on Palmyra's street
The wheel rut in the ruined stone
And Lebanon fade out and Crete
High through the clouds and overblown

And over Sicily the air
Still flashing with the landward gulls
And loom and slowly disappear
The sails above the shadowy hulls

And Spain go under and the shore
Of Africa the gilded sand
And evening vanish and no more
The low pale light across that land

Nor now the long light on the sea . . .

And here face downward in the sun
To feel how swift how secretly
The shadow of the night comes on . . .

The End of the World

Quite unexpectedly, as Vasserot
The armless ambidextrian was lighting
A match between his great and second toe,
And Ralph the lion was engaged in biting
The neck of Madame Sossman while the drum
Pointed, and Teeny was about to cough
In waltz-time swinging Jocko by the thumb—
Quite unexpectedly the top blew off:

And there, there overhead, there, there hung over
Those thousands of white faces, those dazed eyes,
There in the starless dark the poise, the hover,
There with vast wings across the cancelled skies,
There in the sudden blackness the black pall
Of nothing, nothing, nothing—nothing at all.

e. e. cummings

All in green went my love riding

All in green went my love riding
on a great horse of gold
into the silver dawn.

four lean hounds crouched low and smiling
the merry deer ran before.

Fleeter be they than dappled dreams
the swift sweet deer
the red rare deer.

Four red roebuck at a white water
the cruel bugle sang before.

Horn at hip went my love riding
riding the echo down
into the silver dawn.

four lean hounds crouched low and smiling
the level meadows ran before.

Softer be they than slippered sleep
the lean lithe deer
the fleet flown deer.

Four fleet does at a gold valley
the famished arrow sang before.

Bow at belt went my love riding
riding the mountain down
into the silver dawn.

four lean hounds crouched low and smiling
the sheer peaks ran before.

Paler be they than daunting death
the sleek slim deer
the tall tense deer.

Four tall stags at a green mountain
the lucky hunter sang before.

All in green went my love riding
on a great horse of gold
into the silver dawn.

four lean hounds crouched low and smiling
my heart fell dead before.

if there are any heavens

if there are any heavens my mother will(all by herself)have
one. It will not be a pansy heaven nor
a fragile heaven of lilies-of-the-valley but
it will be a heaven of blackred roses

my father will be(deep like a rose
tall like a rose)

standing near my

(swaying over her
silent)
with eyes which are really petals and see

nothing with the face of a poet really which
is a flower and not a face with
hands
which whisper
This is my beloved my

                  (suddenly in sunlight
he will bow,

& the whole garden will bow)

W. H. AUDEN

Voltaire at Ferney

Almost happy now, he looked at his estate.
An exile making watches glanced up as he passed,
And went on working; where a hospital was rising fast
A joiner touched his cap; an agent came to tell
Some of the trees he'd planted were progressing well.
The white alps glittered. It was summer. He was very great.

Far off in Paris, where his enemies
Whispered that he was wicked, in an upright chair
A blind old woman longed for death and letters. He would write
"Nothing is better than life." But was it? Yes, the fight
Against the false and the unfair
Was always worth it. So was gardening. Civilise.

Cajoling, scolding, scheming, cleverest of them all,
He'd led the other children in a holy war
Against the infamous grown-ups; and, like a child, been sly
And humble when there was occasion for
The two-faced answer or the plain protective lie,
But patient like a peasant waited for their fall.

And never doubted, like D'Alembert, he would win:
Only Pascal was a great enemy, the rest
Were rats already poisoned; there was much, though, to be done,
And only himself to count upon.
Dear Diderot was dull but did his best;
Rousseau, he'd always known, would blubber and give in.

So, like a sentinel, he could not sleep. The night was full of wrong,
Earthquakes and executions. Soon he would be dead,
And still all over Europe stood the horrible nurses
Itching to boil their children. Only his verses
Perhaps could stop them: He must go on working. Overhead
The uncomplaining stars composed their lucid song.

Musée des Beaux Arts

About suffering they were never wrong,
The Old Masters: how well they understood
Its human position; how it takes place
While someone else is eating or opening a window or just walking dully
    along;

How, when the aged are reverently, passionately waiting
For the miraculous birth, there always must be
Children who did not specially want it to happen, skating
On a pond at the edge of the wood:
They never forgot
That even the dreadful martyrdom must run its course
Anyhow in a corner, some untidy spot
Where the dogs go on with their doggy life and the torturer's horse
Scratches its innocent behind on a tree.

In Brueghel's *Icarus*, for instance: how everything turns away
Quite leisurely from the disaster; the ploughman may
Have heard the splash, the forsaken cry,
But for him it was not an important failure; the sun shone
As it had to on the white legs disappearing into the green
Water; and the expensive delicate ship that must have seen
Something amazing, a boy falling out of the sky,
Had somewhere to get to and sailed calmly on.

In Memory of W. B. Yeats

(d. Jan. 1939)

1

He disappeared in the dead of winter:
The brooks were frozen, the airports almost deserted,
And snow disfigured the public statues;
The mercury sank in the mouth of the dying day.
O all the instruments agree
The day of his death was a dark cold day.

Far from his illness
The wolves ran on through the evergreen forests,
The peasant river was untempted by the fashionable quays;
By mourning tongues
The death of the poet was kept from his poems.

But for him it was his last afternoon as himself,
An afternoon of nurses and rumours;
The provinces of his body revolted,
The squares of his mind were empty,
Silence invaded the suburbs,
The current of his feeling failed: he became his admirers.

Now he is scattered among a hundred cities
And wholly given over to unfamiliar affections;
To find his happiness in another kind of wood
And be punished under a foreign code of conscience.
The words of a dead man
Are modified in the guts of the living.

But in the importance and noise of tomorrow
When the brokers are roaring like beasts on the floor of the Bourse,
And the poor have the sufferings to which they are fairly accustomed,
And each in the cell of himself is almost convinced of his freedom;
A few thousand will think of this day
As one thinks of a day when one did something slightly unusual.
O all the instruments agree
The day of his death was a dark cold day.

2

You were silly like us: your gift survived it all;
The parish of rich women, physical decay,
Yourself; mad Ireland hurt you into poetry.
Now Ireland has her madness and her weather still,
For poetry makes nothing happen: it survives
In the valley of its saying where executives
Would never want to tamper; it flows south
From ranches of isolation and the busy griefs,
Raw towns that we believe and die in; it survives,
A way of happening, a mouth.

3

Earth, receive an honoured guest;
William Yeats is laid to rest:
Let the Irish vessel lie
Emptied of its poetry.

Time that is intolerant
Of the brave and innocent,
And indifferent in a week
To a beautiful physique,

Worships language and forgives
Everyone by whom it lives;
Pardons cowardice, conceit,
Lays its honours at their feet.

Time that with this strange excuse
Pardoned Kipling and his views,
And will pardon Paul Claudel,
Pardons him for writing well.

In the nightmare of the dark
All the dogs of Europe bark,
And the living nations wait,
Each sequestered in its hate;

Intellectual disgrace
Stares from every human face,
And the seas of pity lie
Locked and frozen in each eye.

Follow, poet, follow right
To the bottom of the night,
With your unconstraining voice
Still persuade us to rejoice;

With the farming of a verse
Make a vineyard of the curse,
Sing of human unsuccess
In a rapture of distress;

In the deserts of the heart
Let the healing fountain start,
In the prison of his days
Teach the free man how to praise.

As I Walked Out One Evening

As I walked out one evening,
  Walking down Bristol Street,
The crowds upon the pavement
  Were fields of harvest wheat.

And down by the brimming river
  I heard a lover sing
Under an arch of the railway:
  "Love has no ending.

I'll love you, dear, I'll love you
  Till China and Africa meet,
And the river jumps over the mountain
  And the salmon sing in the street.

I'll love you till the ocean
  Is folded and hung up to dry,
And the seven stars go squawking
  Like geese about the sky.

The years shall run like rabbits,
  For in my arms I hold
The Flower of the Ages,
  And the first love of the world."

But all the clocks in the city
  Began to whirr and chime:
"O let not Time deceive you,
  You cannot conquer Time.

In the burrows of the Nightmare
  Where Justice naked is,
Time watches from the shadow
  And coughs when you would kiss.

In headaches and in worry
   Vaguely life leaks away,
And Time will have his fancy
   Tomorrow or today.

Into many a green valley
   Drifts the appalling snow;
Time breaks the threaded dances
   And the diver's brilliant bow.

O plunge your hands in water,
   Plunge them in up to the wrist;
Stare, stare in the basin
   And wonder what you've missed.

The glacier knocks in the cupboard,
   The desert sighs in the bed,
And the crack in the tea-cup opens
   A lane to the land of the dead.

Where the beggars raffle the banknotes
   And the Giant is enchanting to Jack,
And the Lily-white Boy is a Roarer,
   And Jill goes down on her back.

O look, look in the mirror,
   O look in your distress;
Life remains a blessing
   Although you cannot bless.

O stand, stand at the window
   As the tears scald and start;
You shall love your crooked neighbor
   With your crooked heart."

It was late, late in the evening,
   The lovers they were gone;
The clocks had ceased their chiming,
   And the deep river ran on.

STEPHEN SPENDER

I Think Continually of Those Who Were Truly Great

I think continually of those who were truly great.
Who, from the womb, remembered the soul's history
Through corridors of light where the hours are suns
Endless and singing. Whose lovely ambition
Was that their lips, still touched with fire,
Should tell of the Spirit clothed from head to foot in song.
And who hoarded from the Spring branches
The desires falling across their bodies like blossoms.

What is precious is never to forget
The essential delight of the blood drawn from ageless springs
Breaking through rocks in worlds before our earth.
Never to deny its pleasure in the morning simple light
Nor its grave evening demand for love.
Never to allow gradually the traffic to smother
With noise and fog the flowering of the spirit.

Near the snow, near the sun, in the highest fields
See how these names are fêted by the waving grass
And by the streamers of white cloud
And whispers of wind in the listening sky.
The names of those who in their lives fought for life
Who wore at their hearts the fire's centre.
Born of the sun they travelled a short while towards the sun,
And left the vivid air signed with their honour.

DYLAN THOMAS

Poem in October

It was my thirtieth year to heaven
Woke to my hearing from harbour and neighbour wood
   And the mussel pooled and the heron
      Priested shore
     The morning beckon
With water praying and call of seagull and rook
And the knock of sailing boats on the net webbed wall
     Myself to set foot
      That second
In the still sleeping town and set forth.

My birthday began with the water—
Birds and the birds of the winged trees flying my name
   Above the farms and the white horses
      And I rose
     In rainy autumn
And walked abroad in a shower of all my days.
High tide and the heron dived when I took the road
     Over the border
      And the gates
Of the town closed as the town awoke.

A springful of larks in a rolling
Cloud and the roadside bushes brimming with whistling
   Blackbirds and the sun of October
      Summery
     On the hill's shoulder,
Here were fond climates and sweet singers suddenly
Come in the morning where I wandered and listened
     To the rain wringing
      Wind blow cold
In the wood faraway under me.

Pale rain over the dwindling harbour
And over the sea wet church the size of a snail
With its horns through mist, and the castle
Brown as owls,
But all the gardens
Of spring and summer were blooming in the tall tales
Beyond the border and under the lark full cloud.
There could I marvel
My birthday
Away but the weather turned around.

It turned away from the blithe country
And down the other air and the blue altered sky
Streamed again a wonder of summer
With apples
Pears and red currants
And I saw in the turning so clearly a child's
Forgotten mornings when he walked with his mother
Through the parables
Of sun light
And the legends of the green chapels

And the twice told fields of infancy
That his tears burned my cheeks and his heart moved in mine.
These were the woods the river and sea
Where a boy
In the listening
Summertime of the dead whispered the truth of his joy
To the trees and the stones and the fish in the tide.
And the mystery
Sang alive
Still in the water and singing birds.

And there could I marvel my birthday
Away but the weather turned around. And the true
Joy of the long dead child sang burning
In the sun.
It was my thirtieth
Year to heaven stood there then in the summer noon
Though the town below lay leaved with October blood.

O may my heart's truth
  Still be sung
On this high hill in a year's turning.

In Memory of Ann Jones

After the funeral, mule praises, brays,
Windshake of sailshaped ears, muffle-toed tap
Tap happily of one peg in the thick
Grave's foot, blinds down the lids, the teeth in black,
The spittled eyes, the salt ponds in the sleeves,
Morning smack of the spade that wakes up sleep,
Shakes a desolate boy who slits his throat
In the dark of the coffin and sheds dry leaves
That breaks one bone to light with a judgment clout,
After the feast of tear-stuffed time and thistles
In a room with a stuffed fox and a stale fern,
I stand, for this memorial's sake, alone
In the snivelling hours with dead, humped Ann
Whose hooded fountain heart once fell in puddles
Round the parched worlds of Wales and drowned each sun
(Though this for her is a monstrous image blindly
Magnified out of praise; her death was a still drop;
She would not have me sinking in the holy
Flood of her heart's fame; she would lie dumb and deep
And need no druid of her broken body).
But I, Ann's bard on a raised hearth, call all
The seas to service that her wood-tongued virtue
Babble like a bellbuoy over the hymning heads,
Bow down the walls of the ferned and foxy woods
That her love sing and swing through a brown chapel,
Bless her bent spirit with four, crossing birds.

Her flesh was meek as milk, but this skyward statue
With the wild breast and blessed and giant skull
Is carved from her in a room with a wet window
In a fiercely mourning house in a crooked year.
I know her scrubbed and sour humble hands
Lie with religion in their cramp, her threadbare
Whisper in a damp word, her wits drilled hollow,
Her fist of a face died clenched on a round pain;
And sculptured Ann is seventy years of stone.
These cloud-sopped, marble hands, this monumental
Argument of the hewn voice, gesture and psalm
Storm me forever over her grave until
The stuffed lung of the fox twitch and cry Love
And the strutting fern lay seeds on the black sill.

LETTERS
AND DIARIES

DOROTHY OSBORNE

To Sir William Temple

[Undated. Assumed date, Sunday, January 22, 1654]

'Tis but an hour since you went, and I am writing to you already; is not this kind? How do you after your journey; are you not weary; do you not repent that you took it to so little purpose? Well, God forgive me, and you too, you made me tell a great lie. I was fain to say you came only to take your leave before you went abroad; and all this not only to keep quiet, but to keep him [her brother Henry] from playing the madman; for when he has the least suspicion, he carries it so strangely that all the world takes notice on't, and so often guess at the reason, or else he tells it. Now, do but you judge whether if by mischance he should discover the truth, whether he would not rail most sweetly at me (and with some reason) for abusing him. Yet you helped to do it; a sadness that he discovered at your going away inclined him to believe you were ill satisfied, and made him credit what I said. He is kind now in extremity, and I would be glad to keep him so till a discovery is absolutely necessary. Your going abroad will confirm him much in his belief, and I shall have nothing to torment me in this place but my own doubts and fears. Here I shall find all the repose I am capable of, and nothing will disturb my prayers and wishes for your happiness which only can make mine. Your journey cannot be to your disadvantage neither; you must needs be pleased to visit a place you are so much concerned in, and to be a witness yourself of the probability of your hopes, though I will believe you need no other inducement to this voyage than my desiring it. I know you love me, and you have no reason to doubt my kindness. Let us both have patience to wait what time and fortune will do for us; they cannot hinder our being perfect friends.

Lord, there were a thousand things I remembered after you were gone that I should have said, and now I am to write, not one of them will come into my head. Sure as I live it is not settled yet! Good God!

279

the fears and surprises, the crosses and disorders of that day, 'twas confused enough to be a dream, and I am apt to think sometimes it was no more. But no, I saw you; when I shall do it again, God only knows! Can there be a more romance story than ours would make if the conclusion should prove happy? Ah! I dare not hope it; something that I cannot describe draws a cloud over all the light my fancy discovers sometimes, and leaves me so in the dark with all my fears about me that I tremble to think on't. But no more of this sad talk.

Who was that Mr. Dr. told you I should marry? I cannot imagine for my life; tell me, or, I shall think you made it to excuse yourself. Did not you say once you knew where good French tweezers were to be had? Pray send me a pair; they shall cut no love. Before you go I must have a ring from you, too, a plain gold one; if I ever marry it shall be my wedding ring; or when I die I'll give it you again. What a dismal story this is you sent me; but who could expect better from a love begun upon such grounds? I cannot pity neither of them, they were both so guilty. Yes, they are the more to be pitied for that.

Here is a note comes to me just now, will you do this service for a fair lady that is my friend; have not I taught her well, she writes better than her mistress? How merry and pleased she is with her marrying because there is a plentiful fortune; otherwise she would not value the man at all. This is the world; would you and I were out on't: for, sure, we were not made to live in it. Do you remember Arme and the little house there? Shall we go thither? that's next to being out of the world. There we might live like Baucis and Philemon, grow old together in our little cottage, and for our charity to some ship-wrecked strangers obtain the blessing of dying both at the same time. How idly I talk; 'tis because the story pleases me—none in Ovid so much. I remember I cried when I read it. Methought they were the perfectest characters of a contented marriage, where piety and love were all their wealth, and in their poverty feasted the gods when rich men shut them out. I am called away—farewell!

Your faithful.

JONATHAN SWIFT

To Pope

September 29 1725

I am now returning to the noble scene of Dublin, into the *grande monde*, for fear of burying my parts, to signalize myself among curates and vicars, and correct all corruptions crept in, relating to the weight of bread and butter, through those dominions where I govern. I have employed my time (beside ditching) in finishing, correcting, amending, and transcribing my travels, in four parts complete, newly augmented, and intended for the press, when the world shall deserve them, or rather when a printer shall be found brave enough to venture his ears.

I like the scheme of our meeting after distresses and dispersions, but the chief end I propose to myself in all my labours is, to vex the world rather than divert it; and if I could compass that design, without hurting my own person or fortune, I would be the most indefatigable writer you have ever seen, without reading. I am exceeding pleased that you have done with translations: Lord-treasurer Oxford often lamented that a rascally world should lay you under a necessity of misemploying your genius for so long a time. But since you will now be so much better employed, when you think of the world give it one lash the more, at my request. I have ever hated all nations, professions, and communities; and all my love is toward individuals; for instance, I hate the tribe of lawyers, but I love Counsellor Such-a-one, and Judge Such-a-one: It is so with physicians, (I will not speak of my own trade,) soldiers, English, Scotch, French, and the rest. But principally I hate and detest that animal called man; although I heartily love John, Peter, Thomas, and so forth. This is the system upon which I have governed myself many years, (but do not tell); and so I shall go on till I have done with them. I have got materials towards a treatise, proving the falsity of that definition *animal rationale*, and to show it should be only *rationais capax*. Upon this great foundation of misanthropy, (though not in Timon's manner), the whole building of my travels is erected;

and I never will have peace of mind till all honest men are of my opinion: by consequence you are to embrace it immediately, and procure that all who deserve my esteem may do so too. The matter is so clear that it will admit of no dispute; nay, I will hold a hundred pounds that you and I agree in the point.

I did not know your Odyssey was finished, being yet in the country, which I shall leave in three days. I thank you kindly for the present, but shall like it three-fourths the less, from the mixture you mention of other hands; however, I am glad you saved yourself so much drudgery. —I have been long told by Mr. Ford of your great achievements in building and planting, and especially of your subterranean passage to your garden, whereby you turned a blunder into a beauty, which is a piece of *Ars Poetica*.

I have almost done with harridans, and shall soon become old enough to fall in love with girls of fourteen. The lady whom you describe to live at court, to be deaf, and no party-woman, I take to be mythology, but know not how to moralize it. She cannot be Mercy, for Mercy is neither deaf, nor lives at court: Justice is blind, and perhaps deaf, but neither is she a court lady: Fortune is both blind and deaf, and a court lady: but then she is a most damnable party-woman, and will never make me easy, as you promise. It must be Riches, which answers all your description: I am glad she visits you, but my voice is so weak that I doubt she will never hear me. . . .

Are you altogether a country gentleman, that I must address to you out of London, to the hazard of your losing this precious letter, which I will now conclude, although so much paper is left. I have an ill name, and therefore shall not subscribe it, but you will guess it comes from one who esteems and loves you about half as much as you deserve, I mean as much as he can.

I am in great concern at what I am just told is in some of the newspapers, that Lord Bolingbroke is much hurt by a fall in hunting. I am glad he has so much youth and vigour left (of which he has not been thrifty), but I wonder he has no more discretion.

RICHARD STEELE

~~~~~~

To Mary Scurlock

[afterwards his wife]

Aug. 16 1707

Madam: Before the light this morning dawn'd upon the earth I awak'd and lay in expectation of its return, not that it could give any new sense of joy to me, but as I hop'd it would blesse you with it's chearfull face, after a quiet which I wish'd you last night. If my prayers are heard the day appear'd with all the influence of a merciful Creator upon your person and actions. Let others, my lovely charmer, talk of a blind being that disposes their hearts, I contemn their low images of love. I have not a thought which relates to you that I cannot with confidence beseech the all-seeing power to bless me in. May He direct you in all your steps, and reward your innocence, your sanctity of manners, your prudent youth, and becoming piety, with the continuance of His grace and protection. This is an unusuall language to ladies, but you have a mind elevated above the giddy motions of a sex insnar'd by flattery, and misled by a false and short adoration into a solid and long contempt. Beauty, my fairest creature, palls in the possession, but I love also your mind; your soul is as dear to me as my own, and if the advantages of a liberall education, some knowledge and as much contempt of the world join'd with the endeavours towards a life of strict vertue and religion, can qualifie me to raise new ideas in a breast so well dispos'd as yours is, our days will passe away with joy, and old age instead of introducing melancholy prospects of decay, give us hope of eternal youth in a better life. I have but a few minutes from the duty of my employment to write in, and without time to read over what I have writ, therefore beseech you to pardon the first hints of my mind which I have express'd in so little order.

I am, dearest creature,
Your most obedient, most devoted servant.

ALEXANDER POPE

To Lady Mary Wortley Montagu

August 18th, 1716.

. . . I think I love you as well as King Herod could Herodias (though I never had so much as one dance with you) and would as freely give you my heart in a dish as he did another's head.

But since Jupiter will not have it so, I must be content to show my taste in life, as I do my taste in painting, by loving to have as little drapery as possible, "not that I think every body naked altogether so fine a sight as yourself and a few more would be"; but because it is good to use people to what they must be acquainted with; and there certainly will come some day of judgment to uncover every soul of us. We shall then see how the prudes of this world owed all their fine figures only to their being a little straiter-laced, and that they were naturally as arrant squabs as those that went more loose, nay as those that never girded their loins at all.

. . . You may easily imagine how desirous I must be of corresponding with a person who had taught me long ago that it was as possible to esteem at first sight, as to love; and who have since ruined me for all the conversation of one sex, and almost all the friendship of the other.

How often have I been quietly going to take possession of that tranquillity and indolence I had so long found in the country, when one evening of your conversation has spoiled me for a solitaire too. Books have lost their effect upon me, and I was convinced, since I saw you, that there is something more powerful than philosophy, and, since I heard you, that there is one alive wiser than all the sages. A plague of female wisdom! it makes a man ten times more uneasy than his own.

LADY MARY WORTLEY MONTAGU

To the Countess of Mar

Cavendish-Square, 1727

This is a vile world, dear sister, and I can easily comprehend, that whether one is at Paris or London, one is stifled with a certain mixture of fool and knave, that most people are composed of. I would have patience with a parcel of polite rogues, or your downright honest fools; but father Adam shines through his whole progeny. So much for our inside,—then our outward is so liable to ugliness and distempers, that we are perpetually plagued with feeling our own decays and seeing those of other people. Yet, sixpennyworth of common sense, divided among a whole nation, would make our lives roll away glibly enough; but then we make laws, and we follow customs. By the first we cut off our own pleasures, and by the second we are answerable for the faults and extravagances of others. All these things, and five hundred more, convince me (as I have the most profound veneration for the Author of nature) that we are here in an actual state of punishment; I am satisfied I have been one of *the condemned* ever since I was born; and in submission to the divine justice I don't at all doubt but I deserved it in some pre-existent state. I will still hope that I am only in purgatory; and that after whining and grunting a certain number of years, I shall be translated to some more happy sphere, where virtue will be natural, and custom reasonable; that is, in short, where common sense will reign. I grow very devout, as you see, and place all my hopes in the next life, being totally persuaded of the nothingness of this. Don't you remember how miserable we were in the little parlour at Thoresby? we then thought marrying would put us at once into possession of all we wanted. Then came being with child, etc., and you see what comes of being with child. Though, after all, I am still of my opinion, that it is extremely silly to submit to ill fortune. One should pluck a spirit, and live upon cordials when one can have no other nourishment. These are my present endeavours, and I run about, though I have five thousand pins and needles running into my heart. I try to console myself with a small damsel, who is at present every thing I like—but, alas! she is yet in a white frock. At fourteen, she may run away with the butler:—there's one of the blessed consequences of great disappointments; you are not only hurt by the thing present, but it cuts off all future hopes, and makes your very expectations melancholy. *Quelle vie!!!*

M. W. M.

wwwwwwwwwwwwwwwwwwwwwwwwwwwwwwwwwwwwwwwwwwwwwwwwwwwwwwwwwwwwwwwwwwwwwwwwwwww

To the Countess of Bute

Sept. 30, 1757.

My dear Child,—Lord Bute has been so obliging as to let me know your safe delivery, and the birth of another daughter; may she be as meritorious in your eyes as you are in mine! I can wish nothing better to you both, though I have some reproaches to make you. Daughter! daughter! don't call names; you are always abusing my pleasures, which is what no mortal will bear. Trash, lumber, sad stuff, are the titles you give to my favourite amusement. If I called a white staff a stick of wood, a gold key gilded brass, and the ensigns of illustrious orders coloured strings, this may be philosophically true, but would be very ill received. We have all our playthings: happy are they that can be contented with those they can obtain: those hours are spent in the wisest manner, that can easiest shade the ills of life, and are least productive of ill consequences. I think my time better employed in reading the adventures of imaginary people, than the Duchess of Marlborough's, who passed the latter years of her life in padding with her will, and contriving schemes of plaguing some, and extracting praise from others, to no purpose; eternally disappointed, and eternally fretting. The active scenes are over at my age. I indulge, with all the art I can, my taste for reading. If I would confine it to valuable books, they are almost as rare as valuable men. I must be content with what I can find. As I approach a second childhood, I endeavour to enter into the pleasures of it. Your youngest son is, perhaps, at this very moment riding on a poker with great delight, not at all regretting that it is not a gold one, and much less wishing it an Arabian horse, which he would not know how to manage. I am reading an idle tale, not expecting wit or truth in it, and am very glad it is not metaphysics to puzzle my judgment, or history to mislead my opinion. He fortifies his health by exercise; I calm my cares by oblivion. The methods may appear low to busy people; but, if he improves his strength, and I forget my infirmities, we attain very desirable ends. I shall be much pleased if you would send your letters in Mr. Pitt's packet.

I have not heard from your father of a long time. I hope he is well, because you do not mention him.

I am ever, dear child, your most affectionate mother.

My compliments to Lord Bute, and blessing to all yours.

To Miss Anne Wortley

August 21 1709

I am infinitely obliged to you, my dear Mrs. Wortley, for the wit, beauty, and other fine qualities, you so generously bestow upon me. Next to receiving them from Heaven, you are the person from whom I would chuse to receive gifts and graces: I am very well satisfied to owe them to your own delicacy of imagination, which represents to you the idea of a fine lady, and you have good nature enough to fancy I am she. All this is mighty well, but you do not stop there; imagination is boundless. After giving me imaginary wit and beauty, you give me imaginary passions, and you tell me I'm in love: if I am, 'tis a perfect sin of ignorance, for I don't so much as know the man's name: I have been studying these three hours, and cannot guess who you mean. I passed the days of Nottingham races, [at] Thoresby, without seeing or even wishing to see one of the sex. Now, if I am in love, I have very hard fortune to conceal it so industriously from my own knowledge, and yet discover it so much to other people. 'Tis against all form to have such a passion as that, without giving one sigh for the matter. Pray tell me the name of him I love, that I may (according to the laudable cus-tom of lovers) sigh to the woods and groves hereabouts, and teach it to the echo. You see, being I am in love, I am willing to be so in order and rule; I have been turning over God knows how many books to look for precedents.

Recommend an example to me; and, above all, let me know whether 'tis most proper to walk in the woods, encreasing the winds with my sighs, or to sit by a purling stream, swelling the rivulet with my tears; may be, both may do well in their turns:—but to be a minute serious, what do you mean by this reproach of inconstancy? I confess you give me several good qualities I have not, and I am ready to thank you for them, but then you must not take away those few I have. No, I will never exchange them; take back the beauty and wit you bestow upon me, leave me my own mediocrity of agreeableness and genius, but leave me also my sincerity, my constancy, and my plain dealing; 'tis all I have to recommend me to the esteem either of others or my-self. How should I despise myself if I could think I was capable of either inconstancy or deceit! I know not how I may appear to other people, nor how much my face may belie my heart, but I know that I never was or can be guilty of dissimulation or inconstancy—you will think this vain, but 'tis all that I pique myself upon. Tell me you be-lieve me and repent of your harsh censure. Tell it me in pity to my uneasiness, for you are one of those few people about whose good opinion I am in pain. I have always took so little care to please the generality of the world, that I am never mortified or delighted by its reports, which is a piece of stoicism born with me; but I cannot be one minute easy while you think ill of

Your faithful.

This letter is a good deal grave, and, like other grave things, dull; but I won't ask pardon for what I can't help.

SAMUEL JOHNSON AND MRS. PIOZZI

Letters on Mrs. Thrale's marriage to Piozzi

MRS. PIOZZI TO DR. JOHNSON

Bath, June 30 [1784]

My dear Sir,

The enclosed is a circular letter which I have sent to all the guardians, but our friendship demands somewhat more; it requires that I should beg your pardon for concealing from you a connexion which you must have heard of by many, but I suppose never believed. Indeed, my dear Sir, it was concealed only to save us both needless pain; I could not have borne to reject that counsel it would have killed me to take, and I only tell it you now because all is irrevocably settled, and out of your power to prevent. I will say, however, that the dread of your disapprobation has given me some anxious moments, and though, perhaps, I am become by many privations the most independent woman in the world, I feel as if acting without a parent's consent till you write kindly to

Your faithful servant.

CIRCULAR

Sir,

As one of the executors of Mr. Thrale's will and guardian to his daughters, I think it my duty to acquaint you that the three eldest left Bath last Friday for their own house at Brighthelmstone in company with an amiable friend, Miss Nicholson, who has sometimes resided with us here, and in whose society they may, I think, find some advantages and certainly no disgrace. I waited on them to Salisbury, Wilton, &c., and offered to attend them to the seaside myself, but they preferred this lady's company to mine, having heard that Mr. Piozzi is coming back from Italy, and judging perhaps by our past friendship and continued correspondence that his return would be succeeded by our marriage.

I have the honor to be, Sir, your obedient servant.

DR. JOHNSON TO MRS. PIOZZI

Madam,

If I interpret your letter right, you are ignominiously married; if it is yet undone, let us once more talk together. If you have abandoned your children and your religion, God forgive your wickedness: If you have forfeited your fame and your country, may your folly do no further mischief. If the last act is yet to do, I have loved you, esteemed you, reverenced you, and served you, I who long thought you the first of mankind, entreat that, before your fate is irrevocable, I may once more see you. I was, I once was,

Madam, most truly yours,
Sam. Johnson.

I will come down, if you permit it.

MRS. PIOZZI TO DR. JOHNSON

Sir,

I have this morning received from you so rough a letter in reply to one which was both tenderly and respectfully written, that I am forced to desire the conclusion of a correspondence which I can bear to continue no longer. The birth of my second husband is not meaner than that of my first; his sentiments are not meaner; his profession is not meaner, and his superiority in what he professes acknowledged by all mankind. It is want of fortune then that is ignominious; the character of the man I have chosen has no other claim to such an epithet. The religion to which he has always been a zealous adherent will, I hope, teach him to forgive insults he has not deserved; mine will, I hope, enable me to bear them at once with dignity and patience. To hear that I have forfeited my fame is indeed the greatest insult I ever yet received. My fame is as unsullied as snow, or I should think it unworthy of him who is henceforth to protect it.

I write by the coach the more speedily and effectually to prevent your coming hither. Perhaps by my fame (and I hope it is so) you mean only that celebrity which is a consideration of a much lower kind. I care for that only as it may give pleasure to my husband and his friends.

Farewell, dear Sir, and accept my best wishes. You have always commanded my esteem, and long enjoyed the fruits of a friendship never infringed by one harsh expression on my part during twenty years of familiar talk. Never did I oppose your will, or control your wish; nor can your unmerited severity itself lessen my regard; but till you have changed your opinion of Mr. Piozzi let us converse no more. God bless you.

DR. JOHNSON TO MRS. PIOZZI

Dear Madam,

What you have done, however I may lament it, I have no pretence to resent, as it has not been injurious to me: I therefore breathe out one sigh more of tenderness, perhaps useless, but at least sincere.

I wish that God may grant you every blessing, that you may be happy in this world for its short continuance, and eternally happy in a better state; and whatever I can contribute to your happiness I am very ready to repay, for that kindness which soothed twenty years of a life radically wretched.

Do not think slightly of the advice which I now presume to offer. Prevail upon Mr. Piozzi to settle in England: you may live here with more dignity than in Italy, and with more security: your rank will be higher, and your fortune more under your own eye. I desire not to detail all my reasons, but every argument of prudence and interest is for England, and only some phantoms of imagination seduce you to Italy.

I am afraid, however, that my counsel is vain, yet I have eased my heart by giving it.

When Queen Mary took the resolution of sheltering herself in England, the Archbishop of St. Andrew's, attempting to dissuade her, attended on her journey; and when they came to the irremeable stream that separated the two kingdoms, walked by her side into the water, in the middle of which he seized her bridle, and with earnestness proportioned to her danger and his own affection pressed her to return. The Queen went forward—If the parallel reaches thus far, may it go no further. The tears stand in my eyes.

I am going into Derbyshire, and hope to be followed by your good wishes, for I am, with great affection,

Your, etc.,
Sam. Johnson.

THOMAS GRAY

wwwwwwwwwwwwwwwwwwwwwwwwwwwwwwwwwwwwwwwwwwwwwwwwwwwwwwwwwwwwwwwwwwwwwwwwwwww

To West

Peterhouse, December, 1736

You must know that I do not take degrees, and, after this term, shall have nothing more of college impertinencies to undergo, which I trust will be some pleasure to you, as it is a great one to me. I have endured lectures daily and hourly since I came last, supported by the hopes of being shortly at full liberty to give myself up to my friends and classical companions, who, poor souls! though I see them fallen into great contempt with most people here, yet I cannot help sticking to them, and out of a spirit of obstinacy (I think) love them the better for it; and indeed, what can I do else? Must I plunge into metaphysics? Alas, I cannot see in the dark; nature has not furnished me with the optics of a cat. Must I pore upon mathematics? Alas, I cannot see in too much light; I am no eagle. It is very possible that two and two make four, but I would not give four farthings to demonstrate this ever so clearly; and if these be the profits of life, give me the amusements of it. The people I behold all around me, it seems, know all this and more, and yet I do not know one of them who inspires me with any ambition of being like him. Surely it was of this place, now Cambridge, but formerly known by the name of Babylon, that the prophet spoke when he said, 'the wild beasts of the desert shall dwell there, and their houses shall be full of doleful creatures, and owls shall build there, and satyrs shall dance there; their forts and towers shall be a den for ever, a joy of wild asses; there shall the great owl make her nest, and lay and hatch and gather under her shadow; it shall be a court of dragons; the screech owl also shall rest there, and find for herself a place or rest'. You see here is a pretty collection of desolate animals, which is verified in this town to a tittle, and perhaps it may also allude to your habitation, for you know all types may be taken by abundance of handles; however, I defy your owls to match mine.

If the default of your spirits and nerves be nothing but the effect of the hyp, I have no more to say. We all must submit to that wayward Queen; I too in no small degree own her sway,

I feel her influence while I speak her power. But if it be a real distemper, pray take more care of your health, if not for your own at least for our sakes, and do not be so soon weary of this little world: I do not know what refined friendships you may have contracted in the other, but pray do not be in a hurry to see your acquaintance above; among your terrestrial familiars, however, though I say it that should not say it, there positively is not one that has a greater esteem for you than Yours most sincerely, &c.

DAVID GARRICK

To Mr. Hogarth

Our friend Wilson hinted to me that the last time I saw him, that I had of late been remiss in my visits to you—it may be so, though upon my word I am not conscious of it; for such ceremonies I look upon as mere counters, where there is no remission of regard and good wishes. As Wilson is not an accurate observer of things, not even of those which concern him most, I must imagine that the hint came from you, and therefore, I shall say a word or two to you upon it.

Montaigne, who was a good judge of human nature, takes notice that when friends grow exact and ceremonious, it is a certain sign of coolness, for that the spirit of friendship keeps no account of trifles. We are, I hope, a strong exception to this rule. Poor Draper, whom I loved better than any man breathing, once asked me smiling,—'How long is it, think you, since you were at my house?'—'How long?—Why a month, or six weeks.'—'A year and five days', replied he; 'but don't imagine that I have kept an account; my wife told me so this morning, and bid *me scold you for it*'. If Mrs. Hogarth has observed my neglect, I am flattered by it; but if it is your observation, woe betide you! Could I follow my own wishes, I would see you every day in the week, and not care whether it was in Leicester-fields or Southampton-street; but what with an indifferent state of health, and the care of a large family

[Drury Lane Theatre], in which there are many froward children, I have scarce half an hour to myself.

However, since you are grown a polite devil, and have a mind to play at lords and ladies, have at you.

I will certainly call upon you soon, and if you should not be at home, I will leave my card.

HORACE WALPOLE

To the Countess of Ossory

Jan. 15, 1797

My dear Madam,

You distress me infinitely by showing my idle notes, which I cannot conceive can amuse anybody. My old-fashioned breeding impels me every now and then to reply to the letters you honour me with writing, but in truth very unwillingly, for I seldom can have anything particular to say; I scarce go out of my own house, and then only to two or three very private places, where I see nobody that really knows anything, and what I learn comes from Newspapers, that collect intelligence from coffee-houses, consequently what I neither believe nor report. At home I see only a few charitable elders, except about four-score nephews and nieces of various ages, who are each brought to me about once a-year, to stare at me as the Methusalem of the family, and they can only speak of their own contemporaries, which interest me no more than if they talked of their dolls, or bats and balls. Must not the result of all this, Madam, make me a very entertaining correspondent? And can such letters be worth showing? or can I have any spirit when so old and reduced to dictate?

Oh! my good Madam, dispense with me from such a task, and think how it must add to it to apprehend such letters being shown. Pray send me no more such laurels, which I desire no more than their leaves when decked with a scrap of tinsel and stuck on twelfth-cakes that lie on the shop-boards of pastry-cooks at Christmas. I shall be quite content with a sprig of rosemary thrown after me, when the parson of the parish commits my dust to dust. Till then, pray, Madam, accept the resignation of your

Ancient servant,
Orford.

MRS. ELIZABETH MONTAGU

To Leonard Smelt

Sandleford, October ye 28 [1776]

From a gay Parisian Dame visiting the Beau Monde, and conversing with the Beaux Esprits of the Academies, I am at once metamorphosed into a plain Country Farmeress. I have the same love for my pigs, pride in my potatoes, solicitude for my Poultry, care of my wheat, attention to my barley, and application to the regulation of the dairy as formerly. My fable is that of Dame Baucis inverted. I believe my friends at Paris would be amazed and scandalized at the joy I feel in this way of life, for they have not any taste of rural pleasures. A French Lady told me, she thought the English Women not so happy as the French; I smiled, and said I was not sure of that. She gave it as one reason, that they were obliged to spend part of the year in the Country. I combated her opinion, but found it was impossible to make her comprehend the pleasures of a morning or evening walk, the delight of animating the industry, or relieving the little wants of a district; or the dignity of that independence which we all feel in retirement. The business of the toilette, the amusement of les spectacles, and the pleasures of conversation engross their whole attention; in the first and the latter of these they show skill and taste; as to their Spectacles I cannot commend them. Their Theatres, except the Opera, are mean, dirty, and dark. Their bombast Tragedies are so extravagantly acted, it is hardly possible not to laugh, but Punch is as like to a grave Magistrate as their Actors to a real Hero. Moliere is out of fashion, they have pretty comick pieces which are tolerably acted. The Dancers and scenery at the Opera are fine, but the musick bad, and the singers scream most insufferably. As the French Ladies dine at ½ after two they have a long afternoon, and the spectacles are necessary to amuse the hours between dinner and supper. To me the most interesting object was the French themselves, and their conversation much the most agreeable thing I found at Paris, so that I went seldom to the Plays.

I am glad that your sentiments so perfectly confirm mine upon Voltaire's letter. Your observation on his translating for the use of the Queen and Mesdames of France what should not have been translated at all is very just. Voltaire views Shakespear at the summit of Parnassus with the same malice with which Satan beheld Adam in the midst of Paradise; I dare say Mons' Satan was very witty on our general Parents' unsophisticated state and unadorned condition, but oh Messieurs Satan and Voltaire! know that in a state of innocence and simplicity, nakedness is not a sign of impudence, nor either the Child or the Parent of wantoness. It is the evil of our disposition that renders the guard of caution necessary.

FANNY BURNEY

From her *Diary*

London, August [1778]. I have now to write an account of the most consequential day I have spent since my birth; namely, my Streatham visit.

Our journey to Streatham was the least pleasant part of the day, for the roads were dreadfully dusty, and I was really in the fidgets from thinking what my reception might be, and from fearing they would expect a less awkward and backward kind of person than I was sure they would find.

Mr. Thrale's house is white, and very pleasantly situated, in a fine paddock. Mrs. Thrale was strolling about, and came to us as we got out of the chaise.

She then received me, taking both my hands, and with mixed politeness and cordiality welcoming me to Streatham. She led me into

the house, and addressed herself almost wholly for a few minutes to
my father, as if to give me an assurance she did not mean to regard
me as a show, or to distress or frighten me by drawing me out. Afterwards she took me upstairs, and showed me the house, and said she
had very much wished to see me at Streatham, and should always
think herself much obliged to Dr. Burney for his goodness in bringing
me, which she looked upon as a very great favour. . . .

When we were summoned to dinner, Mrs. Thrale made my father
and me sit on each side of her. I said that I hoped I did not take Dr.
Johnson's place—for he had not yet appeared.

'No,' answered Mrs. Thrale, 'he will sit by you, which I am sure
will give him great pleasure.'

Soon after we were seated, this great man entered. I have so true
a veneration for him, that the very sight of him inspires me with delight
and reverence, notwithstanding the cruel infirmities to which he is
subject; for he has almost perpetual convulsive movements, either of
his hands, lips, feet, or knees, and sometimes all together.

Mrs. Thrale introduced me to him, and he took his place. We had
a noble dinner, and a most elegant dessert. Dr. Johnson, in the middle
of the dinner, asked Mrs. Thrale what was in some little pies that were
near him.

'Mutton,' answered she, 'so I don't ask you to eat any, because I
know you despise it.'

'No, madam, no,' cried he; 'I despise nothing that is good of its
sort; but I am too proud now to eat of it. Sitting by Miss Burney makes
me very proud to-day.'

'Miss Burney,' said Mrs. Thrale, laughing, 'you must take great
care of your heart if Dr. Johnson attacks it; for I assure you he is not
often successless.'

'What's that you say, madam?' cried he; 'are you making mischief
between the young lady and me already?'

A little while after he drank Miss Thrale's health and mine, and
then added:

' 'Tis a terrible thing that we cannot wish young ladies well without wishing them to become old women.'

'But some people,' said Mr. Seward, 'are old and young at the
same time, for they wear so well that they never look old.'

'No, sir, no,' cried the doctor, laughing; 'that never yet was; you
might as well say they are at the same time tall and short. I remember
an epitaph to that purpose, which is in——'

(I have quite forgot what—and also the name it was made upon, but the rest I recollect exactly:)

> '—— lies buried here;
> So early wise, so lasting fair,
> That none, unless her years you told,
> Thought her a child, or thought her old.'

Mrs. Thrale then repeated some lines in French, and Dr. Johnson some more in Latin. An epilogue of Mr. Garrick's to *Bonduca* was then mentioned, and Dr. Johnson said it was a miserable performance, and everybody agreed it was the worst he had ever made.

'And yet,' said Mr. Seward, 'It has been very much admired; but it is in praise of English valour, and so I suppose the subject made it popular.'

'I don't know, sir, said Dr. Johnson, 'anything about the subject, for I could not read on till I came to it; I got through half a dozen lines, but I could observe no other subject than eternal dullness. I don't know what is the matter with David; I am afraid he is grown superannuated, for his prologues and epilogues used to be incomparable.'

'Nothing is so fatiguing,' said Mrs. Thrale, 'as the life of a wit; he and Wilkes are the two oldest men of their ages I know, for they have both worn themselves out by being eternally on the rack to give entertainment to others.'

'David, madam,' said the doctor, 'looks much older than he is; for his face has had double the business of any other man's; it is never at rest; when he speaks one minute, he has quite a different countenance to what he assumes the next; I don't believe he ever kept the same look for half an hour together in the whole course of his life; and such an eternal, restless, fatiguing play of the muscles must certainly wear out a man's face before its real time.'

'Oh, yes,' cried Mrs. Thrale; 'we must certainly make some allowance for such wear and tear of a man's face.'

We left Streatham at about eight o'clock, and Mr. Seward, who handed me into the chaise, added his interest to the rest, that my father would not fail to bring me again next week to stay with them for some time. In short, I was loaded with civilities from them all. And my ride home was equally happy with the rest of the day, for my kind and most beloved father was so happy in *my* happiness, and congratulated me so sweetly, that he could, like myself, think on no other subject.

SIR WALTER SCOTT

~~~~~~

From his *Journal*

[*Abbotsford,*] *May 16 [1826]*—She died at nine in the morning, after being very ill for two days,—easy at last. . . . For myself, I scarce know how I feel, sometimes as firm as the Bass Rock, sometimes as weak as the wave that breaks on it.

I am as alert at thinking and deciding as I ever was in my life. Yet, when I contrast what this place now is, with what it has been not long since, I think my heart will break. Lonely, aged, deprived of my family—all but poor Anne, an impoverished and embarrassed man, I am deprived of the sharer of my thoughts and counsels, who could always talk down my sense of the calamitous apprehensions which break the heart that must bear them alone. Even her foibles were of service to me, by giving me things to think of beyond my weary self-reflections.

I have seen her. The figure I beheld is, and is not, my Charlotte—my thirty years' companion. There is the same symmetry of form, though those limbs are rigid which were once so gracefully elastic—but that yellow masque, with pinched features, which seems to mock life rather than emulate it, can it be the face that was once so full of lively expression? I will not look on it again. Anne thinks her little changed, because the latest idea she had formed of her mother is as she appeared under circumstances of sickness and pain. Mine go back to a period of comparative health. If I write long in this way, I shall write down my resolution, which I should rather write up, if I could. I wonder how I shall do with the large portion of thoughts which were hers for thirty years. I suspect they will be hers yet for a long time at least. But I will not blaze cambric and crape in the public eye like a disconsolate widower, that most affected of all characters. . . .

May 18.—Another day, and a bright one to the external world, again opens on us; the air soft, and the flowers smiling, and the leaves glittering. They cannot refresh her to whom mild weather was a natural enjoyment. Cerements of lead and of wood already hold her; cold earth must have her soon. But it is not my Charlotte, it is not the bride of my youth, the mother of my children, that will be laid among the ruins of Dryburgh, which we have so often visited in gaiety and pastime. No, no. She is sentient and conscious of my emotions some-where—somehow; *where* we cannot tell; *how* we cannot tell; yet would I not at this moment renounce the mysterious yet certain hope that I shall see her in a better world, for all that this world can give me. The necessity of this separation,—that necessity which rendered it even a relief,—that and patience must be my comfort. I do not experi-ence those paroxysms of grief which others do on the same occasion. I can exert myself and speak even cheerfully with the poor girls. But alone, or if anything touches me—the choking sensation. I have been to her room: there was no voice in it—no stirring; the pressure of the coffin was visible on the bed, but it had been removed elsewhere; all was neat as she loved it, but all was calm—calm as death. I remembered the last sight of her; she raised herself in bed, and tried to turn her eyes after me, and said, with a sort of smile, "You all have such melancholy faces." They were the last words I ever heard her utter, and I hurried away, for she did not seem quite conscious of what she said. When I returned, immediately [before] departing, she was in a deep sleep. It is deeper now. This was but seven days since.

They are arranging the chamber of death; that which was long the apartment of connubial happiness, and of whose arrangements (better than in richer houses) she was so proud. They are treading fast and thick. For weeks you could have heard a foot-fall. Oh, my God! . . .

May 21. . . . I wish to-morrow were over; not that I fear it, for my nerves are pretty good, but it will be a day of many recollections. . . .

May 23. . . . The whole scene floats as a sort of dream before me—the beautiful day, the grey ruins covered and hidden among clouds of foliage and flourish, where the grave, even in the lap of beauty, lay lurking and gaped for its prey. Then the grave looks, the hasty im-portant bustle of men with spades and mattocks—the train of carriages—the coffin containing the creature that was so long the dearest on earth to me, and whom I was to consign to the very spot which in pleasure-parties we so frequently visited. It seems still as if this could not be really so. But it is so—and duty to God and to my children must teach me patience. . . .

May 26. . . . Dull, drooping, cheerless has the day been. I cared not to carry my own gloom to the girls, and so sate in my own room, dawdling with old papers, which awakened as many stings as if they had been the nest of fifty scorpions. Then the solitude seemed so absolute—my poor Charlotte would have been in the room half-a-score of times to see if the fire burned, and to ask a hundred kind questions. Well, that is over—and if it cannot be forgotten, must be remembered with patience. . . .

June 11.—Bad dreams about poor Charlotte. Woke, thinking my old and inseparable friend beside me; and it was only when I was fully awake that I could persuade myself that she was dark, low, and distant, and that my bed was widowed. I believe the phenomena of dreaming are in a great measure occasioned by the *double touch*, which takes place when one hand is crossed in sleep upon another. Each gives and receives the impression of touch to and from the other, and this complicated sensation our sleeping fancy ascribes to the agency of another being, when it is in fact produced by our own limbs acting on each other. Well, here goes—*incumbite remis*.

DOROTHY WORDSWORTH

From her *Grasmere Journal*

[April] 15th, Thursday. . . . When we were in the woods beyond Gowbarrow Park we saw a few daffodils close to the water-side. We fancied that the lake had floated the seeds ashore, and that the little colony had so sprung up. But as we went along there were more and yet more; and at last, under the boughs of the trees, we saw that there was a long belt of them along the shore, about the breadth of a country turnpike road. I never saw daffodils so beautiful. They grew among the mossy stones about and about them; some rested their heads

upon these stones as on a pillow for weariness; and the rest tossed and reeled and danced, and seemed as if they verily laughed with the wind, that blew upon them over the lake; they looked so gay, ever glancing, ever changing. This wind blew directly over the lake to them. There was here and there a little knot, and a few stragglers a few yards higher up; but they were so few as not to disturb the simplicity, unity, and life of that one busy highway.

[*Friday*], *September 24th*. . . . On Monday, 4th October 1802, my brother William was married to Mary Hutchinson. I slept a good deal of the night, and rose fresh and well in the morning. At a little after 8 o'clock I saw them go down the avenue towards the church. William had parted from me upstairs. When they were absent my dear little Sara prepared the breakfast. I kept myself as quiet as I could, but when I saw the two men running up the walk, coming to tell us it was over, I could stand it no longer and threw myself on the bed, where I lay in stillness, neither hearing or seeing anything till Sara came upstairs to me, and said, "They are coming". This forced me from the bed where I lay, and I moved, I knew not how, straight forward, faster than my strength could carry me, till I met my beloved William, and fell upon his bosom. He and John Hutchinson led me to the house, and there I stayed to welcome my dear Mary. As soon as we had breakfasted, we departed. It rained when we set off. Poor Mary was much agitated, when she parted from her brothers and sisters, and her home. Nothing particular occurred till we reached Kirby. We had sunshine and showers, pleasant talk, love and chearfulness. We were obliged to stay two hours at K. while the horses were feeding. We wrote a few lines to Sara, and then walked out; the sun shone, and we went to the churchyard after we had put a letter into the postoffice for the *York Herald*. We sauntered about, and read the grave-stones. There was one to the memory of five children, who had all died within five years, and the longest lived had only lived four years. There was another stone erected to the memory of an unfortunate woman (as we supposed, by a stranger). The verses engraved upon it expressed that she had been neglected by her relations, and counselled the readers of those words to look within, and recollect their own frailties. We left Kirby at about half-past two. . . . Every foot of the road was, of itself, interesting to us, for we had travelled along it on foot, Wm. and I, when we went to fetch our dear Mary, and had sate upon the turf by the roadside more than once. Before we reached Helmsley, our driver told us that he could not take us any further, so we stopped at the same inn where we had slept before. My heart danced at the sight of its cleanly outside, bright yellow walls, casements overshadowed with jasmine, and its low, double gavel-ended front. We were not shown into the same parlour where Wm. and I were; it was a small room with a drawing over the chimney piece which the woman told us had been bought at a sale. Mary and I warmed ourselves at the kitchen fire. We then walked into the garden, and looked over a gate, up to the old ruin which stands at the top of a mount, and round about it the moats are grown up into soft green cradles, hollows surrounded with green grassy hillocks, and these are overshadowed by old trees, chiefly ashes. I prevailed upon William to go up with me to the ruins. We left Mary sitting by the kitchen fire. The sun shone, it was warm and very pleasant. One part of the castle seems to be inhabited. There was a man mowing nettles in the open space which had most likely once been the castle-court. There is one gateway exceedingly beautiful. Children were playing upon the sloping ground. We came home by the street. . . . We breakfasted next morning and set off at about ½-past 8 o'clock. It was a chearful, sunny morning. We soon turned out of Leeming Lane and passed a nice village with a beautiful church. . . . One of our horses seemed to grow a little restive as we went through the first village, a long village on the side of a hill. It grew worse and worse, and at last we durst not go on any longer. We walked a while, and then the post boy was obliged to take the horse out, and go back for another. We seated ourselves again snugly in the postchaise. . . .

Wm. fell asleep, lying upon my breast, and I upon Mary. I lay motionless for a long time, but I was at last obliged to move. I became very sick and continued so for some time after the boy brought the horse to us. Mary had been a little sick, but it soon went off. We had a sweet ride till we came to a publick-house on the side of a hill, where we alighted and walked down to see the waterfalls. . . .

At our return to the inn, we found new horses and a new driver, and we went on nicely to Hawes, where we arrived before it was quite dark. Mary and I got tea and William had a partridge and mutton chops and tarts for his supper. Mary sate down with him. We also had a shilling's worth of negus, and Mary made me some broth, for all which supper we were only charged 2/-. I could not sit up long, I vomited and took the broth and then slept sweetly. We rose at six o'clock—a rainy morning. We had a good breakfast and then departed. . . . The afternoon was not chearful but it did not rain till we came near Winder--

mere. I am always glad to see Stavely; it is a place I dearly love to think of—the first mountain village that I came to with Wm. when we first began our pilgrimage together. Here we drank a bason of milk at a publick house, and here I washed my feet in the brook, and put on a pair of silk stockings by Wm.'s advice. . . . We sate in the rain at Wilcock's to change horses and arrived at Grasmere at about 6 o'clock on Wednesday evening, the 6th of October 1802. Molly was overjoyed to see us, for my part I cannot describe what I felt, and our dear Mary's feelings would I dare say not be easy to speak of. We went by candle light into the garden, and were astonished at the growth of the brooms, Portugal laurels, etc. etc. etc. The next day, Thursday, we unpacked the boxes. On Friday, 8th, we baked bread and Mary and I walked, first upon the hill-side, and then in John's Grove, then in view of Rydale, the first walk that I had taken with my sister.

ROBERT SOUTHEY

To Charlotte Brontë

. . . It is not my advice that you have asked as to the direction of your talents, but my opinion of them, and yet the opinion may be worth little, and the advice much. You evidently possess, and in no inconsiderable degree, what Wordsworth calls the "faculty of verse." I am not depreciating it when I say that in these times it is not rare. Many volumes of poems are now published every year without attracting public attention, any one of which, if it had appeared half a century ago, would have obtained a high reputation for its author. Whoever, therefore, is ambitious of distinction in this way ought to be prepared for disappointment.

But it is not with a view to distinction that you should cultivate this talent, if you consult your own happiness. I, who have made literature my profession, and devoted my life to it, and have never for a moment repented of the deliberate choice, think myself, nevertheless, bound in duty to caution every young man who applies as an aspirant to me for encouragement and advice against taking so perilous a course.

You will say that a woman has no need of such a caution; there can be no peril in it for her. In a certain sense this is true; but there is a danger of which I would, with all kindness and all earnestness, warn you. The day dreams in which you habitually indulge are likely to induce a distempered state of mind; and, in proportion as all the ordinary uses of the world seem to you flat and unprofitable, you will be unfitted for them without becoming fitted for anything else. Literature cannot be the business of a woman's life, and it ought not to be. The more she is engaged in her proper duties, the less leisure will she have for it, even as an accomplishment and a recreation. To those duties you have not yet been called, and when you are you will be less eager for celebrity. You will not seek in imagination for excitement, of which the vicissitudes of this life, and the anxieties from which you must not hope to be exempted, be your state what it may, will bring with them but too much.

But do not suppose that I disparage the gift which you possess, nor that I would discourage you from exercising it. I only exhort you so to think of it, and so to use it, as to render it conducive to your own permanent good. Write poetry for its own sake; not in a spirit of emulation, and not with a view to celebrity; the less you aim at that the more likely you will be to deserve and finally to obtain it. So written it is wholesome both for the heart and soul; it may be made the surest means, next to religion, of soothing the mind and elevating it. You may embody in it your best thoughts and your wisest feelings, and in so doing discipline and strengthen them.

Farewell, madam. It is not because I have forgotten that I was once young myself that I write to you in this strain, but because I remember it. You will neither doubt my sincerity nor my good-will; and however ill what has here been said may accord with your present views and temper, the longer you live the more reasonable it will appear to you. Though I may be an ungracious adviser, you will allow me, therefore, to subscribe myself, with the best wishes for your happiness here and hereafter, your friend,

Robert Southey

[Charlotte Brontë's reply to Southey's letter may be found on p. 319.]

CHARLES LAMB

wwwwwwwwwwwwwwwwwwwwwwwwwwwwwwwwwwwwwwwwwwwwwwwwwwwwwwwwwwwwwwwwwwwww

To S. T. Coleridge

March 9, 1822.

Dear C.,—It gives me great satisfaction to hear that the pig turned out
so well,*—they are interesting creatures at a certain age; what a pity
such buds should blow out into the maturity of rank bacon! You had
all some of the crackling—and brain sauce; did you remember to rub it
with butter, and gently dredge it a little, just before the crisis? Did the
eyes come away kindly, with no Oedipean avulsion? Was the crackling
the color of the ripe pomegranate? Had you no cursed complement of
boiled neck of mutton before it, to blunt the edge of delicate desire?
Did you flesh maiden teeth in it? Not that I sent the pig, or can form
the remotest guess what part Owen could play in the business. I never
knew him give anything away in my life. He would not begin with
strangers. I suspect the pig, after all, was meant for me; but at the
unlucky juncture of time being absent, the present somehow went
round to Highgate. To confess an honest truth, a pig is one of those
things I could never think of sending away. Teals, widgeons, snipes,
barn-door fowl, ducks, geese, . . . Welsh mutton, collars of brawn, stur-
geon, fresh or pickled, your potted char, Swiss cheeses, French pies,
early grapes, muscadines, I impart as freely unto my friends as to myself. They are but self-extended; but pardon me if I stop somewhere.
Where the fine feeling of benevolence giveth a higher smack than the
sensual rarity, there my friends (or any good man) may command me;
but pigs are pigs, and I myself therein am nearest to myself. Nay, I
should think it an affront, an undervaluing done to Nature, who bestowed such a boon upon me, if in a churlish mood I parted with the
precious gift. One of the bitterest pangs I ever felt of remorse was
when a child. My kind old aunt had strained her pocket-strings to bestow a sixpenny whole plum-cake upon me. In my way home through

---

* Someone had sent Coleridge a pig, and the gift was erroneously credited to
Lamb.

the Borough, I met a venerable old man, not a mendicant, but there-abouts,—a look-beggar, not a verbal petitionist; and in the coxcombry of taught-charity, I gave away the cake to him. I walked on a little in all the pride of an Evangelical peacock, when of a sudden my old aunt's kindness crossed me,—the sum it was to her; the pleasure she had a right to expect that I—not the old impostor—should take in eating her cake; the cursed ingratitude by which, under the color of a Christian virtue, I had frustrated her cherished purpose. I sobbed, wept, and took it to heart so grievously that I think I never suffered the like; and I was right. It was a piece of unfeeling hypocrisy, and proved a lesson to me ever after. The cake has long been masticated, consigned to dunghill with the ashes of that unseasonable pauper.

But when Providence, who is better to us all than our aunts, gives me a pig, remembering my temptation and my fall, I shall endeavor to act towards it more in the spirit of the donor's purpose.

Yours (short of pig) to command in everything,

C. L.

BENJAMIN ROBERT HAYDON

From his *Journals*

30th.—Last day but one of 1845. Well; I have not been perfect, but I have struggled to be so, and I have less vice to lament than any previous year since I was fourteen. The first step towards fitting the soul to stand before its Maker is a conviction of its unworthiness. . . .

31st.—. . . 'O God, not mine, but Thy will be done! Give me eyes and intellect, and energy and health, till the last gush of existence, and I'll bear up, and get through, under Thy blessing, my six works to illustrate the best government for mankind.

O Lord! let not this be presumption, but that just confidence inspired by Thee, O God! This year is closing rapidly. I almost hear the rush and roar of the mighty wave from eternity that will overwhelm it for ever! O Lord, accept my deep, deep gratitude for all Thy mercies this last year; and grant I may deserve a continuance of such mercies, and conclude by the end of 1846 two more great works of my series! Amen, Amen, Amen.' . . .

[January] 12th.—O God! bless the beginning, progression and conclusion of my taking my rooms for exhibition of my pictures this day. Amen.

Took my rooms: so the die is cast!

25th.—My birthday, sixty years old! O God! continue my eyes and faculties to the last hour of my existence. Bless me through my ensuing years. Grant I may live to accomplish my six great works, and leave my family in competence.

April 1st.—Hung up all my remaining drawings, and finally arranged the exhibition. My pictures looked well. God bless it with success!

4th.—It rained the whole day. Nobody came except Jerrold, Bowring, Fox Maule, and Hobhouse. Twenty-six years ago, the rain would not have prevented them. But now it is not so. However I do not despair. . . .

Omens of failure in this exhibition.

1st.—The cab-horse slipped on the wood, and tumbled.

2nd.—I let all the letters tumble for the private day, and to-day, in trying to put up Wordsworth, he tumbled, knocked down Lord Althorp, broke the frame, and played the devil.

After this what success can come?

Do I believe this, or don't I? Half inclined.

• • •

13th.—Easter Monday. . . .

They rush by thousands to see Tom Thumb. They push, they fight, they scream, they faint, they cry help and murder! and oh! and ah! They see my bills, my boards, my caravans, and don't read them. Their eyes are open, but their sense is shut. It is an insanity, a *rabies,* a madness, a furor, a dream.

I would not have believed it of the English people . . .

16th.—My situation is now of more extreme peril than even when I began Solomon, thirty-three years ago. Involved in debt, mortified by the little sympathy the public display towards my best pictures, with several private engagements yet to fulfil . . .

21st.—Tom Thumb had 12,000 people last week; B. R. Haydon, 133½ (the ½ a little girl). Exquisite taste of the English people! . . .

[May] 5th.—Came home in excruciating anxiety, not being able to raise the money for my rent for the Hall, and found a notice from a broker for a quarter's rent from Newton, my old landlord for twenty-two years. For a moment my brain was confused. I had paid him half; and, therefore, there was only £10 left. I went into the painting-room in great misery of mind. That so old a friend should have chosen such a moment to do such a thing is painful. After an hour's dulness, my mind suddenly fired up, with a new background for Alfred. I dashed at it, and at dinner it was enormously improved. I make a sketch to-morrow; then begin to finish with the Saxon noble.

6th.— . . . I came home with great pain of mind; yet would any man believe, as I waited in the lawyer's chambers, the whole background of Alfred flashed into my head? I dwelt on it, foresaw its effects, and came home in sorrow, delight, anxiety and anticipation. I set my palette with a disgust, and yet under irresistible impulse. In coming into the parlour, the cook, whose wages I had not been able to pay, handed me a card from a broker, saying he called for a quarter's rent from Mr. Newton. I felt my heart sink, my brain confused, as I foresaw ruin, misery and a prison! It was hoisting the standard!

This is temper. I went on with my palette in a giddy fidget. I brought it out, and looking at my great work rejoiced inwardly at the coming background. But my brain, harassed and confused, fell into a deep slumber, from which I did not awake for an hour. I awoke cold, the fire out; but I flew at my picture, and dashing about like an inspired devil by three had arranged and put in the alteration. . . .

14th.—This day forty-two years I left my native Plymouth for London and life. O God, bless me through the numerous anxieties of this day satisfactorily.

18th.—I closed my exhibition this day, and have lost £111, 8s. 10d.

No man can accuse me of showing less energy, less spirit, less genius, than I did twenty-six years ago. I have not decayed, but the people have been corrupted. I am the same, they are not; and I have suffered in consequence. . . .

19th.—Cleared out my exhibition. Removed Aristides and Themistocles, and all my drawings. Next to a victory is a skilful retreat; and I marched out before General Thumb, a beaten but not conquered exhibitor.

23rd.—Awoke at three, in very great agony of mind; and lay awake till long after five, affected by my position. Prayed God, as David did, and fell asleep happier, but still fearing. . . .

June 1st.—O God I begin this month, June, in fear and submission. Thy will, not mine, be done. Carry me through, in spite of all appearances and realities of danger, for Jesus Christ's sake; and enable me to keep my health in eyes and mind, and to bear up and get through my six great works in spite of all the difficulties, calamities or obstructions which ever afflicted humanity. . . .

Sunday, 14th.—O God! Let it not be presumption in calling for Thy blessing on my six works. Let no difficulty on earth stop or impede their progression for one moment.

15th.—Passed in great anxiety; finally painted the background in the sketch, after harassing about to no purpose in the heat.

16th.—I sat from two till five staring at my picture like an idiot. My brain pressed down by anxiety and anxious looks of my dear Mary and children, whom I was compelled to inform. I dined, after having raised money on all our silver, to keep us from want in case of accidents . . .

18th.—O God, bless me through the evils of this day. Great anxiety. My landlord, Newton, called. I said "I see a quarter's rent in thy face; but none from me." I appointed to-morrow night to see him, and lay before him every iota of my position.

"Good-hearted Newton!" I said, "don't put in an execution."

"Nothing of the sort," he replied, half hurt.

I sent the Duke, Wordsworth, dear Fred's and Mary's heads, to Miss Barrett to protect. I have the Duke's boots and hat and Lord Grey's coat, and some more heads.

20th.—O God, bless us all through the evils of this day. Amen.

21st.—Slept horribly. Prayed in sorrow, and got up in agitation.

22nd.—God forgive me. Amen.

Finis

of

B. R. HAYDON.

"Stretch me no longer on this rough world."—*Lear.*

End of Twenty-sixth Volume.

[This closing entry was made between half-past ten and a quarter to eleven o'clock, on the morning of Sunday the 22nd of June. Before eleven the hand that wrote it was stiff and cold in self-inflicted death.]

LORD BYRON

To the Countess of————

Albany, October 5, 1814.

Dear Lady ————,

Your recollection and invitation do me great honour; but I am going to be "married, and can't come." My intended is two hundred miles off, and the moment my business here is arranged, I must set out in a great hurry to be happy. Miss Milbanke is the good-natured person who has undertaken me, and, of course, I am very much in love, and as silly as all single gentlemen must be in that sentimental situation. I have been accepted these three weeks; but when the event will take place, I don't exactly know. It depends partly upon lawyers, who are never in a hurry. One can be sure of nothing; but, at present, there appears no other interruption to this intention, which seems as mutual as possible, and now no secret, though I did not tell first,—and all our relatives are congratulating away to right and left in the most fatiguing manner.

You perhaps know the lady. She is niece to Lady Melbourne, and cousin to Lady Cowper and others of your acquaintance, and has no fault, except being a great deal too good for me, and that I must pardon, if nobody else should. It might have been *two* years ago, and, if it had, would have saved me a world of trouble. She has employed the interval in refusing about half a dozen of my particular friends, (as she did me once, by the way,) and has taken me at last, for which I am very much obliged to her. I wish it was well over, for I do hate bustle, and there is no marrying without some;—and then, I must not marry in a black coat, they tell me, and I can't bear a blue one.

Pray forgive me for scribbling all this nonsense. You know I must be serious all the rest of my life, and this is a parting piece of buffoonery, which I write with tears in my eyes, expecting to be agitated. Believe me, most seriously and sincerely your obliged servant,

Byron.

To Lady Byron

Venice, March 5, 1817.

A letter from Mr. Hanson apprizes me of the result of his correspondence with Sir Ralph Noel (of which he has transmitted a copy), and of his interviews with Dr. Lushington on the subject of our daughter. I am also informed of a bill in Chancery filed against me last Spring by Sir Ralph Noel, of which this is the first intimation, and of the subject of which I am ignorant.

Whatever may be the result of these discussions and the measures, which have led to them, and to which they may lead, remember, that

I have not been the first to begin; but, being begun, neither shall I be the first to recede. I feel at length convinced that the feeling which I had cherished through all and in spite of all, namely—the hope of a reconciliation and reunion, however remote,—is indubitably useless; and although, all things considered, it could not be very sanguine, still it was sincere, and I cherished it as a sickly infatuation: and now I part with it with a regret, perhaps bitterer [than] that which I felt in parting with yourself.

It was generally understood, if not expressed, that all legal proceedings were to terminate in the act of our separation: to what then I am to attribute the bill, of which I am apprized, I am at a loss to conjecture. The object, however, is evident: it is to deprive me of my paternal right over my child, which I have the less merited, as I neither abused nor intended to abuse it. You and yours might have been satisfied with the outrages I have already suffered, if not by your design, at least by your means. I know your defence and your apology—duty and Justice; but *Qui n'est que juste, est dur:* or if the French aphorism should seem light in the balance, I could refer you to an older language and a higher authority for the condemnation of conduct, which you may yet live to condemn in your own heart.

Throughout the whole of this unhappy business, I have done my best to avoid the bitterness, which, however, is yet amongst us; and it would be as well if even you at times recollected, that the man who has been sacrificed in fame, in feelings, in every thing, to the convenience of your family, was he whom you once loved, and who—whatever you may imagine to the contrary—loved you. If you conceive that I could be actuated by revenge against you, you are mistaken: I am not humble enough to be vindictive. Irritated I may have been, and may be—is it a wonder? but upon such irritation, beyond its momentary expression, I have not acted, from the hour that you quitted me to that in which I am made aware that our daughter is to be the entail of our disunion, the inheritor of our bitterness. If you think to reconcile yourself to yourself by accumulating harshness against me, you are again mistaken: you are not happy, nor even tranquil, nor will you ever be so, even to the very moderate degree which is permitted to general humanity. For myself, I have a confidence in my Fortune, which will yet bear me through. . . . The reverses, which have occurred, were what I should have expected; and, in considering you and yours merely as the instruments of my more recent adversity, it would be difficult for me to blame you, did not every thing appear to intimate a deliberate intention of as wilful malice on your part as could well be digested into a system. However, time and Nemesis will do that, which I would not, even were it in my power remote or immediate. You will smile at this piece of prophecy—do so, but recollect it: it is justified by all human experience. No one was ever even the involuntary cause of great evils to others, without a requital: I have paid and am paying for mine—so will you.

JOHN KEATS

To Fanny Brawne

Wednesday Morng.
[5 July? 1820]

My dearest Girl,

I have been a walk this morning with a book in my hand, but as usual I have been occupied with nothing but you I wish I could say in an agreeable manner. I am tormented day and night. They talk of my going to Italy. 'Tis certain I shall never recover if I am to be so long separate from you yet with all this devotion to you I cannot persuade myself into any confidence of you. Past experience connected with the fact of my long separation from you gives me agonies which are scarcely to be talked of. When your mother comes I shall be very sudden and expert in asking her whether you have been to Mrs Dilke's, for she might say no to make me easy. I am literally worn to death, which seems my only recourse. I cannot forget what has pass'd. What? nothing with a man of the world, but to me deathful. I will get rid of this as much as possible. When you were in the habit of flirting with Brown you would have left off, could your own heart have felt one half of one pang mine did. Brown is a good sort of Man—he did not know he was doing me to death by inches. I feel the effect of every one of those hours in my side now; and for that cause, though he has done me many services, though I know his love and friendship for me, though at this moment I should be without pence were it not for his assistance, I will never see or speak to him until we are both old men, if we are to be.

I *will* resent my heart having been made a football. You will call this madness. I have heard you say that it was not unpleasant to wait a few years—you have amusements—your mind is away—you have not brooded over one idea as I have, and how should you? You are to me an object intensely desireable—the air I breathe in a room empty of you is unhealthy. I am not the same to you—no—you can wait—you have a thousand activities—you can be happy without me. Any party, any thing to fill up the day has been enough. How have you pass'd this month? Who have you smil'd with? All this may seem savage in me. You do not feel as I do—you do not know what it is to love—one day you may—your time is not come. Ask yourself how many unhappy hours Keats has caused you in Loneliness. For myself I have been a Martyr the whole time, and for this reason I speak; the confession is forc'd from me by the torture. I appeal to you by the blood of that Christ you believe in: Do not write to me if you have done anything this month which it would have pained me to have seen. You may have altered—if you have not—if you still behave in dancing rooms and other societies as I have seen you—I do not want to live—if you have done so I wish this coming night may be my last. I cannot live without you, and not only you but *chaste you; virtuous you.* The Sun rises and sets, the day passes, and you follow the bent of your inclination to a certain extent—you have no conception of the quantity of miserable feeling that passes through me in a day.—Be serious! Love is not a plaything—and again do not write unless you can do it with a crystal conscience. I would sooner die for want of you than——

> *Yours for ever*
> *J. Keats.*

JANE WELSH CARLYLE

To John Welsh

Chelsea: July 18, 1843.

Dearest, dear only Uncle of me,—I would give a crown that you could see me at this moment through a powerful telescope! You would laugh for the next twelve hours. I am doing the rural after a fashion so entirely my own! To escape from the abominable paint-smell, and the infernal noise within doors, I have erected, with my own hands, a gipsy-tent in the garden, constructed with clothes lines, long poles, and an old brown floor cloth! under which remarkable shade I sit in an arm-chair at a small round table, with a hearth rug for carpet under my feet, writing-materials, sewing-materials, and a mind superior to Fate!

The only drawback to this retreat is its being exposed to 'the envy of surrounding nations'; so many heads peer out on me from all the windows of the Row, eager to penetrate my meaning! If I had a speak-ing trumpet I would address them once for all:—'Ladies and Gentle-men,—I am not here to enter my individual protest against the progress of civilisation! nor yet to mock you with an Arcadian felicity, which you have neither the taste nor the ingenuity to make your own! but simply to enjoy Nature according to ability, and to get out of the smell of new paint! So, pray you, leave me to pursue my innocent avocations in the modest seclusion which I covet!'

Not to represent my contrivance as too perfect, I must also tell you that a strong puff of wind is apt to blow down the poles, and then the whole tent falls down on my head! This has happened once already since I began to write, but an instant puts it all to rights again. Indeed, without counteracting the indoors influences by all lawful means, I could not stay here at present without injury to my health, which is at no time of the strongest. Our house has for a fortnight back been a house possessed by seven devils! a painter, two carpenters, a paper-hanger, two nondescript apprentice-lads, and 'a spy;' all playing the devil to the utmost of their powers: hurrying and scurrying 'upstairs, down stairs, and in my lady's chamber!' affording the liveliest image of a sacked city!

When they rush in at six of the morning, and spread themselves over the premises, I instantly jump out of bed, and 'in wera desperation' take a shower bath. Then such a long day to be virtuous in! I make chair and sofa covers; write letters to my friends; scold the work-people, and suggest improved methods of doing things. And when I go to bed at night I have to leave both windows of my room wide open (and plenty of ladders lying quite handy underneath), that I may not, as old Sterling predicted, 'awake dead' of the paint.

The first night that I lay down in this open state of things, I recol-lected Jeannie's house-breaker adventure last year, and, not wishing that all the thieves who might walk in at my open windows should take me quite unprepared, I laid my policeman's rattle and my dagger on the spare pillow, and then I went to sleep quite secure. But it is to be confidently expected that, in a week or more, things will begin to subside into their normal state; and meanwhile it were absurd to expect that any sort of revolution can be accomplished. There! the tent has been down on the top of me again, but it has only upset the ink.

Jeannie appears to be earthquaking with like energy in Maryland Street, but finds time to write me nice long letters nevertheless, and even to make the loveliest pin-cushion for my birthday; and my birthday was celebrated also with the arrival of a hamper, into which I have not yet penetrated. Accept kisses *ad infinitum* for your kind thought of me, dearest uncle. I hope to drink your health many times in the Madeira when I have Carlyle with me again to give an air of respectability to the act. Nay, on that evening when it came to hand, I was feeling so sad and dreary over the contrast between this Fourteenth of July—alone, in a house like a sacked city, and other Fourteenths that I can never forget, that I hesitated whether or no to get myself out a bottle of the Madeira there and then, and try for once in my life the hitherto unknown comfort of being dead drunk. But my sense of the respectable overcame the temptation.

My husband has now left his Welshman, and is gone for a little while to visit the Bishop of St. David's. Then he purposes crossing over somehow to Liverpool, and, after a brief benediction to Jeannie, passing into Annandale. He has suffered unutterable things in Wales from the want of any adequate supply of tea! For the rest, his visit appears to have been pretty successful; plenty of sea-bathing; plenty of riding on horseback, and of lying under trees! I wonder it never enters his head to lie under the walnut-tree here at home. It is a tree! leaves as green as any leaves can be, even in South Wales! but it were too easy to repose under that: if one had to travel a long journey by railway to it, then indeed it might be worth while!

But I have no more time for scribbling just now; besides, my pen is positively declining to act. So, God bless you, dear, and all of them.

Ever your affectionate
Jane Carlyle.

MARJORIE FLEMING

[Marjorie, not yet six years old, writes to her sister.]

Probably 1809.

My Dear Isa,—

I now sit down on my botom to answer all your kind and beloved letters which you was so so good as to write to me. This is the first time I ever wrote a letter in my Life.

There are a great number of Girls in the Square and they cry just like a pig when we are under the painfull necessity of putting it to Death.

Miss Potune a lady of my acquaintance, praises me dreadfully. I repeated something out of Deen Swift and she said I was fit for the stage, and you may think I was primmed up with majestick Pride, but upon my word I felt myselfe turn a little birsay—birsay is a word which is a word that William composed which is as you may suppose a little enraged. This horid fat Simpliton says that my Aunt is beautifull which is intirely impossible for that is not her nature.

ROBERT BROWNING

To Elizabeth Barrett

New Cross, Hatcham, Surrey.
[Post-mark, January 10, 1845.]

I love your verses with all my heart, dear Miss Barrett,—and this is no off-hand complimentary letter that I shall write,—whatever else, no prompt matter-of-course recognition of your genius, and there a graceful and natural end of the thing. Since the day last week when I first read your poems, I quite laugh to remember how I have been turning and turning again in my mind what I should be able to tell you of their effect upon me, for in the first flush of delight I thought I would this once get out of my habit of purely passive enjoyment, when I do really enjoy, and thoroughly justify my admiration—perhaps even, as a loyal fellow-craftsman should, try and find fault and do you some little good to be proud of hereafter!—but nothing comes of it all—so into me has it gone, and part of me has it become, this great living poetry of yours, not a flower of which but took root and grew—Oh, how different that is from lying to be dried and pressed flat, and prized highly, and put in a book with a proper account at top and bottom, and shut up and put away . . . and the book called a 'Flora,' besides! After all, I need not give up the thought of doing that, too, in time; because even now, talking with whoever is worthy, I can give a reason for my faith in one and another excellence, the fresh strange music, the affluent language, the exquisite pathos and true new brave thought; but in this addressing myself to you—your own self, and for the first time, my feeling rises altogether. I do, as I say, love these books with all my heart —and I love you too. Do you know I was once not very far from seeing— really seeing you? Mr. Kenyon said to me one morning 'Would you like to see Miss Barrett?' then he went to announce me,—then he returned . . . you were too unwell, and now it is years ago, and I feel as at some untoward passage in my travels, as if I had been close, so close, to some world's-wonder in chapel or crypt, only a screen to push and I might have entered, but there was some slight, so it now seems, slight and just sufficient bar to admission, and the half-opened door shut, and I went home my thousands of miles, and the sight was never to be?

Well, these Poems were to be, and this true thankful joy and pride with which I feel myself,

Yours ever faithfully,
Robert Browning.

CHARLOTTE BRONTË

To Robert Southey

March 16.

Sir,—I cannot rest till I have answered your letter, even though by addressing you a second time I should appear a little intrusive; but I must thank you for the kind and wise advice you have condescended to give me. I had not ventured to hope for such a reply; so considerate in its tone, so noble in its spirit. I must suppress what I feel, or you will think me foolishly enthusiastic.

At the first perusal of your letter I felt only shame and regret that I had ever ventured to trouble you with my crude rhapsody; I felt a painful heat rise to my face when I thought of the quires of paper I had covered with what once gave me so much delight, but which now was only a source of confusion; but after I had thought a little, and read it again and again, the prospect seemed to clear. You do not forbid me to write; you do not say that what I write is utterly destitute of merit. You only warn me against the folly of neglecting real duties for the sake of imaginative pleasures; of writing for the love of fame; for the selfish excitement of emulation. You kindly allow me to write poetry for its own sake, provided I leave undone nothing which I ought to do, in order to pursue that single, absorbing, exquisite gratification. I am afraid, sir, you think me very foolish. I know the first letter I wrote to you was all senseless trash from beginning to end; but I am not altogether the idle dreaming being it would seem to denote. My father is a clergyman of limited though competent income, and I am the eldest of his children. He expended quite as much in my education as he could afford in justice to the rest. I thought it therefore my duty, when I left school, to become a governess. In that capacity I find enough to occupy my thoughts all day long, and my head and hands too, without having a moment's time for one dream of the imagination. In the evenings, I confess, I do think, but I never trouble any one else with my thoughts. I carefully avoid any appearance of preoccupation and eccentricity, which might lead those I live amongst to suspect the nature of my pursuits. Following my father's advice—who from my childhood has counselled me, just in the wise and friendly tone of your letter—I have endeavoured not only attentively to observe all the duties a woman ought to fulfil, but to feel deeply interested in them. I don't always succeed, for sometimes when I'm teaching or sewing I would rather be reading or writing; but I try to deny myself; and my father's approbation amply rewarded me for the privation. Once more allow me to thank you with sincere gratitude. I trust I shall never more feel ambitious to see my name in print; if the wish should rise, I'll look at Southey's letter, and suppress it. It is honour enough for me that I have written to him, and received an answer. That letter is consecrated; no one shall ever see it but papa and my brother and sisters. Again I thank you. This incident, I suppose, will be renewed no more; if I live to be an old woman, I shall remember it thirty years hence as a bright dream. The signature which you suspected of being fictitious is my real name. Again, therefore, I must sign myself

C. Brontë

P. S.—Pray, sir, excuse me for writing to you a second time; I could not help writing, partly to tell you how thankful I am for your kindness, and partly to let you know that your advice shall not be wasted, however sorrowfully and reluctantly it may at first be followed.

C. B.

[Robert Southey's letter is to be found on p. 304.]

WALT WHITMAN

To his mother and to the newspapers

[*The following extracts are taken in part from Whitman's letters written from Washington, D. C. for publication in* The Brooklyn Eagle, *March 19, 1863, and* The New York Times, *December 11, 1864, and in part from private letters written to his mother on March 31 and August 18, 1863, March 29 and June 14, 1864.*]

... I go around, distributing myself and the contents of my pockets and haversack in infinitesimal quantities, with faith that nearly all of it will, somehow or other, fall on good ground. In many cases, where I find a soldier "dead broke" and pretty sick, I give half a tumbler of good jelly. I carry a good-sized jar to a ward, have it opened, get a spoon, and taking the head nurse in tow, I go around and distribute it to the most appropriate cases. To others I give an orange or an apple; to others some spiced fruits; to others a small quantity of pickles. Many want tobacco: I do not encourage any of the boys in its use, but where I find they crave it I supply them. I always carry some, cut up in small plugs, in my pocket. Then I have commissions: some New York or Connecticut, or other soldier, will be going home on sick leave, or perhaps discharged, and I must fit him out with good new undershirt, drawers, stockings, etc.

.   .   .

By these and like means one comes to be better acquainted with individual cases, and so learns every day peculiar and interesting character, and gets on intimate and soon affectionate terms with noble American young men; and now is where the real good begins to be done . . . I can testify that friendship has literally cured a fever, and the medicine of daily affection, a bad wound. . . .

As I write, I have lying before me a little discarded note-book, filled with memoranda of things wanted by the sick—special cases. I use up one of these little books in a week. See from this sample, for instance, after walking through a ward or two: Bed 53 wants some liquorice; Bed 6—erysipelas—bring some raspberry vinegar to make a cooling drink, with water; Bed 18 wants a good book—a romance; Bed 25—a manly, friendly young fellow . . . of the Twenty-seventh Connecticut, an independent young soul—refuses money and eatables, so I will bring him a pipe and tobacco, for I see he much enjoys a smoke; Bed 45—sore throat and cough—wants horehound candy; Bed 11, when I come again, don't forget to write a letter for him; etc. The wants are a long and varied list: some need to be humored and forgotten, others need to be especially remembered and obeyed. One poor German, dying—in the last stage of consumption—wished me to find him, in Washington, a German Lutheran clergyman, and send him to him; I did so. One patient will want nothing but a toothpick, another a comb, and so on. All whims are represented, and all the States. There are many New York State soldiers here; also Pennsylvanians. I find, of course, many from Massachusetts, Connecticut, and all the New England States, and from the Western and Northwestern States. Five sixths of the soldiers are young men.

.   .   .

He who goes among the soldiers with gifts, etc., must beware how he proceeds. It is much more of an art than one would imagine. They are not charity-patients, but American young men, of pride and independence. The spirit in which you treat them, and bestow your donations, is just as important as the gifts themselves; sometimes more so. Then there is continual discrimination necessary. Each case requires some peculiar adaptation to itself. It is very important to slight nobody—not a single case. Some hospital visitors, especially the women, pick out the handsomest looking soldiers, or have a few for their pets. Of course some will attract you more than others, and some will need more attention than others; but be careful not to ignore any patient. A word, a friendly turn of the eye or touch of the hand in passing, if nothing more.

. . .

One poor boy—this is a sample of one case out of the 600—he seemed to be quite young, he was quite small (I looked at his body afterwards), he groaned some as the stretcher bearers were carrying him along, and again as they carried him through the hospital gate. They set down the stretcher and examined him, and the poor boy was dead. They took him into the ward, and the doctor came immediately, but it was all of no use. The worst of it is, too, that he is entirely unknown—there was nothing on his clothes, or any one with him to identify him, and he is altogether unknown. Mother, it is enough to rack one's heart—such things. Very likely his folks will never know in the world what has become of him. Poor, poor child, for he appeared as though he could be but 18. I feel lately as though I must have some intermission. I feel well and hearty enough, and was never better, but my feelings are kept in a painful condition a great part of the time.

. . .

I *have* felt quite well of my deafness and cold in my head for four days or so, but it is back again bad as ever this morning.

. . .

It has been awful hot here now for twenty-one days; ain't that a spell of weather? The first two weeks I got along better than I would have thought, but the last week I have felt it more, have felt it in my head a little—I no more stir without my umbrella, in the day time, than I would without my boots. I am afraid of the sun affecting my head and move pretty cautious.

. . .

I am not feeling very well these days—the doctors have told me not to come inside the hospitals for the present. . . . It is probable that the hospital poison has affected my system, and I find it worse than I calculated. I have spells of faintness and very bad feeling in my head, fullness and pain—and besides sore throat. My boarding place, 502 Pennsylvania av., is a miserable place, very bad air. But I shall feel better soon, I know—the doctors say it will pass over—they have long told me I was going in too strong. . . .

JOHN RUSKIN

To Effie Gray

Denmark Hill
9 November 1847

My own Effie—my kind Effie—my mistress—my friend—my queen—my darling—my only love—how good of you—and I can't answer you a word today. I am going into town with my mother in half an hour—and have all manner of things to do, first—but I am so glad that you have my letter speaking about this very thing— Indeed I *never* will be jealous of you—and I will keep that purer form of jealousy—that longing for more love—within proper limits—and you will soon find out how to manage this weakness—and perhaps to conquer it altogether; I can't enter into details today—but indeed it was anxiety and weakness of nerve which made me so fretful when you were here—natural enough I think—and even then, I was only jealous of *some* people—and that because I was hurt by your *condescension*—it was, I think—at the root—more pride than jealousy—I was speaking of large parties to my mother yesterday for you—she said "You would'nt like to see her surrounded by a circle of gentlemen like Mrs. Liddell?" "Indeed I should," I said.

Denmark Hill
11 November 1847

My Dearest Euphemia,
What a pretty name you have—I like to write it full, sometimes, it puts me in mind of old times— Do you recollect the first time I ever called you "Effie"—when I was frightened at finding you practising in the cold drawing-room and stopped, and begged pardon—and your giving me leave an evening or two afterwards— What a luxury it was to call you Effie—and is— By the bye—you haven't told me anything about Captn. C.—and the happiness he looked forward to—Grant him *that*—but—I'm very sorry—I can't help it—don't be angry with me—I *would* rather he did'nt call you Effie any more! *please!* . . .

Folkestone
30 November 1847

My Beloved Effie

I never thought to have felt time pass slowly any more—but—foolish that I am, I cannot help congratulating myself on this being the last day of November— Foolish, I say—for what pleasure soever may be in store for us, we ought not to wish to lose the treasure of time—nor to squander away the heap of gold even though its height should keep us from seeing each other for a little while. But your letter of last night shook all the philosopher out of me. That little undress bit! Ah—my sweet Lady— What naughty thoughts had I.—Dare I say?—I was thinking—thinking, naughty—happy thought, that you would soon have—some one's arms to keep you from being cold! Pray don't be angry with me. How *could* I help it?—how can I? I'm thinking so just now, even. Oh—my dearest— I am not so "scornful" neither, of all that I hope for— Alas—I know not what I would not give for one glance of your fair eyes.—your fair—saucy eyes. You cruel, cruel girl—now that was *just* like you—to poor William at the Ball. I can see you at this moment—*hear* you. "*If* you wanted to dance with *me*, William! *If*!! You saucy—wicked—witching—malicious— merciless—mischief loving—torturing—martyrizing—unspeakably to be feared and fled—mountain nymph that you are— "If !" When you knew that he would have given a year of his life for a touch of your hand. Ah's me—what a world this is, when its best creatures and kindest—will do such things. What a sad world. Poor fellow,—How the lights of the ballroom would darken and its floor sink beneath him— Earthquake and eclipse at once. and to be "if'd" at by you, too; Now—I'll take up his injured cause—I'll punish you for that—Effie—some time—see if I don't— *If* I don't. It deserves—oh—I don't know what it doesn't deserve—nor what I can do. . . .

To Effie Gray's father

Chamonix
5 July 1849

Having heard the late correspondence between you and my father I think it well that you should know from myself my feelings respecting

Effie's illness as this knowledge may more straitly direct your influence over her. I have no fault to find with her; if I had it would not be to her father that I should complain: I am simply sorry for the suffering she has undergone and desirous that you should understand in what way your advice may prevent its recurrence. If she had not been seriously ill I *should* have had fault to find with her: but the state of her feelings I ascribe, now, simply to bodily weakness; that is to say—and this is a serious and distressing admission—to a nervous disease affecting the brain. . . . You know—better than I—what is likely now to benefit her—but I look forward with confidence to her restoration of health by simple physical means—and I am delighted to hear of the shower bath and the riding and the milk instead of tea—and the quiet. When I have her to manage again, I hope to do it better—and not to reason with—nor blame a physical weakness—which the course of time will, I doubt not, entirely cure. In all this, however, you will perceive that I look upon the thing as a purely medical question—not a moral one.

If Effie had in *sound mind* been annoyed by the contemptible trifles which have annoyed her: if she had cast back from her the kindness and affection with which my parents received her and refused to do her duty to them under any circumstances whatever but those of an illness bordering in many of its features on incipient insanity, I should not now have written you this letter respecting her. . . . I hope to see her outgrow with her girl's frocks that contemptible dread of interference and petulant resistance of authority which begins in pride and is nourished in folly and ends in pain. Restiveness I am accustomed to regard as unpromising character even in horses and asses.

EMILY DICKINSON

To Austin Dickinson

17 October 1851

We are waiting for breakfast, Austin, the meat and potato and a little pan of your favorite brown bread are keeping warm at the fire, while father goes for shavings.

While we were eating supper Mr Stephen Church rang the door bell very violently and offered to present us with *three barrels of shavings*. We are much overcome by this act of magnanimity and father has gone this morning to claim his proffered due. He wore a palm leaf hat, and his pantaloons tucked in his boots and I could'nt help thinking of *you* as he strode along by the window.

I dont think "negligé" quite becoming to so mighty a man. I had rather a jacket of green and your barndoor apparrel, than all the mock simplicity of a lawyer and a man. The breakfast is so warm and pussy is here a singing and the teakettle sings too as if to see which was loudest and I am so afraid lest kitty should be beaten—yet a *shadow* falls upon my morning picture—where is the youth so bold, the bravest of our fold, a seat is empty here—spectres sit in your chair and now and then nudge father with their long, bony elbows. I wish you were here dear Austin—the dust falls on the bureau in your deserted room and gay, frivolous spiders spin away in the corners. I dont go there after dark whenever I can help it, for the twilight seems to pause there and I am half afraid, and if ever I have to go, I hurry with all my might and never look behind me for I know who I should see.

Before next Tuesday—Oh before the coming stage will I not brighten and brush it, and open the long closed blinds, and with a sweeping broom will I not bring each spider down from its home so high and tell it it may come back again when master has gone—and oh I will bid it to be a tardy spider, to tarry on the way, and I will think my eye is fuller than sometimes, tho' *why* I cannot tell, when it shall rap on the window and come to live again. I am so happy when I know how soon you are coming that I put away my sewing and go out in the yard to think. I have tried to delay the frosts, I have coaxed the fading flowers, I thought I *could* detain a few of the crimson leaves until you had smiled upon them, but their companions call them and they cannot stay away—you will find the blue hills, Austin, with the autumnal shadows silently sleeping on them, and there will be a glory lingering round the day, so you'll know autumn has been here, and the *setting sun* will tell you, if you dont get home till evening. How glad I am you are well—you must try hard to be careful and not get sick again. I hope you will be better than ever you were in your life when you come home *this time*, for it never seemed so long since we have seen you. I thank you for such a long letter, and yet if I might choose, *the next* should be a longer. I think a letter just about *three days* long would make me happier than any other kind of one—if you please, dated at Boston, but thanks be to our Father, you may conclude it *here*. Everything has changed since my other letter—the doors are shut this morning, and all the kitchen wall is covered with chilly flies who are trying to warm themselves—poor things, they do not understand that there are no summer mornings remaining to them and me and they have a bewildered air which is really very droll, did'nt one feel *sorry* for them. You would say t'was a gloomy morning if you were sitting here—the frost has been severe and the few lingering leaves seem anxious to be going and wrap their faded cloaks more closely about them as if to shield them from the chilly northeast wind. The earth looks like some poor old lady who by dint of pains has bloomed e'en till *now,* yet in a forgetful moment a few silver hairs from out her cap come stealing, and she tucks them back so hastily and thinks nobody *sees.* The cows are going to pasture and little boys with their hands in their pockets are whistling to try to keep warm. Dont think that the sky will frown so the day when you come home! She will smile and look happy, and be full of sunshine *then* —and even *should* she frown upon her child returning, there is *another* sky ever serene and fair, and there is *another* sunshine, tho' it be darkness there—never mind faded forests, Austin, never mind silent fields— *here* is a little forest whose leaf is ever green, here is a *brighter* garden, where not a frost has been, in its unfading flowers I hear the bright bee hum, prithee, my Brother, into *my* garden come!

> *Your very aff*
> *Sister.*

LOUISA MAY ALCOTT

To her sister

[*1861?*]

My Lass:

This must be a frivolous and dressy letter, because you always want to know about our clothes, and we have been at it lately. May's bonnet is a sight for gods and men. Black and white outside, with a great cockade boiling over the front to meet a red ditto surging from the interior, where a red rainbow darts across the brow, and a surf of white lace foams up on each side. I expect to hear that you and John fell flat in the dust with horror on beholding it.

My bonnet has nearly been the death of me; for, thinking some angel might make it possible for me to go to the mountains, I felt a wish for a tidy hat, after wearing an old one till it fell in tatters from my brow. Mrs. P. promised a bit of gray silk, and I built on that; for when I went for it I found my hat was founded on sand; for she let me down with a crash, saying she wanted the silk herself, and kindly offering me a flannel petticoat instead. I was in woe for a spell, having one dollar in the world, and scorning debt even for that prop of life, a "bonnet". Then I roused myself, flew to Dodge, demanded her cheapest bonnet, found one for a dollar, took it, and went home wondering if the sky would open and drop me a trimming. I am simple in my tastes, but a naked straw bonnet is a little too severely chaste even for me. Sky did not open; so I went to the "Widow Cruise's oil bottle"—my ribbon box—which, by the way, is the eighth wonder of the world, for nothing is ever put in, yet I always find some old dud when all other hopes fail. From this salvation bin I extracted the remains of the old white ribbon (used up, as I thought, two years ago), and the bits of black lace that have adorned a long line of departed hats. Of the lace I made a dish, on which I thriftily served up bows of ribbon, like meat on toast. Inside put the lace bow, which adorns my form anywhere when needed. A white flower A. H. gave me sat airily on the brim,—fearfully unbecoming, but pretty in itself, and in keeping. Strings are yet to be evolved from chaos. I feel that they await me somewhere in the dim future. Green ones *pro tem.* hold this wonder of the age upon my gifted brow, and I survey my hat with respectful awe. I trust you will also, and see in it another great example of the power of mind over matter, and the convenience of a colossal brain in the primeval wrestle with the unruly atoms which have harassed the feminine soul ever since Eve clapped on a modest figleaf and did up her hair with a thorn for a hairpin.

I feel very moral today, having done a big wash alone, baked, swept the house, picked the hops, got dinner, and written a chapter in "Moods". May gets exhausted with work, though she walks six miles without a murmur.

It is dreadfully dull, and I work so that I may not "brood". Nothing stirring but the wind; nothing to see but dust; no one comes but rosebugs; so I grub and scold at the "A." because it takes a poor fellow's tales and keeps 'em years without paying for 'em. If I think of my woes

I fall into a vortex of debts, dishpans, and despondency awful to see. So I say, "every path has its puddle," and try to play gaily with the tadpoles in *my* puddle, while I wait for the Lord to give me a lift, or some gallant Raleigh to spread his velvet cloak and fetch me over dry shod.

L. W. adds to my woe by writing of the splendours of Gorham, and says, "When tired, run right up here and find rest among these everlasting hills." All very aggravating to a young woman with one dollar, no bonnet, half a gown, and a discontented mind. It's a mercy the mountains are everlasting, for it will be a century before *I* get there. Oh, me, such a life!

Now I've done my Jeremiad, and I will go on twanging my harp in the "willow tree".

You ask what I am writing. Well, two books half done, nine stories simmering, and stocks of fairy stories moulding on the shelf. I can't do much, as I have no time to get into a real good vortex. It unfits me for work, worries Ma to see me look pale, eat nothing, and ply by night. These extinguishers keep genius from burning as I could wish, and I give up ever hoping to do anything unless luck turns for your

Lu

LEWIS CARROLL

To Adelaide Paine

Christ Church, Oxford, March 8, 1880

My dear Ada—(Isn't that your short name? "Adelaide" is all very well, but you see when one is *dreadfully* busy one hasn't time to write such long words—particularly when it takes one half-hour to remember how to spell it—and even then one has to go and get a dictionary to see if one has spelt it right, and of course the dictionary is in another room, at the top of a high bookcase—where it has been for months and months—and has got all covered with dust. So one has to get a duster first of all, and nearly choke oneself in dusting it—and when one *has* made out at last which is dictionary and which is dust, *even* then there is the job of remembering which end of the alphabet "A" comes—for one feels pretty certain it isn't in the *middle*—then one has to go and wash one's hands before turning over the leaves—for they've got so thick with dust, one hardly knows them by sight—and, as likely as not, the soap is lost, and the jug is empty, and there's no towel, and one has to spend hours and hours in finding things—and perhaps after all, one has to go off to the shop to buy a new cake of soap. So, with all this bother, I hope you won't mind my writing it short and saying, "My dear Ada"), — You said in your letter you would like a likeness of me: so here it is, and I hope you will like it. I won't forget to call the next time but one I'm in Wallington. — Your very affectionate friend,

Lewis Carroll

To Gertrude Chataway

Christ Church, Oxford, October 13, 1875

My dear Gertrude,—I never give birthday *presents*, but you see I *do* sometimes write a birthday *letter*: so, as I've just arrived here, I am writing this to wish you many and many a happy return of your birthday to-morrow. I will drink your health if only I can remember, and if you don't mind—but perhaps you object?

You see, if I were to sit by you at breakfast, and to drink your tea, you wouldn't like that, would you? You would say, "Boo! hoo! Here's Mr. Dodgson drunk all my tea, and I haven't got any left!" So I am very much afraid, next time Sybil looks for you, she'll find you sitting by the sad sea-waves and crying "Boo! hoo! Here's Mr. Dodgson has drunk my health, and I haven't got any left!"

And how it will puzzle Mr. Maund, when he is sent for to see you! "My dear madam, I'm sorry to say your little girl has got no health at all! I never saw such a thing in my life!" "You see she would go and make friends with a strange gentleman, and yesterday he drank her health!" "Well, Mrs. Chataway," he will say, "the only way to cure her is to wait till his next birthday, and then for *her* to drink *his* health."

And then we shall have changed healths. I wonder how you'll like mine! Oh, Gertrude, I wish you would not talk such nonsense! . . . Your loving friend,

Lewis Carroll

MARK TWAIN

To Olivia Langdon

Please address *"Everett House, Union Square, New York"*
Nov. 28 [*1868*]

My dear, dear Livy: When I found myself comfortably on board the cars last night (I see Dan has just come in from breakfast, & he will be back here, within five minutes & interrupt me)—when I found myself comfortably on board the cars, I said to myself: "Now whatever others may think, it is *my* opinion that I am blessed above all other men that live; I have known supreme happiness for two whole days, & now I ought to be ready & willing to pay a little attention to necessary duties, & do it cheerfully." Therefore I resolved to go deliberately through that lecture, without notes, & so impress it upon my memory & my understanding as to secure myself against any such lame delivery of it in future as *I* thought characterized it in Elmira. But I had little calculated the cost of such a resolution. Never was a lecture so full of parentheses before. It was Livy, Livy, Livy, Livy, all the way through! It was one sentence of Vandal* to ten sentences about *you.* The insignificant lecture was hidden, lost, overwhelmed & buried under a boundless universe of Livy! I was sorry I had ever made so reckless a resolve, for its accomplishment seemed entirely hopeless. Still, having *made* it, I *would* stick to it till it was finished, & I *did*—but it was rather late at night. Then, having a clear conscience, I prayed, & with good heart—but it was only when I prayed

---

* "The American Vandal Abroad" was the title of his lecture.

for you that my tongue was touched with inspiration. You will smile at the idea of *my* praying for *you*—I, who so need the prayers of all good friends, praying for you who surely need the prayers of none. But never mind, Livy, the prayer was honest & sincere—it was *that*, at least—& I know it was heard. . . .

I do love, love, *love* you, Livy! My whole being is permeated, is renewed, is leavened with this love, & with every breath I draw its noble influence makes of me a better man. And I shall yet be *worthy* of your priceless love, Livy. It is the glad task of my life—it is the purest ambition & the most exalted, that ever I have known, & I shall never, never swerve from the path it has marked out for me, while the goal & *you* are before me. Livy, I could not tell your honored father & mother how deeply I felt for them, & how heartless it seemed in me to come, under cover of their trusting, generous hospitality, & try to steal away the sun out of their domestic firmament & rob their fireside heaven of its angel. . . . & yet there was nothing criminal in my *intent*, Livy—nothing wilfully & deliberately underhanded & dishonorable—I could say it in the high court of Heaven. *You* know I would scorn to do a shameful act, my darling—you know it & will maintain it—for never yet had any friend a stauncher, braver defender than *you*—you—you Perfection! Ah, how "deluded" I am, & how I do love to be so "deluded"! I could not tell them those things, Livy, but if it shall seem necessary, I know that *you* can. And moreover you can always say, with every confidence, that I have been through the world's "mill"—I have traversed its ramifications from end to end—I have searched it, & probed it, & put it under the microscope & I *know* it, through & through, & from back to back—its follies, its frauds & its vanities—all by personal *experience* & not through dainty *theories* culled from nice moral books in luxurious parlors where temptation never comes & it is easy to be good & keep the heart warm & one's [generous] best impulses fresh & strong & uncontaminated—& now I know *how* to be a better man, & the *value* of so being, & when I say that I *shall* be, it is just the same as if I *swore* it! *Now!*

Good-bye, Livy. You are so pure, so great, so good, so beautiful. *How* can I help loving you? Say, rather, how can I keep from *worshipping* you, you dear little paragon? *If* I could only see you! I do *wish* I could. Write me im-*mediately*. Don't wait a minute. . . .

Most lovingly, Yours
Forever—Samuel

P. S. I do LOVE you, Livy!

SAMUEL BUTLER AND MISS E. M. A. SAVAGE

A correspondence

22 Beaumont Street,
Portland Place, W.
Oct. 23rd, 1884

Dear Mr. Butler,

With this letter I send a little present for you. I have lately developed an extraordinary talent for knitting stockings, and was so enchanted with the first *one* I made, that I immediately began to wear it, regardless of the fact that it was of a lightish blue colour while the other was black. You should be thankful that I have not required you to do likewise. I can knit much better now, and I mean *always* to make your stockings for the future. The next pair are to be thicker and softer and looser in texture; these are rather harsh and inelastic. I shall not however, begin them, till I have heard these do. If they don't fit (and I dare say they won't) you can give them to Mr. Jones with my kind regards. If he doesn't have them you can give them to any one you please, without my kind regards . . . You will be pleased to hear that the socks were made entirely on the Sabbath. Sunday afternoons I retired in my closet, and shut the door (as we are told to do in the Bible) and knitted. So that they represent a religious service, and are sanctified. I think you had better let me have an old sock that fits you, as a pattern to do the next by.

Yours very truly,
E. M. A. Savage

15 Clifford's Inn, E. C.
Friday, Oct. 24th, 1884

Dear Miss Savage,

Now I have tried your socks on and I don't quite know whether they fit me or no. They are long enough in the foot—well—just long

enough now, but I shall wear them through at the toe after they have
been washed, if they get smaller, but the main difficulty is in getting
them on, I mean in getting them to come round the heel and up the
calf. They were beautiful when once on, and I do not doubt will give
and stretch with wear; however we shall see. As for doing me any more,
I flatly forbid it; I believe you don't like my books, and want to make
me say I won't give you any more if you make me any more socks, and
then you will make me some more, in order not to get the books. No,
I will let you read my stupid books in MS. and help me that way. If
you like to make me a kettleholder you may, for I have only one just
now, and I like to have two because I always mislay one, but I won't
have people working their fingers out to knit me stockings. This one
pair I accept gratefully, and if it does not wear right I will get you to
enlarge it a little at the top, if it can be enlarged. You shall hear from
me again later on.

Yours very truly,
S. *Butler*

22 Beaumont Street, W.
Monday [Oct. 27th, 1884]

Dear Mr. Butler,
    Here is a kettleholder, and I can only say that a man who is equal
to the control of two kettleholders fills me with awe, and I shall begin
to be afraid of you. The vagaries of one drive me nearly mad—two
would send me straight into a Lunatic Asylum. . . .
    The kettleholder is very clumsy and ugly, but please to remember
that I am not a very many-sided genius, and to expect me to excel in
kettleholders *and* stockings is unreasonable. I take credit to myself,
however, for affixing a fetter to it, so that you may chain it up if it
is too much disposed to wander. My expectation is that it is too thick
for you to grasp the kettle with, and the kettle will slip out of your
hand and scald you frightfuly. I shall be sorry for you, but you would
have it, so upon your own head be it.

Yours very truly,
E. *M. A. Savage*

15 Clifford's Inn, E. C.
Tuesday, Oct. 28th, 1884

Dear Miss Savage,

The kettleholder is beautiful—it is like a filleted sole and I am very fond of filleted soles— It is not at all too thick, and fits my kettle to perfection. I have been lifting my kettle on and off the fire with it, and then hanging the kettleholder on its nail again, all day—ever since I got it this morning, and I like it better and better continually—only you never made it. You bought it at a bazaar and that little touch about the affixing a fetter to it, is just like one of my own lies—very circumstantial and like where the subject comes in again in a chorus as a counterpoint to some other subject, as though it were quite an accident, when all the time it was tried on another piece of paper beforehand to see whether it would or no. You hadn't time to think it all out, and invent so much, and do all that work, since you got my letter. I won't say that I don't think you could have done the knitting, because you can do anything you like—still I don't believe you did do it.

I am wearing the socks. They fit very well now—and come on and off quite easily—still, when the toes begin to wear out (which perhaps they won't) I will get you to add a little to the length, and will carefully keep the wool you sent against this contingency. . . .

Yours very truly,
S. Butler

PS. If you did knit that kettleholder I shall think you even cleverer than I did before. If you did not knit it, I shall think that you are just as clever as I have always thought you.

22 Beaumont Street, W.
Nov. 1st [1884]

Dear Mr. Butler,

No doubt your powers of lying are great, but when you assert that my TRUTH is like your lies, you considerably overestimate their value and some day you will get into a scrape from your over-confidence. It is entirely in your interests, therefore, that I have procured the enclosed affidavits—not on my own account, for my character for veracity is *spotless*. Besides I never lie with a circumstance; I have not done so for many years, having found the inconvenience, and I recommend you to follow my example. Affidavit No. 1 is from Miss Johnson's aunt, so you can easily verify her statement—but I have not disclosed your name to either of the ladies—I have called you simply a 'person.' If their testimony does not convince you, I can have two more for the asking I dare say. I could have three, but one of the witnesses is a man hater, and calls men 'vile Creech-Haughs' and 'base Monst-Haughs' and she would triumph over me too much, because I take the part of the poor men, and she would say 'Now you have discovered the wickedness of men', and she would call you a *villain*, which I should not like.

Like many, perhaps I should say most, of the members of the Somerville club, she does not like her husband, and the very first time I saw her, she told me of his iniquities with details that are usually suppressed. There were many details, and every time I have seen her since, she has added more, till I begin to suspect that she sometimes borrows details from other people's husbands. In conclusion I can only say that if you *repent*, you may have the forgiveness of yours truly,

E. M. A. Savage

15 *Clifford's Inn, E. C.*
Nov. 3rd, 1884

Dear Miss Savage,

What penance shall I perform? I know *you* are above trampling on a fallen man—I should have said worm—*you* don't like to wound any one's feelings—*you* don't wish to be like my sisters— There! I know that *no* member of the Somerville Club would forge a certificate (that is more correct is it not?) and even if I didn't, if you tell me that you wish me to say I believe you really did make the kettleholder, that is quite enough. I do believe firmly that you made that kettleholder—I know it—my profoundest apologies—my diffusest thanks—and my expression of enhanced admiration for your great and versatile powers.

Believe me, Yours very truly,
S. Butler

SIDNEY LANIER

To his wife

1

Baltimore, December 2, 1873

Well, Flauto Primo hath been to his first rehearsal.

Fancy thy poor lover, weary, worn, and stuffed with a cold, arriving after a brisk walk—he was *so* afraid he might be behind time—at the hall of Peabody Institute. He passeth down betwixt the empty benches, turneth through the greenroom, emergeth on the stage, greeteth the Maestro, is introduced by the same to Flauto Secondo, and then, with as much carelessness as he can assume, he sauntereth in among the rows of music-stools, to see if peradventure he can find the place where he is to sit—for he knoweth not, and liketh not to ask. He remembereth where the flutes sit in Thomas' Orchestra; but on going to the corresponding spot he findeth the part of Contra-Basso on the music-stand, and fleeth therefrom in terror. In despair, he is about to endeavor to get some information on the sly, when he seeth the good Flauto Secondo sitting down far in front, and straightway marcheth to his place on the left of the same, with the air of one that had played there since babyhood. This Hamerik of ours hath French ideas about his orchestral arrangements and places his pieces very differently from Thomas. Well, I sit down, some late-comers arrive, stamping and blowing—for it is snowing outside—and pull the green-baize covers off their big horns and bass-fiddles. Presently the Maestro, who is rushing about, hither and thither, in some excitement, falleth to striking a great tuning-fork with a mallet, and straightway we all begin to toot A, to puff it, to groan it, to squeak it, to scrape it, until I sympathize with the poor letter, and glide off in some delicate little runs; and presently the others begin to flourish also, and here we have it, up chromatics, down diatonics, unearthly buzzings from the big fiddles, diabolical four-string chords from the 'cellos, passionate shrieks from the clarionets and oboes, manly remonstrances from the horns, querulous complaints from the bassoons, and so on. Now the Maestro mounteth to his perch. I am seated immediately next the audience, facing the first violins, who are separated from me by the conductor's stand. I place my part (of the Fifth Symphony of Beethoven, which I had procured two days before, in order to look over it, being told that on the first rehearsal we would try nothing but the Fifth Symphony) on my stand, and try to stop my heart from beating so fast—with unavailing arguments. Maestro rappeth with his *bâton,* and magically stilleth all the shrieks and agonies of the instruments. "Fierst" (he saith, with the Frenchiest of French accents—tho' a Dane, he was educated in Paris) "I wish to present to ze gentlemen of ze orchestra our fierst flutist, Mr. Sidney Lanier, also our fierst oboe, Mr. (I didn't catch his name)." Whereupon, not knowing what else to do—and the pause being somewhat awkward—I rise and make a profound bow to the Reeds, who sit behind me, another to the 'Celli, the Bassi, and the Tympani, in the middle, and a third to the Violins opposite. This appeareth to be the right thing, for Oboe jumpeth up also, and boweth, and the gentlemen of the orchestra all rise and bow, some of them with great *empressement.* Then there is a little idiotic hum and simper, such as newly introduced people usually affect. Then cometh a man— whom I should always hate, if I *could* hate anybody always—and, to my horror, putteth on my music-stand the flauto primo part of Niels Gade's Ossian Overture, and thereupon the Maestro saith, "We will try *that* fierst." Horrors! They told me they would play nothing but the Fifth Symphony, and this Ossian Overture I have never seen or heard! This does not help my heart-beats nor steady my lips—thou canst believe. However, there is no time to tarry, the *bâton* rappeth, the horns blow, my five bars' rest is out—I plunge.

—Oh! If thou couldst but be by me in this sublime glory of music! All through it I yearned for thee with heart-breaking eagerness. The beauty of it maketh me catch my breath—to write of it. I will not attempt to describe it. It is the spirit of the poems of Ossian done in music by the wonderful Niels Gade.

I got through it without causing any disturbance. Maestro had to stop twice on account of some other players. I failed to come in on time twice in the Symphony. I am too tired now to give thee any further account. I go again to rehearsal to-morrow.

2

Baltimore, February 8, 1874.

If the constituents and guardians of my childhood—those good Presbyterians who believed me a model for the Sunday-school children of all time—could have witnessed my acts and doings this day, I know not what groans of sorrowful regret would arise in my behalf. For— the same being Sunday—I went at two o'clock to rehearse with an orchestra in which I was engaged, under Herr Leuschow, for the concert of the Germania Männerchor of Baltimore, which is to be next Wednesday night. . . . Having arrived at the beautiful new hall which this Männerchor have just built—and the opening of which is the occasion of the concert—I found they were waiting for me, and so quickly took my seat and fell to. First, a Concerto for Violin and Orchestra, by De Beriot, light, lovely, airy and wondrous delicate; then the "Jübel" overture of Weber, full of glory and triumph, ending with "God Save the Queen," which is set in four sharps and carrieth the poor, straining Flauto Primo clear up to

and thereabouts, without pity; then in filed a great chorus of male and female voices, and we all plunged into that great "Athalia" of Mendelssohn for orchestra and chorus. Borne on the noble surges of the up-swelling tones, I floated hither and thither in that sea of glory-turned-into-music. Presently I found myself playing almost alone, in octaves with a lovely soprano voice; I turned my eyes involuntarily, as we sailed along together, and my gaze fell full upon a pair of beautiful liquid, gazelle eyes which, by a similar impulse, I suppose, had sought mine; she—I mean the Eyes—looked me full in the face for a moment, then with a half-smile, full of dignity and sweetness, turned to her notes again: which also I had to do, not having seen or heard the piece before, and so, mutually cheered by this dumb exchange of sympathy, we sang and played together to the end of the piece, which occupied, I should think, near three-quarters of an hour. When we had finished I rushed to Herr Leuschow and procured a presentation to the fair Soprano. I found her a charming young woman, bright-faced and witty, . . . and had a little, really refreshing, champagny talk with her. . . . Then we played a cavatina from "Ernani," sung by a stout German lady; then the "Sonnenuntergang" by Flamma, for chorus of men's voices and orchestra.

Then I took a great draught of beer, and found it was six o'clock. I had had nothing to eat since eight this morning: so hied me to a restaurant, and dined on oysters and a chop. Then home, laid me down for twenty minutes, rose, dressed in full concert-suit, and went forth with —— to the great hall of the Masonic Temple. Here we found a large audience assembled to hear a concert for the benefit of the Carmelite Nuns, and being quickly called, forth stepped the little man and I on the stage, and dashed into the elaborate tootle-ty-tootle-ty of Rabboni's duo on themes from "Rigoletto." I did laugh inwardly, as I looked about the hall, to see the big Irishmen, servant-maids and all, good Catholics every one, gazing and listening, rapt. They encored us, and we responded with "Adieu, Dear Land."

Then, home, and here sit I . . . famished for . . . my highest-of-life. . . .

Bohemianism and compliments fill not my heart.

WILLIAM JAMES

~~~~~~

To his father

Bolton St., London, Dec. 14, 1882.

Darling old Father,—Two letters, one from my Alice last night, and one from Aunt Kate to Harry just now, have somewhat dispelled the mystery in which the telegrams left your condition; and although their news is several days earlier than the telegrams, I am free to suppose that the latter report only an aggravation of the symptoms the letters describe. It is far more agreeable to think of this than of some dreadful unknown and sudden malady.

We have been so long accustomed to the hypothesis of your

being taken away from us, especially during the past ten months, that the thought that this may be your last illness conveys no very sudden shock. You are old enough, you've given your message to the world in many ways and will not be forgotten; you are here left alone, and on the other side, let us hope and pray, dear, dear old Mother is waiting for you to join her. If you go, it will not be an inharmonious thing. Only, if you are still in possession of your normal consciousness, I should like to see you once again before we part. I stayed here only in obedience to the last telegram, and am waiting now for Harry—who knows the exact state of my mind, and who will know yours—to telegraph again what I shall do. Meanwhile, my blessed old Father, I scribble this line (which may reach you though I should come too late), just to tell you how full of the tenderest memories and feelings about you my heart has for the last few days been filled. In that mysterious gulf of the past into which the present soon will fall and go back and back, yours is still for me the central figure. All my intellectual life I derive from you; and though we have often seemed at odds in the expression thereof, I'm sure there's a harmony somewhere, and that our strivings will combine. What my debt to you is goes beyond all my power of estimating,—so early, so penetrating and so constant has been the influence. You need be in no anxiety about your literary remains. I will see them well taken care of, and that your words shall not suffer for being concealed. At Paris I heard that Milsand, whose name you may remember in the "Revue des Deux Mondes" and elsewhere, was an admirer of the "Secret of Swedenborg," and Hodgson told me your last book had deeply impressed him. So will it be; especially, I think, if a collection of *extracts* from your various writings were published, after the manner of the extracts from Carlyle, Ruskin, & Co. I have long thought such a volume would be the best monument to you.—As for us; we shall live on each in his way,—feeling somewhat unprotected, old as we are, for the absence of the parental bosoms as a refuge, but holding fast together in that common sacred memory. We will stand by each other and by Alice, try to transmit the torch in our offspring as you did in us, and when the time comes for being gathered in, I pray we may, if not all, some at least, be as ripe as you. As for myself, I know what trouble I've given you at various times through my peculiarities; and as my own boys grow up, I shall learn more and more of the kind of trial you had to overcome in superintending the development of a creature different from yourself, for whom you felt responsible. I say this merely to show how my *sympathy* with you is likely to grow much livelier, rather than to fade—and not for the sake of regrets.—As for the other side, and Mother, and our all possibly meeting, I *can't* say anything. More than ever at this moment do I feel that if that *were* true, all would be solved and justified. And it comes strangely over me in bidding you good-bye how a life is but a day and expresses mainly but a single note. It is so much like the act of bidding an ordinary good-night. Good-night, my sacred old Father! If I don't see you again—Farewell! a blessed farewell! Your

William.

GERARD MANLEY HOPKINS

wwwwwwwwwwwwwwwwwwwwwwwwwwwwwwwwwwwwwwwwwwwwwwwwwwwwwwwwwwwwwwwwwwwwwwwwwwwwww

To his sister Kate Hopkins

Stonyhurst, April 25, 1871.

My dear Katie,—Many thanks for your letter, which I was delighted to get. When it first came to hand I stood balancing in my mind who it could be from, there was such a youngladyship and grownupdom about the address, until I remembered that you were older than you used to be. As for me I will say no more than this, that I have prescribed myself twenty four hourglasses a day (which I take even during sleep, such is the force of habit) and that even this does not stop the ravages of time.

What month in the year it may be at Hampstead I will not be sure; with us it is a whity-greeny January. What with east winds, cloud, and rain I think it will never be spring. If we have a bright afternoon the next morning it is winter again.

We were all vaccinated the other day. The next day a young Portug[u]ese came up to me and said 'Oh misther 'Opkins, do *you* feel the cows in *yewer* arm?' I told him I felt the horns coming through. I do I am sure. I cannot remember now whether one ought to say the calf of the arm or the calf of the leg. My shoulder is like a shoulder of beef. I dare not speak above a whisper for fear of bellowing—there now, I was going to say I am obliged to speak low for fear of lowing.

I dream at night that I have only two of my legs in bed. I think there is a split coming in both my slippers. Yesterday I could not think why it was that I would wander about on a wet grass-plot: I see now. I chew my pen a great deal. The long and short of it is that my left forequarter is swollen and painful (I meant to have written arm but I cowld not). Besides the doctor has given us medicine, so that I am in a miserable way just now.

From cows I will turn to lambs. Our fields are full of them. When they were a little younger and nicer and sillier they wd. come gambolling up to one as if one were their mother. One of them sucked my finger and my companion took another up in his arms. The ewes then came up and walked round us making suspicious sheep's eyes at us, as people say. Now, when they are not sucking the breast (to do which they make such terrific butts and digs at the old dam that two of them together will sometimes lift her off her hind legs) they spend their time in bounding and spinning round as if they were tumblers. The same thing is I daresay to be seen (and earlier than this) about Hampstead: still as many of these lambs are ours I cannot pass it by and must tell you of it in black and white.

One thing made me very sad the day we were vaccinated. I was coming away: I left a number of my companions in a room in the infirmary—some had come from the doctor and others were waiting for their turn—all laughing and chatting. As I came down one of the galleries from the room I saw one of our young men standing there looking at a picture. I wondered why he stayed by himself and did not join the rest and then afterwards I remembered that he had had the smallpox and was deeply marked with it and all his good looks gone which he would have had and he did not want to face the others at that time when they were having their fun taking safe precautions against catching what it was too late for him to take any precautions against.

I want to know two things by the next person who writes—first some particulars from Arthur about the American yacht Sappho which seems to have had such great successes last year and next whether it is true that the cuckoo has come unusually early this year, as I heard said. It has not come here yet and I do not know if it will.

With best love to all believe me your loving brother

Gerard M. Hopkins.

ROBERT LOUIS STEVENSON

‹‹

To Edmund Gosse

San Francisco, Cal., April 16 [*1880*]

My dear Gosse,—You have not answered my last; and I know you will repent when you hear how near I have been to another world. For about six weeks I have been in utter doubt; it was a toss-up for life or death all that time; but I won the toss, sir, and Hades went off once more discomfited. This is not the first time, nor will it be the last, that I have a friendly game with that gentleman. I know he will end by cleaning me out; but the rogue is insidious, and the habit of that sort of gambling seems to be a part of my nature; it was, I suspect, too much indulged in youth; break your children of this tendency, my dear Gosse, from the first. It is, when once formed, a habit more fatal than opium—I speak, as St. Paul says, like a fool. I have been very very sick; on the verge of a galloping consumption, cold sweats, prostrating attacks of cough, sinking fits in which I lost the power of speech, fever, and all the ugliest circumstances of the disease; and I have cause to bless God, my wife that is to be, and one Dr. Bamford (a name the Muse repels), that I have come out of all this, and got my feet once more upon a little hilltop, with a fair prospect of life and some new desire of living. Yet I did not wish to die, neither; only I felt unable to go on farther with that rough horseplay of human life: a man must be pretty well to take the business in good part. Yet I felt all the time that I had done nothing to entitle me to an honourable discharge; that I had taken up many obligations and begun many friendships which I had no right to put away from me; and that for me to die was to play the cur and slinking sybarite, and desert the colours on the eve of the decisive fight. Of course I have done no work for I do not know how long; and here you can triumph. I have been reduced to writing verses for amusement. A fact. The whirligig of time brings in its revenges, after all. But I'll have them buried with me, I think, for I have not the heart to burn them while I live. Do write. I shall go to the mountains as soon as the weather clears; on the way thither, I marry myself; then I set up my family altar among the pinewoods, 3000 feet, sir, from the disputatious sea.—I am, dear Weg, most truly yours,

R. L. S.

J. M. BARRIE

wwwwwwwwwwwwwwwwwwwwwwwwwwwwwwwwwwwwwwwwwwwwwwwwwwwwwwwwwwwwwwwwwwwwwwwwwwwwwwwwwwww

To Mrs. Patrick Campbell

Island of Harris, N. B. 7 September '12

Dear Stella

I thought when I saw your nice little monogram that it meant you no longer adored G. B. S., and that you had crossed the street again to me. You see, I had watched you (a bitter smile on my face) popping in at his door instead of at mine. For the moment I am elated, though well I know that you will soon be off with me again and on with him. He and I live in the weather house with two doors, and you are the figure that smiles on us and turns up its nose at us alternately. However, I would rather see you going in at his door than not see you at all, and as you are on elastic I know that the farther you go with him the farther you will have to bound back. I wish I had not thought of this because it suddenly fills me with a scheme for a play called *The Weather House.* Will stop this letter presently to think scheme out, but as I see it just now I feel that G. B. S. and I must write alternate acts (according to which door you go in at). When I wrote that, I meant that we should each write the acts in which you were nice to him, but on reflection I am not sure that I would not prefer to write the scenes which took place across the way and leave him to write those of No. 3.

I have done no work here except a one act play, which striketh me as being no great shakes, for the Duke of York's, where a triple bill is to be done; I daresay I'll go on with the other, but why, oh, why don't you post, or, better, call on Frohman, as it goes to him if it's done? This place is very remote—nothing alive but salmon, deer, and whales, and I return to London in a fortnight, when I hope this comedy of the doors will begin again.

Yours, J. M. B.

VIRGINIA WOOLF

From her *Diary*

Monday, August 4th [1918]

While waiting to buy a book in which to record my impressions first of Christina Rossetti, then of Byron, I had better write them here. For one thing I have hardly any money left, having bought Leconte de Lisle in great quantities. Christine has the great distinction of being a born poet, as she seems to have known very well herself. But if I were bringing a case against God she is one of the first witnesses I should call. It is melancholy reading. First she starved herself of love, which meant also life; then of poetry in deference to what she thought her religion demanded. There were two good suitors. The first indeed had his peculiarities. He had a conscience. She could only marry a particular shade of Christian. He could only stay that shade for a few months at a time. Finally he developed Roman Catholicism and was lost. Worse still was the case of Mr. Collins—a really delightful scholar—an unworldly recluse—a single-minded worshipper of Christina, who could never be brought into the fold at all. On this account she could only visit him affectionately in his lodgings, which she did to the end of her life. Poetry was castrated too. She would set herself to do the psalms into verse; and to make all her poetry subservient to the Christian doctrines. Consequently, as I think, she starved into austere emaciation a very fine original gift, which only wanted licence to take to itself a far finer form than, shall we say, Mrs. Browning's. She wrote very easily; in a spontaneous childlike kind of way one imagines, as is the case generally with a true gift; still undeveloped. She has the natural singing power. She thinks too. She has fancy. She could, one is profane enough to guess, have been ribald and witty. And, as a reward for all her sacrifices, she died in terror, uncertain of salvation. I confess though that I have only turned her poetry over, making my way inevitably to the ones I knew already.

Wednesday, August 7th [1919]

Asheham diary drains off my meticulous observations of flowers, clouds, beetles and the price of eggs; and, being alone, there is no other event to record. Our tragedy has been the squashing of a caterpillar; our excitement the return of the servants from Lewes last night, laden with all L.'s war books and the English review for me, with Brailsford upon a League of Nations, and Katherine Mansfield on *Bliss*. I threw down *Bliss* with the exclamation, "She's done for!" Indeed I don't see how much faith in her as woman or writer can survive that sort of story. I shall have to accept the fact, I'm afraid, that her mind is a very thin soil, laid an inch or two deep upon very barren rock. For *Bliss* is long enough to give her a chance of going deeper. Instead she is content with superficial smartness; and the whole conception is poor, cheap, not the vision, however imperfect, of an interesting mind. She writes badly too. And the effect was as I say, to give me an impression of her callousness and hardness as a human being. I shall read it again; but I don't suppose I shall change. She'll go on doing this sort of thing, perfectly to her and Murry's satisfaction. I'm relieved now that they didn't come. Or is it absurd to read all this criticism of her personally into a story?

Anyhow I was very glad to go on with my Byron. He has at least the male virtues. In fact, I'm amused to find how easily I can imagine the effect he had upon women—especially upon rather stupid or uneducated women, unable to stand up to him. So many, too, would wish to reclaim him. Ever since I was a child (as Gertler would say, as if it proved him a particularly remarkable person) I've had the habit of getting full of some biography and wanting to build up my imaginary figure of the person with every scrap of news I could find about him. During the passion, the name of Cowper or Byron or whoever it might be, seemed to start up in the most unlikely pages. And then, suddenly, the figure becomes distant and merely one of the usual dead. I'm much impressed by the extreme badness of B.'s poetry—such of it as Moore quotes with almost speechless admiration. Why did they think this Album stuff the finest fire of poetry? It reads hardly better than L. E. L. or Ella Wheeler Wilcox. And they dissuaded him from doing what he knew he could do, which was to write satire. He came home from the East with satires (parodies of Horace) in his bag and *Childe Harold*. He was persuaded that *Childe Harold* was the best poem ever written. But he never as a young man believed in his poetry;

a proof, in such a confident dogmatic person, that he hadn't the gift. The Wordsworths and Keats' believe in that as much as they believe in anything. In his character, I'm often reminded a little of Rupert Brooke, though this is to Rupert's disadvantage. At any rate Byron had superb force; his letters prove it. He had in many ways a very fine nature too; though as no one laughed him out of his affectations he became more like Horace Cole than one could wish. He could only be laughed at by a woman, and they worshipped instead. I haven't yet come to Lady Byron, but I suppose, instead of laughing, she merely disapproved. And so he became Byronic.

Monday, January 20th [*1919*]

I mean to copy this out when I can buy a book, so I omit the flourishes proper to the new year. It is not money this time that I lack, but the capacity, after a fortnight in bed, to make the journey to Fleet Street. Even the muscles of my right hand feel as I imagine a servant's hand to feel. Curiously enough, I have the same stiffness in manipulating sentences, though by rights I should be better equipped mentally now than I was a month ago. The fortnight in bed was the result of having a tooth out, and being tired enough to get a headache—a long dreary affair, that receded and advanced much like a mist on a January day. One hour's writing daily is my allowance for the next few weeks; and having hoarded it this morning I may spend part of it now, since L. is out and I am much behind-hand with the month of January. I note however that this diary writing does not count as writing, since I have just re-read my year's diary and am much struck by the rapid haphazard gallop at which it swings along, sometimes indeed jerking almost intolerably over the cobbles. Still if it were not written rather faster than the fastest type-writing, if I stopped and took thought, it would never be written at all; and the advantage of the method is that it sweeps up accidentally several stray matters which I should exclude if I hesitated, but which are the diamonds of the dustheap. If Virginia Woolf at the age of 50, when she sits down to build her memoirs out of these books, is unable to make a phrase as it should be made, I can only condole with her and remind her of the existence of the fireplace, where she has my leave to burn these pages to so many black films with red eyes in them. But how I envy her the task I am preparing for her! There is none I should like better. Already my 37th birthday next Saturday is robbed of some of its terrors by the thought.

Partly for the benefit of this elderly lady (no subterfuges will then be possible: 50 is elderly, though I anticipate her protest and agree that it is not old) partly to give the year a solid foundation I intend to spend the evenings of this week of captivity in making out an account of my friendships and their present condition, with some account of my friends' characters; and to add an estimate of their work and a forecast of their future works. The lady of 50 will be able to say how near to the truth I come; but I have written enough for tonight (only 15 minutes, I see).

WILLIAM CARLOS WILLIAMS

To Ezra Pound

Nov. 6, 1936

Dea Rezra: Always delighted to hear from you. I began to think you had gone up into some more rarefied stratum than that to which I have grown accustomed. Truly, truly, my friend, you have greatly alleviated the passage of my years—. Don't stop now. My only regret has been that you have not been closer to these here diggins. Damn it to hell, it's been a serious loss to us all that you haven't set your flowers to clambering on our walls. I planted three small clematis vines in my back yard this morning. Very mild weather here so far.

I approve of your proposed manifesto and think that this is of all times the most propitious in which to release it. The American political upheaval having for the moment practically eliminated the Communist party from our midst, it would seem to be THE moment for redirecting sane minds toward the need for an actual radicalism—which would concern precisely the things your nine or ten categories included. . . .

And James Laughlin (bless his heart) has just offered to do my *White Mule. That* finished me. It sure was a bolt out of the blue of almost despair. His impetus has set me polishing (that is, rewriting) the last chapters to make this a definite Book. It is to be Book I and ends with proper regard for an ending. I'm going to like this book. It's put ten years on my life; out next spring.

Besides which I've about made up my mind to write my mother's story this winter. I have an idea for it that I can't detail now. I've been collecting her sayings and letters for years. You'll see.

And I've done seven new short poems—two of them as good as anything I've ever done, maybe the best.

And then there's that magnum opus I've always wanted to do: the poem PATERSON. Jeez how I'd like to get at that. I've been sounding myself out in these years working toward a form of some sort. . . .

Oh yeah, there's a good guy named Bernard de Voto; he has taken the place of Henry Seidel Canby as editor of the *Saturday Review of Literature* and MAY come to something. He's got a face like a spoiled potato but they say his heart is in the right place. I'm going to meet him first, through a woman, a real fine woman, and we'll see what happens.

I'm never hopeless, as you seem to suggest—but I have always been hopeless of doing anything with other people. I know I am wrong, but then, that's the way I am.

You see, I live a very obscure but very complete life in my own petty world, I know its smells and its bouquets. They are not to be ignored. I tell you when I went in to Rockefeller City today and saw that beeg building and then entered it and rode on the escalator and walked about the book show—I tells you my little suburb just bust right out laughing. SUCH a lot of cheap crap I NEVER encountered. There in the middle of everything was our old, very old friend Edwin Markham parading his innocent white beard about, wanting to be spoken to and admired. I tell you I was not envious, nor did I wish I had been paraded about the walls to sell for them.

Me Mother is helping me translate an old book I think it was you left here once: *El Perro y la Calentura,* by Quevedo.

Well, write me again. Floss is fine. Best to Dorothy. I'd enjoy playing you a game of tennis.

.

Yrs.,
BILL

D. H. LAWRENCE

To J. M. Murry

Lerici, per Fiascherino, Golfo della Spezia, Italy.
Thursday (1913)

Dear Murry,

I'm going to answer your letter immediately, and frankly.

When you say you won't take Katherine's money, it means you don't trust her love for you. When you say she needs little luxuries, and you couldn't bear to deprive her of them, it means you don't respect either yourself or her sufficiently to do it.

It looks to me as if you two, far from growing nearer, are snapping the bonds that hold you together, one after another. I suppose you must both of you consult your own hearts, honestly. She must see if she really wants *you*, wants to keep you and to have no other man all her life. It means forfeiting something. But the only principle I can see in this life, is that one *must* forfeit the less for the greater. Only one must be thoroughly honest about it.

She must say, "Could I live in a little place in Italy, with Jack, and be lonely, have rather a bare life, but be happy?" If she could, then take her money. If she doesn't want to, don't try. But don't beat about the bush. In the way you go on, you are inevitably coming apart. She is perhaps beginning to be unsatisfied with you. And you can't make her more satisfied by being unselfish. You must say, "How can I make myself most healthy, strong, and satisfactory to myself and to her?" If by being lazy for six months, then be lazy, and take her money. It doesn't matter if she misses her luxuries; she won't die of it. What luxuries do you mean?

. . . If you work yourself sterile to get her chocolates, she will most justly detest you—she is *perfectly* right. She doesn't want you to sacrifice herself to you, you fool. Be more natural, and positive, and stick to your own guts. You spread them on a tray for her to throw to the cats.

If you want things to come right—if you are ill and exhausted, then take her money to the last penny, and let her do her own house-work. Then she'll know you love her. You can't blame her if she's not satisfied with you. If I haven't had enough dinner, you can't blame *me.* But, you fool, you squander yourself, not for *her*, but to provide her with petty luxuries she doesn't really want. You insult her. A woman unsatisfied must have luxuries. But a woman who loves a man would sleep on a board.

It strikes me you've got off your lines, somewhere you've not been man enough: you've felt it rested with your honour to give her a place to be proud of. It rested with your honour to give her a man to be satisfied with—and satisfaction is never accomplished even physically unless the man is strongly and surely himself, and doesn't depend on anything but his own *being* to make a woman love him. You've tried to satisfy Katherine with what you could earn for her, give her: and she will only be satisfied with what you *are.*

And you don't know what you are. You've never come to it. You've always been dodging round, getting Rhythms and flats and doing criticism for money. You are a fool to work so hard for Katherine —she hates you for it—and quite right. You want to be strong in the possession of your own soul. Perhaps you will only come to that when this affair of you and her has gone crash. I should be sorry to think that—I don't believe it. You must save yourself, and your self-respect, by making it complete between Katherine and you—if you devour her money till she walks in rags, if you are both outcast. Make her certain —don't pander to her—stick to *yourself*—do what you *want* to do—don't *consider* her—she hates and loathes being considered. You insult her in saying you wouldn't take her money.

. . .

Get up, lad, and be a man for yourself. It's the man who dares to take, who is independent, not he who gives.

I think Oxford did you harm.

It is beautiful, wonderful, here.

A ten-pound note is 253 lire. We could get you, I believe, a jolly nice apartment in a big garden, in a house alone, for 80 lire a month. Don't waste yourself—don't be silly and floppy. You know what you *could* do—you *could* write—then prepare yourself: and first make Katherine at rest in her love for you. Say, "This I will certainly do"—it would be a relief for her to hear you. Don't be a child—don't keep that rather childish charm. Throw everything away, and say, "Now I act for my own good, at last."

We are getting gradually nearer again, Frieda and I. It is very beautiful here.

We are awfully sorry Katherine is so seedy. She ought to write to us. Our love to her and you.

D. H. Lawrence

If you've got an odd book or so you don't want to read, would you send it us? There is nothing for Frieda to read—and we like everything and anything.

BARTOLOMEO VANZETTI

To Mrs. Elizabeth Glendower Evans

July 22, 1921. Charlestown Prison

My dear Mrs. Glendower Evans:

I was just thinking what I would to do for past the long days jail: I was saying to myself: Do some work. But what? Write. A gentle motherly figure came to my mind and I rehear the voice: Why don't you write something now? It will be useful to you when you will be free. Just at that time I received your letter.

Thanks to you from the bottom of my heart for your confidence in my innocence; I am so. I did not spittel a drop of blood, or steal a cent in all my life. A little knowledge of the past; a sorrowful experience of the life itself had gave to me some ideas very different from those of many other umane beings. But I wish to convince my fellowmen that only with virtue and honesty is possible for us to find a little happiness in the world. I preached: I worked. I wished with all my faculties that the social wealth would belong to every umane creatures, so well as it was the fruit of the work of all. But this do not mean robbery for a insurrection.

The insurrection, the great movements of the soul, do not need dollars. It need love, light, spirit of sacrifice, ideas, conscience, instincts. It need more conscience, more hope and more goodness. And all this blessed things can be seeded, awoked, growed up in the heart of man in many ways, but not by robbery and murder for robbery.

. . . A little roof, a field, a few books and food is all what I need. I do not care for money, for leisure, for mondane ambition. And honest, even in this world of lambs and wolves I can have those things. My father has many field, houses, garden. He deal in wine and fruits and granaries. He wrote to me many times to come back home, and be a business man. Well, this supposed murderer had answered to him that my conscience do not permit to me to be a business man and I will gain my bread by work his field.

And more: The clearness of mind, the peace of the conscience, the determination and force of will, the intelligence, all, all what make the man feeling to be a part of the life, force and intelligence of the universe, will be brake by a crime. I know that, I see that, I tell that to everybody: Do not violate the law of nature, if you do not want to be a miserable. I remember: it was a night without moon, but starry. I sit alone in the darkness, I was sorry, very sorry. With the face in my hands I began to look at the stars. I feel that my soul want goes away from my body, and I have had to make an effort to keep it in my chest. So, I am the son of Nature, and I am so rich that I do not need any money. And for this they say I am a murderer and condemned me to death. Death? It is nothing. Abbominium is cruel thing.

. . . I hope to see you very soon; I will tell you more in the matter. I will write something, a meditation perhaps and name it: Waiting for the Hanger. I have lost the confidence in the justice of man. I mean in what is called so; not of course, of that sentiment which lay in the heart of man, and that no infernal force will be strong enough to soffocate it. Your assistance and the assistance of so many good men and women, had made my cross much more light. I will not forget it.

I beg your pardon for such a long letter, but I feel so reminiscent to you that hundred pages would not be sufficient to extern my sentiments and feelings. I am sure you will excuse me. Salve.

NICOLA SACCO

To Mrs. Cerise Jack

February 26, 1924. Dedham Jail

My dear Friend Mrs. Jack:

. . . . Every night when the light goes out I take a long walk and really I do not know how long I walk, because the most of the time I forget myself to go to sleep, and so I continue to walk and I count, one, two, three, four steps and turn backward and continue to count, one, two, three four and so on. But between all this time my mind it is always so full of ideas that one gos and one comes. . . . I find one of my mostly beautiful remembrance while I am thinking and walking, frequently I stop to my window cell and through those sad bars I stop and look at the nature into crepuscular of night, and the stars in the beauti blue sky. So last night the stars they was moor bright and the sky it was moor blue than I did ever seen; while I was looking it appear in my mind the idea to think of something of my youth and write the idea to my good friend Mrs. Jack first thing in morning. So here where I am right with you, and always I will try to be, yes, because I am study to understand your beautiful language and I know I will love it. And I will hope that one day I could surprise the feel of my gratitude towards all this fierce legion of friends and comrades.

The flowers you send to me last week it renew in my mind the remembrance of my youth. It complete sixteen years ago this past autumn that I left my father vineyards. Every year in autumn right after the collection I usd take care my father vineyard and sometime I usd keep watch, because near our vineyard they was a few big farmer and surronder our vineyard they was vast extension of prairie and hundreds animal they used pasturage day and night on those vast prairie. So the most of night I remane there to sleep to watch the animal to not let coming near our vineyard. The little town of Torre-maggiore it is not very far from our vineyard, only twenty minete of walk and I used go back and forth in morning an night and I usd bring to my dear an poor mother two big basket full of vegetables and fruits and big bounch flowers. The place where I used to sleep it was a big large hayrick that my good father and my brothers and I build. The hayrick it was set in one corner near the well in the middle of our vineyard, and surronde this sweet hayrick they was many plants and flowers except the red rose, because they was pretty hard to find the good red rose and I did love them so much that I was always hunting for find one plant of those good—red rose!

About sixty step from our vineyard we have a large piece of land full of any quantity of vegetables that my brothers and I we used cultivate them. So every morning before the sun shining used comes up and at night after the sun goes out I used put one quart of water on every plant of flowers and vegetables and the smal fruit trees. While I was finishing my work the sun shining was just coming up and I used always jump upon well wall and look at the beauty sun shining and I do not know how long I usd remane there look at that enchanted scene of beautiful. If I was a poet probably I could discribe the red rays of the loving sun shining and the bright blue sky and the perfume of my garden and flowers, the smell of the violet that was comes from the vast verdant prairie, and the singing of the birds, that was almost the joy of deliriany. So after all this enjoyment I used come back to my work singing one of my favourite song an on way singing I used full the bascket of fruit and vegetables and bunch of flowers that I used make a lovely bouquet. And in the middle the longuest flowers I used always put one of lovely red rose and I used walk one mile a way from our place to get one of them good red rose that I always hunting and love to find, the good red rose. . . .

P. S. How you find the day of our dear Mrs. Evans birthday? I have here very beauti bag to surprise her. If you hap to see her give my warm regard.

EDNA ST. VINCENT MILLAY

To the Millay family and friends

Box 53
Austerlitz, N. Y.
June 22, 1925

Dearest Mummie:

Here we are, in one of the loveliest places in the world, I am sure, working like Trojans, dogs, slaves, etc., having chimneys put in, & plumbing put in, & a garage built, etc.—We are crazy about it—& I have so many things on my mind at this moment that must be done before I'm an hour older,—you know how it is—that I hardly know if I am writing with a pen or with a screw-driver.—You & Kay & Howard are all invited to come to see us when next you are in these parts again—one at a time or all at once, but the most restful time to come would be after a couple of months—just now there is a little too much mortaring & tearing down of old building going on, & a guest is likely to be pressed into service laying a floor or digging a hole for the septic tank.— . . .

But it's going to be a sweet place when it's finished—and it's ours, all ours, about seven hundred acres of land & a lovely house, & no rent to pay, only a nice gentlemanly mortgage to keep shaving a slice off.

We're so excited about it we are nearly daft in the bean—kidney bean, lima bean, string-bean, butter-bean—you dow whad I bean—ha! ha! ha!—I'm off!—(Now you understand what I have been trying to tell you, that I am very interested in & pleased with the place that Eugen & I have bought.) . . .

Ugin & Edner.

Steepletop
Austerlitz, New York
July 28, 1925.

Dear Friends:

Ugin has just gone off in the Egg-beater to Albany to sell a load of crated huckleberries, and Freddie has to do the dishes. . . .

The kitchen plumbing, you will be glad to hear, is all connected, even to the set tubs, and the guest bath-room nearly so, and the servants' lavatory and seat—we decided after all to postpone the installation of our individual bath until the dormer windows are in and the installation of the dormer windows until the terrace is laid and the laying of the terrace until the swimming pool is dug and the digging of the swimming pool until we get money enough to buy some cocoa-butter against sunburn. The only trouble with our plumbing is that we have no water. . . . So we all took a bath in the brook, at least all but Ugin, who got lost trying to collect fifty cents apiece from the dozens of people who come in motor cars and camp on our land and steal our berries. Anyway, Deems and Freddie and I took a bath in the brook, and I made them give me up-stream because I was cleaner.

· · ·

We have quite a lot of flies. It's hard to keep the doors closed in a house that isn't finished yet. But the nine Polish dogs haven't broken into the spring-house for a long time. . . .

· · ·

What a thrilling time you must be having with that telescope, looking at the stars. There is nothing, not anything, so exciting. We have here no telescope, and for the most part no stars, it having rained here nearly every day since we came. It was pretty dismal at first, with no stove even in the kitchen, except a stinking kerosene modernity. You couldn't step outside the door without getting into grass up to your neck, and there wasn't a dry foot among us for over a fortnight. However, that's all over now, we have three splendid fireplaces and a handsome new range in the kitchen, and all the wood we can burn just lying around cluttering up the grass,—and it hasn't rained today, so far. . . .

If it wasn't for Freddie I don't know what we should do. Freddie is Gene's nephew, Robert's son, such a darling boy, not much over twenty, who is a landscape gardener, and left a growing business in Long Island to the care of his partner for two months to come up here and help us out with gardens and orchards and things, of which we are dismayingly ignorant. His coming has put new courage into us; we were about gone with weariness and confusion when he got here. You see, we have had living with us for three weeks now six masons, four plumbers, two carpenters, two ineffectual and transient servants, and fifteen insubordinate and mischievous berry-picking children. They don't spend the night here, but they might as well, for they appear in the morning before we are dressed, and tramp through the bed-rooms without knocking, bearing ladders and bricks and trowels and buckets of cement. There's not a room in the house that one or another of them isn't boring holes in or something, and there's not a spot within a quarter of a mile where I can stand and brush my teeth except in full sight of some of them.

Well—I would dearly, dearly love to get a letter from you, any of you, all of you. And if any of you should be leaving there, do come here, do. From now on it will be getting better. At least, after a week or so more, the mess will be our own mess, at least,—our own pails of paint and different colored brushes and hammers and nails and yards of cretonne, etc. We have only one guest-room, so far; but Freddie sleeps in the pantry, which leaves the guest-room free, and there will be the big davenport downstairs for one, and the big wide couch in the library for two, and indeed quite a number of nice people could be fairly comfortable here, from the jiffy the water is turned on,— provided any water appears. . . .

Meseems I hear the infernal whirring of the Egg-beater. Ugin will be back from Albany with presents for Ediner,—paint-brushes and loaves of bread and empty blueberry crates, and maybe if I'm very very good some white lead and linseed oil!

Next Day

Eugen read this letter, and he is frightfully jealous because he hasn't had a minute to write to *his* family. So he begs you to return this when you have finished with it or make a copy of it or something, so that he can ship it on to Holland. I tell him there are bad words in it; he says there are bad words in Holland, too.

I send you all much love from both of us.

Vincent.

Steepletop
August 20th, 1925

Dearest Mummie:

. . . Things are slowly getting done here, but we still have six workmen working in the house. Yesterday we got one room into fairly decent order, so that one could retire there and sit in comparative peace,—the only spot within a radius of a thousand feet where one could safely install one's harassed behind for a moment, without becoming firmly imbedded in a half-ton of cement—and today a hive of migrating honey-bees picked out that particular room to swarm in. We smoked them out finally, and nobody got stung; but it's so long since I dared sit, that when I again begin to sit, I shall have to go about it a few minutes at a time at first, as with any other unaccustomed exercise, in order not to get stiff. . . .

Let me know when you want some more money, even if it's by return mail. I can always go out and gather a few dollars for you; but it's been a very wet spring here, and it will be late in October before the dollars are really ripe enough to drop from the bough.

Goo'bye, darling, and ever and ever so much love,

Vincent.

e. e. cummings

From EIMI, a journal of a trip to Russia in 1931

TUES.

. . .

train's. train's Trainlessness. train's trainlessness Expanding. train's trainlessness expanding To. train's trainlessness expanding to Infinity. Train's Trainlessness Expanding To Infinity vanishes!

moscow?

"Dadada" from electrified picture-postcard—vividly(look)exit Swiss-in-tow(alas,without even a farewell nod.) The alcove yields its prey. I typewriter knapsack valise fall all over each other,collectively attaining our individual freedoms per not altogether large(but far from peculiarly small)station. Now wouldn't I be in a nice fix if he didn't take it into his unknown head to show up,that prominent Russian writer; the comrade for whom have a gaudy box of chocolates—the fellow to whom obediently I sent a telegram written and signed by that prominent Russian-in-Paris novelist(to whom was introduced by what's her name,the beauteous lady for whose farfamed sister am bringing all those nifty magazines and all that gudjus perfume)? Suppose he simply wasn't here to welcome his brother in literature,alias me? Such would indeed be droll. But something else would be droller! Suppose he did show up,and neither of us recognized the other(it seems,when I stop to think,considerably possible; for both of us haven't the slightest idea what either of us looks like). However,dogs will be dogs and Pavlov, with the aid of lampposts,may have discovered a brand-new recognition reflex;meanwhile,lampposts being unhandy,our hero may just as well ask certain distinguishedlooking comrades whether or no they happen to coincide with the anonymous celebrity who's to direct my very not unerring footsteps(if only everybody didn't look so equally distinguished,to put it mildly!). I approach jittery dude who's a little taller than the divine average

Excuse me:are you Soandso?

hardly,although he farts with an eyebrow. (That was my best Russian, too). Try next the little chap who's just fallen out of an observation balloon into a glass of sour milk

Pardon me:are you SoandSo?

emphatically nyet. Once again—for luck. And this time I choose a comparatively undistinguished comrade;who may or may not be asleep, feebleminded,or both

Forgive me:are you SoandSo?

he doesn't seem to understand. I reiterate my query;nothing doing. I soar into Heine—and a light dawns;the face opens,contracts,and in perfect American says

Nn-nn.

Then he turns his socalled back.

THOMAS WOLFE

To Aline Bernstein

Brussels
Wednesday, Sept 22, [1926]

My Dear:

. . . I have been in this very gay city for ten days now; in over a week I have not spoken in my own language, or talked with one of my own nation. My talk with nearly everyone has been impersonal—a matter of buying and paying. It's not bad, save at night. I get rather lonely, then.

I have done a great deal of writing—my book is going to enormous length, and I can't get done as quickly as I thought. To-day is the only day I haven't written—I am writing you this at dinner (8 o'clock) and shall try to get my day's work done to-night.

I took the day off and went to Waterloo in a bus—the first trip I've made. There were seven or eight of us only—two or three English, two or three French, and your old friend, James Joyce. He was with a woman about forty, and a young man, and a girl. I noticed him after we had descended at Waterloo—I had seen his picture only a day or two ago in a French publisher's announcements: he was wearing a blind over one eye. He was very simply—even shabbily—dressed. We went into a little café where the bus stopped to look at the battle souvenirs and buy postcards: then we walked up what was once the Sunken Road to a huge circular building that had a panorama of the battle painted around the sides; then we ascended the several hundred steps up the great mound which supports the lion and looks out over the field. The young man, who wore horn-rim spectacles, and a light sporty looking overcoat, looked very much like an American college boy: he began to talk to me going up the steps—I asked him if he knew the man with the eye blind. He said he did, and that it was Joyce. I commented briefly that I had seen Joyce's picture and read his book; after this the young fellow joined me at every point. Walking back down the road to the café, I asked him if Joyce's eyesight was better—he said it had greatly improved. He said Joyce was working on a new book, but thought it impossible to say when it was finished. We went back to the café—they sat down at a table and had tea—the young man seemed about to ask me to join them, and I took a seat quickly at another table, calling for two beers. They all spoke French together—he told them all about it, and they peeked furtively at me from time to time—the great man himself taking an occasional crafty shot at me with his good eye. As they had tea, they all wrote postcards. As they got up to go into the bus, the young man bowed somewhat grandly to me—I don't blame him; I'd be pleased too. I judge the people are Joyce's family—he is a man in the middle forties—old enough to have a son and a daughter like these. The woman had the appearance of a thousand middle class French women I've known—a vulgar, rather loose mouth; not very intelligent looking. The young man spoke English well, but with a foreign accent. It was tragic to see Joyce—one of the gods of the moment—speaking not one word of the language his fame is based on. The girl was rather pretty—I thought at first she was a little American flapper.

Joyce was very simple, very nice. He walked next to the old guide who showed us around, listening with apparent interest to his harangue delivered in broken English, and asking him questions. He came home to Brussels through a magnificent forest, miles in extent— Joyce sat with the driver on the front seat, asked a great many questions. I sat alone on the back seat—it was a huge coach; the woman sat in front of me, the girl in front of her, the young man to one side. Queer arrangement, eh?

Joyce got a bit stagey on the way home, draping his overcoat poetically around his shoulders. But I liked Joyce's looks—not extraordinary at first sight, but growing. His face was highly colored, slightly concave—his mouth thin, not delicate, but extraordinarily humorous. He had a large powerful straight nose—redder than his face, somewhat pitted with scars and boils.

When we got back to Brussels, and stopped in front of the bus office, the young man and two women made a little group, while Joyce went inside. The young fellow was looking at me, and I was swimming in beer. I made a dive for the nearest place, which was under a monument: they are more respectable here than in Paris.

Anyway it was too good to spoil: the idea of Joyce and me being at Waterloo at the same time, and aboard a sight-seeing bus, struck me as insanely funny: I sat on the back seat making idiot noises in my throat, and crooning all the way back through the forest.

I think really they might have been a little grand about it if they had known they were discovered. But they were just like common people out sight-seeing.

I'm going on to Antwerp to-morrow, Bruges the day after, London Sunday or Monday. . . . My life is utterly austere, utterly remote. I have eaten well here—some of the restaurants are excellent. But I have not sat at table or anywhere else with anyone, save a little English merchant who came over on the boat with me: he was a funny little man, . . . who conducted me, with many a sly wink to a table at a most respectable dinner hall: we drank orangeade, the little man looked at the girls, and winked at me, going off into fits of silent laughter.

You get nothing to drink in Brussels but beer and wine unless you buy *bottles* of the stronger stuff at stores. I drink beer mainly:

there are places here where you get iced sparkling champagne for twelve cents a goblet.

Last night about midnight—I had gone out from my room after working, for a walk—a woman stopped me, and began to wheedle me. She was a large strapping blonde prostitute. I gave her money for a beer and sent her on. A few minutes later, I noticed a fearful commotion across the street. Prostitutes, with their eager delight in a brawl, came in magical hordes. My lady had cut a sizable hunk out of a drunken gentleman's neck with a razor, and was fiercely mauling a small man all over the pavement. There were several minor brawls going on between the whores and their pimps. Finally, someone yelled "Police," and the army disappeared up four separate alleys. The police came up and arrested magnificently the man who had been cut. . . .

I am going back to England to try to finish the book—it is a far vaster thing than I had thought, but it grows in clarity and structure every day. This letter is stupid—all my energy . . . has gone into the book. I may go to Oxford next month. Meanwhile I shall try to get back my old apartment in London. . . .

Good-by—God bless you, my dear.

I'm tired after Joyce and Waterloo. Forgive a stupid letter. I just thought that I shall probably be 26 years old when you get this. At 23, hundreds of people thought I'd do something. Now, no one does—not even myself. I really don't care very much. . . .

ALUN LEWIS

To his wife, Gweno, written from Burma, undated [1943-44]

A hasty pot boiler to keep your hands warm. How are you? The sun is bright and gay and everything sparkling and scrubbed, and if it were ten years ago or ahead I'd have a gay scrubbed heart as well. As it is I philosophize and contemplate and remain neutral amid a very massive hurry-scurry of regimental mankind. If by some magic we were together I'd tell you quietly all that I cannot tell you in a letter. The only things they permit me to say are the fundamental unchanging things that don't help the Japs or interest the 5th columnists: things of no consequence to the fighting world, the world of telegrams and troop trains and supply columns. But they sing out in my heart like a branch of cherries and seven singing dwarfs, louder than all the trumpets, and it's the only true meaning in the sunshine and scene.

It's a limping, blinkered correspondence this, and until your letters catch me, one-sided for the both of us. But when you get it it becomes two-sided, doesn't it? And if you get this one and then get no more for a few weeks, it'll still be two-sided and complete. It must be. We must breathe freely, and keep our own world alive with sunlight and growth and health. The darkness and threats are from another part of ourselves. And the long self-torture I've been through is resolving itself now into a discipline of the emotions and hopes of you and me and the Remington baby, and I can feel my reason taking control and working carefully and methodically. I'm becoming my job in a very broad sense and (I may be flattering myself) I feel that my grasp is broader and steadier than it's been for a long time. I hope it's true, because that's how I want to be: and the rest of me is invulnerable. I want you to know that.

I won't be able to do much about your birthday this year, except send my love by pigeon and whistle Cherry Ripe, and I'll get my little gremlin to put a shine on the knob of the kettle and spit into the kettle for luck. And we'll chalk up all the birthday teas and Xmas dinners we've missed and have them all in Greek Street and Charlotte Street in one luxurious and abandoned week in London.

As I write now, Indian troops are shoutnig and squabbling about their dixies full of dahl and chappatis and curry, and the air is trailed and lined with the smell of their food. Hobnailed boots clattering back and fore, and men asking questions, and birds flying over in the wide blue sky. Last night I felt the moving active quality in the star-grown sky and the dark night and the silent watchful land—and there seemed to be a marvellous depth and freedom as well as danger and secrecy in it all. When you see Orion you are looking with my eyes. And the Plough tilts down on us both.

I must run now. Sorry I have to go. And God be in our heads and in our eyes and in our understanding. Buy me a typewriter when someone has one to sell, and I'll buy you a beautiful beautiful emerald or maybe a sapphire or maybe something neither of us knows.

THOMAS MERTON

From his Journal, *The Sign of Jonas*

April 28 [*1947*]

On and off since Easter I have been playing a new game called insomnia. It goes like this: You lie down in your dormitory cell and listen to first one monk and then another monk begin to snore without, however, going to sleep yourself. Then you count the quarter hours by the tower clock and console yourself with an exact knowledge of the amount of sleep you are missing. The fun does not really begin until you get up at 2 A. M. and try to keep awake in choir. All day long you wander around the monastery bumping into the walls.

Insomnia can become a form of contemplation. You just lie there, inert, helpless, alone, in the dark, and let yourself be crushed by the inscrutable tyranny of time. The plank bed becomes an altar and you lie there without trying to understand any longer in what sense you can be called a sacrifice. Outside in the world, where it is night, perhaps there is someone who suddenly sees that something he has done is horrible. He is most unexpectedly sorry and finds himself able to pray. . . .

October 10 Sunday [*1948*]

Sooner or later the world must burn, and all things in it—all the books, the cloister together with the brothel, Fra Angelico together with the Lucky Strike ads which I haven't seen for seven years because I don't remember seeing one in Louisville. Sooner or later it will all be consumed by fire and nobody will be left—for by that time the last man in the universe will have discovered the bomb capable of destroying the universe and will have been unable to resist the temptation to throw the thing and get it over with.

And here I sit writing a diary.

But love laughs at the end of the world because love is the door to eternity and he who loves God is playing on the doorstep of eternity, and before anything can happen love will have drawn him over the sill and closed the door and he won't bother about the world burning because he will know nothing but love.

Today for the first time we tried a schola of eight, singing during the whole Mass, and I can see where it would one day help a great deal. That was one of the ideas Reverend Father brought back from Citeaux.

In Chapter he told us about how it was at Lisieux, and La Grande Trappe, and Port du Salut where they run a power station. At La Trappe our Father Bernard, the sculptor, has discovered a system for making plaques of pious subjects, four at a time, all different sizes, and the notion made me quiver.

But sooner or later the world must burn—and *The Seven Storey Mountain* and *Figures for an Apocalypse*. And I have several times thought how at the Last Day I am likely to be one of the ten most abjectly humiliated sinners in the history of the world, but it will be my joy, and it will fill me with love, and I will fly like an arrow to take a back seat very far in the back where the last shall be first. And perhaps if Saint Francis will pray for me, and Saint John of the Cross, and Saint Mary Magdalen, I'll slide down off my high horse now and begin being the last and the least in everything, but not out of injured vanity as I was this morning in the eight-cylinder schola we had, that sang so fast *vir erat in terra Hus nomine Job.*

Now it is a toss-up whether I should ask Reverend Father to give me another and fatter book to fill with *Journal,* for we have been talking about my writing less. In fact, I have begun to tell him all about my temptations to become a Carthusian and he says he doesn't see why things can't be fixed up right here.

But *nos qui vivimus benedicamus Domino* by love, love, love, in the cloister and in the choir and out there in the presence of the forest and the hills where all the colors are changing, and under the steeple whose topmost cross has been painted with yellow traffic paint by Brother Processus who swung up there for days in the sky with his angel holding on to him. (He upset a bucket of paint and I could see it flying upside down on the end of a rope, and the paint turned to spray before it was half way down, and a drop fell on our Psalter and there were little yellow spots all over the stones and the bushes of the cemetery where today I saw a hawk.)

December 14 [*1948*]

The most precious thing I had today was an hour of silence out be-hind the church. It has been warm and damp and the knobs are hidden in mist. It started to rain a little and I came in but the laybrother novices were practicing part-singing in the choir novitiate and were singing better than the choir novices who were practicing Gregorian chant in the professed singing room. By that time I discovered that it wasn't really raining after all and so I escaped to my silence and stood out there all alone, drugged and happy, with a book under my arm.

Tomorrow: revolution. Self-shaving is to be introduced at Geth-semani for the first time in a century. Father Prior is going to give out brushes and safety razors and small bars of soap and (o horror!) mirrors. Father Abbot has received a letter of instructions from Our Lady of the Valley telling all about how to shave. We are supposed to shave twice a week. Such effeminacy! We shall rake and hack at our own miserable chins; in the end this is going to be more penitential—but faster than the communal electric shave: we won't have to sit around waiting our turn.

Apparently this is what they do in Europe. Dom Gabriel was shocked to see us so hairy.

I am invitator and I sing *"Tota pulchra es, Maria."*

Berliner and Lanigan sent us an Advent house—you open a window each day and lo! a picture symbolizing one of the "O" antiphons. To-morrow is Ember Wednesday—O happy fast!— and the Great "O's" begin Friday.

July 11 [*1949*]

We have a new mechanical monster on the place called a D-4 Trax-cavator which is enormous and rushes at the earth with a wide-open maw and devours everything in sight. It roars terribly, especially when it is hungry. It has been given to the laybrother novices. They feed it every day and you can't hear yourself think in the monastery while the brute is at table. It is yellow and has a face like a drawbridge and is marked all over with signs saying it comes from the Whayne supply company in Louisville, but really, as I know from secret information, it was born on a raft in Memphis, Tennessee. There, the hippopotamus abounds: which this instrument greatly resembles.

Also we have bought fans. They are exhaust fans. You make a

hole in the building and put the fans there and they draw all the hot air out of the dormitory. Nobody knows what happens after that. My guess is that the hot air that went out through the fan is then replaced by the hot air that comes in through the windows. The fans are not yet running because the laybrother novices have not yet made the holes in the building. However, they have begun. They have a scaffold up on the roof of the infirmary and they have been blasting at the gable of that wing with jack-hammers, and two frail novices who are very young were posted down on the ground floor near the doorways with artistic signs which read "Falling Bricks." At first one of them was standing at the precise spot where all the falling bricks would land on his head. He was saying the rosary in an attitude of perfect abandonment. Afterwards he got a stool and moved inside the cloister and propped up the sign in his lap and took to reading the immortal masterpiece of Father Garrigou-Lagrange, *Christian Perfection and Contemplation.*

DRAMA

From *Abraham and Isaac**

[*God's angel has announced to Abraham that God wishes Abraham
to make a sacrifice with the blood of his young son Isaac. God thus
makes proof whether Abraham "better loveth his child or me." The
angel has just left Abraham.*]

ABRAHAM. Now, Isaac, my own son dear,
Where art thou, child? Speak to me.
ISAAC. My fair, sweet father, I am here,
And make my prayers to the Trinity.
ABRAHAM. Rise up, my child, and fast come hither,
My gentle barn, that art so wise;
For we two, child, must go together,
And unto my Lord make sacrifice.
ISAAC. I am full ready, my father, lo!
Even at your hands I stand right here;
And whatsoever ye bid me do,
It shall be done with glad cheer,
Full well and fine.
ABRAHAM. A! Isaac, my own son so dear,
God's blessing I give thee, and mine.
Hold this faggot upon thy back,
And here myself fire shall bring.
ISAAC. Father, all this here will I pack;
I am full fain to do your bidding.
ABRAHAM. A! Lord of heaven, my hands I wring.
This child's words wound sore my heart!
Now, Isaac, son, go we our way
Unto yon mount, with all our main.
ISAAC. Go we, my dear father, as fast as I may;
To follow you I am full fain,
Although I be slender.

* The text of this fifteenth-century miracle play from Brome Hall, Suffolk, has
been slightly modernized.

ABRAHAM. A! Lord, my heart breaketh in twain,
This child's words they be so tender!
                    (They arrive atop the mount.)
A! Isaac, son, now lay it down.
No longer upon thy back it hold,
For I must make ready prayer
To honor my Lord God as I should.
                    (Abraham prepares the fire.)
ISAAC. Lo, my dear father, where it is!
To cheer you always I draw me near.
But, father, I marvel sore of this—
Why that ye make this heavy cheer;
And also, father, evermore dread I:
Where is your quick beast that ye should kill?
Both fire and wood we have ready,
But quick beast have we none on this hill.
A quick beast, I know well, must be dead
Your sacrifice for to make.
      ABRAHAM. Dread thee nought, my child, I bid thee.
Our Lord will send me unto this place
Some manner of beast for to take
Through his sweet command.
      ISAAC. Yea, father, but my heart beginneth to quake
To see that sharp sword in your hand.
Why bear ye your sword drawn so?
Of your countenance I have much wonder.
      ABRAHAM. A! Father of heaven, so am I woe!
This child here breaks my heart asunder.
      ISAAC. Tell me, my dear father, or that ye cease,
Bear ye your sword drawn for me?
      ABRAHAM. A! Isaac, sweet son, peace! peace!
For thou dost break my heart in three.
      ISAAC. Now truly, something, father, ye think,
That ye mourn thus more and more.
      ABRAHAM. A! Lord of Heaven, thy grace let sink,
For my heart was never half so sore.
      ISAAC. I pray you, father, that ye will tell me so
Whether shall I have any harm or no.
      ABRAHAM. Of a truth, sweet son, I may not tell thee yet,
My heart is now so full of woe.

ISAAC. Dear father, I pray you, hide it not from me,
But some of your thought that ye tell me.

ABRAHAM. A! Isaac, Isaac, I must kill thee!

ISAAC. Kill me, father? Alas! what have I done?
If I have trespassed against thee aught,
With a rod ye may make me full mild,
And with your sharp sword kill me not,
For alas, father, I am but a child!

ABRAHAM. I am full sorry, son, thy blood for to spill,
But truly, my child, I may not choose.

ISAAC. Now I would to God my mother were here on this hill!
She would kneel for me on both her knees
To save my life.
And since that my mother is not here,
I pray you, father, change your cheer,
And kill me not with your knife.

ABRAHAM. Forsooth, son! unless I thee kill,
I should grieve God right sore, I fear.
It is his commandment, and also his will,
That I should do this same deed here,
He commanded me, son, for certain,
To make my sacrifice with thy blood.

ISAAC. And is it God's will that I should be slain?

ABRAHAM. Yea, truly, Isaac, my son so good;
And therefore my hands I wring.

ISAAC. Now, father, against my Lord's will
I will never grudge, loud nor still.
He might have sent me a better destiny
If it had been his will.

ABRAHAM. Forsooth, son, unless I did this deed
Grievously displeased our Lord will be.

ISAAC. Nay, nay, father; God forbid
That ever ye should grieve him for me.
Ye have other children, one or two,
The which ye should love well by nature.
I pray you, father, make ye no woe,
For be I once dead and from you go,
I shall be soon out of your mind.
Therefore, do our Lord's bidding.
And when I am dead, then pray for me.

But—good Father—tell ye my mother no thing.
Say—that I am in another country dwelling.

ABRAHAM. A! Isaac, Isaac, blessed may thou be!
My heart beginneth strongly to rise,
To see the blood of thy blessed body.

ISAAC. Father, since it may be no other wise,
Let it pass over as well as I.
But father, or I go unto my death,
I pray you bless me with your hand.

ABRAHAM. Now, Isaac, with all my breath
My blessing I give thee upon this land,
And God's also thereto, surely.
Isaac, Isaac, son, up thou stand,
Thy fair, sweet mouth that I may kiss.

ISAAC. Now farewell, my own father so fine;
And greet well my mother on earth.
But I pray you, father, to hide my eyn
That I see not the stroke of your sharp sword,
That my flesh shall defile.

· · · · ·

ABRAHAM. Thy meek words, child, make me afraid;
So "Welaway!" may be my song,
Except alonely God's will.
A! Isaac, my own sweet child,
Yet kiss me again upon this hill!
In all this world is none so mild.

· · · · ·

ISAAC. A! Mercy, father; mourn ye no more.
Your weeping maketh my heart sore,
As my own death that I shall suffer.
Your kerchief, father, about my eyn ye wind!

ABRAHAM. So I shall, my sweetest child on earth.

ISAAC. Now yet, good father, have this in mind:
And smite me not often with your sharp sword,
But hastily that it be sped.

ABRAHAM. Now farewell, my child, so full of grace.

ISAAC. A! Father, father, turn downward my face,
For of your sharp sword I am ever adread.

· · · · ·

ABRAHAM. Lo! Now is the time come certain
That my sword in his neck shall bite.
A! Lord, my heart riseth thereagainst!
I may not find it in my heart to smite;
My heart will not now thereto.
Yet fain I would work my Lord's will;
But this young innocent lieth so still
I may not find it in my heart him to kill.
O! Father of Heaven! What shall I do?
    ISAAC. A! Mercy, father; why tarry ye so,
And let me lie thus long on this heath?
Now I would to God the stroke were done!
Father, I pray you heartily, cut short my woe,
And let me not look thus after my death,
    ABRAHAM. Now, heart, why wouldst not thou break in three?
Yet shall thou not make me to my God unmild.
I will no longer stay for thee,
For that my God aggrieved would be.
Now hold the stroke, my own dear child!
      (As he is about to strike, the angel reappears,
        and seizes the sword from Abraham.)
    ANGEL. I am an angel, thou mayst see glad,
That from heaven to thee is sent.
Our Lord thanketh thee an hundred times
For the keeping of his commandment.
He knows thy will and also thy heart,
That thou dreadest him above all thing;
And some of thy heaviness for to depart
A fair ram yonder I did bring.
He standeth tied, among the briars.
Now, Abraham, amend thy mood,
For Isaac, thy young son that here is,
This day shall not shed his blood.
Go, make thy sacrifice with yon ram.
Now farewell, blessed Abraham,
For unto Heaven I go now home.
The way is full straight.
Take up thy son so free.
        (ANGEL *leaves.*)

ABRAHAM. A! Lord, I thank thee of thy great grace,
Now am I gladdened in many ways.
Arise up, Isaac, my dear son, arise!
Arise up, sweet child, and come to me!

· · · · · ·

Yon beast shall die here in thy stead,
In the worship of our Lord alone.
Go, fetch him hither, my child, indeed.
 ISAAC. Father, I will go catch him by the head,
And bring yon beast with me straightway.
    (*He brings the ram to* ABRAHAM.)
A! Sheep, sheep, blessed may thou be,
That ever thou wert sent down hither!
Thou shall this day die for me,
In the worship of the holy Trinity.
Now come fast and go we together
To my Father of Heaven.
Thou thou be never so gentle and good,
Yet had I liefer thou sheddest thy blood,
Surely, sheep, than I.
Lo! father, I have brought here full smart
This gentle sheep, and him to you I give;
But Lord God, I thank thee with all my heart,
For I am glad that I shall live
And kiss once my dear mother!

CHRISTOPHER MARLOWE

~~~~~~

From *The Tragical History of Dr. Faustus*

[*This is from the concluding scene of the play. Having sold his soul to the Devil in exchange for magical powers, Faustus now awaits his last hour.*]

(The clock strikes eleven.)

FAUSTUS.   Ah, Faustus,
Now hast thou but one bare hour to live,
And then thou must be damn'd perpetually!
Stand still, you ever-moving spheres of Heaven,
That time may cease, and midnight never come;
Fair Nature's eye, rise, rise again and make
Perpetual day; or let this hour be but
A year, a month, a week, a natural day,
That Faustus may repent and save his soul!
O lente, lente, currite noctis equi!*
The stars move still, time runs, the clock will strike,
The Devil will come, and Faustus must be damn'd.
O, I'll leap up to my God! Who pulls me down?
See, see, where Christ's blood streams in the firmament!
One drop would save my soul—half a drop; ah, my Christ!
Ah, rend not my heart for naming of my Christ!
Yet will I call on him: O spare me, Lucifer!—
Where is it now? 'Tis gone; and see where God
Stretcheth out his arm, and bends his ireful brows!
Mountain and hills come, come and fall on me,
And hide me from the heavy wrath of God!
No! No!
Then will I headlong run into the earth;
Earth, gape! O no, it will not harbour me!
You stars that reign'd at my nativity,
Whose influence hath allotted death and hell,
Now draw up Faustus like a foggy mist
Into the entrails of yon labouring clouds,
That when they vomit forth into the air,
My limbs may issue from their smoky mouths,
So that my soul may but ascend to Heaven.
            (The watch strikes the half hour.)
Ah, half the hour is past! 'T will all be past anon!
O God!
If thou wilt not have mercy on my soul,
Yet for Christ's sake whose blood hath ransom'd me,
Impose some end to my incessant pain;
Let Faustus live in hell a thousand years—

    * "Run softly, softly, horses of the night."—Ovid.

A hundred thousand, and at last be sav'd!
O, no end is limited to damned souls!
Why wert thou not a creature wanting soul?
Or why is this immortal that thou hast?
Ah, Pythagoras' metempsychosis! were that true,
This soul should fly from me, and I be chang'd
Unto some brutish beast! All beasts are happy,
For, when they die,
Their souls are soon dissolv'd in elements;
But mine must live, still to be plagu'd in hell.
Curst be the parents that engend'red me!
No, Faustus: curse thyself: curse Lucifer
That hath depriv'd thee of the joys of Heaven.
        (The clock striketh twelve.)
O, it strikes, it strikes! Now, body, turn to air,
Or Lucifer will bear thee quick to hell.
        (Thunder and lightning)
O soul, be chang'd into little water-drops,
And fall into the ocean—ne'er be found.
My God! my God! look not so fierce on me!
        (Enter DEVILS.*)*
Adders and serpents, let me breathe awhile!
Ugly hell, gape not! come not, Lucifer!
I'll burn my books!—Ah, Mephistophilis!
        (Exeunt DEVILS, *with* FAUSTUS.*)*

WILLIAM SHAKESPEARE

From *Richard II*

[*From Act V. Scene v. Alone in Pomfret Castle, the imprisoned young king awaits his death.*]

        (Enter RICHARD, *alone.)*
    RICHARD. I have been studying how I may compare
This prison where I live unto the world;

And, for because the world is populous,
And here is not a creature but myself,
I cannot do it. Yet I'll hammer it out.
My brain I'll prove the female to my soul,
My soul the father; and these two beget
A generation of still-breeding thoughts;
And these same thoughts people this little world,
In humours like the people of this world,
For no thought is contented. The better sort,
As thoughts of things divine, are intermix'd
With scruples, and do set the world itself
Against the word:
As thus, "Come, little ones," and then again,
"It is as hard to come as for a camel
To thread the postern of a small needle's eye."
Thoughts tending to ambition, they do plot
Unlikely wonders—how these vain weak nails
May tear a passage through the flinty ribs
Of this hard world, my ragged prison walls;
And, for they cannot, die in their own pride.
Thoughts tending to content flatter themselves
That they are not the first of fortune's slaves,
Nor shall not be the last; like seely beggars
Who, sitting in the stocks, refuge their shame,
That many have, and others must sit there.
And in this thought they find a kind of ease,
Bearing their own misfortunes on the back
Of such as have before endur'd the like.
Thus play I in one person many people,
And none contented. Sometimes am I king:
Then treasons make me wish myself a beggar,
And so I am. Then crushing penury
Persuades me I was better when a king;
Then am I king'd again; and by-and-by
Think that I am unking'd by Bolingbroke,
And straight am nothing. But whate'er I be,
Nor I, nor any man that but man is,
With nothing shall be pleas'd till he be eas'd
With being nothing.

(The music plays.)

Music do I hear?
Ha, ha! keep time! How sour sweet music is
When time is broke and no proportion kept!
So is it in the music of men's lives.
And here have I the daintiness of ear
To check time broke in a disorder'd string;
But for the concord of my state and time,
Had not an ear to hear my true time broke.
I wasted time, and now doth time waste me;
For now hath time made me his numbering clock:
My thoughts are minutes; and with sighs they jar
Their watches on unto mine eyes, the outward watch,
Whereto my finger, like a dial's point,
Is pointing still, in cleansing them from tears.
Now, sir, the sounds that tell what hour it is
Are clamorous groans, that strike upon my heart,
Which is the bell. So sighs, and tears, and groans
Show minutes, times, and hours. But my time
Runs posting on in Bolingbroke's proud joy,
While I stand fooling here, his Jack o' th' clock.
This music mads me! Let it sound no more!
For though it have holp madmen to their wits,
In me it seems it will make wise men mad.
Yet blessing on his heart that gives it me!
For 'tis a sign of love, and love to Richard
Is a strange brooch in this all-hating world.

~~~~~~

From *Twelfth Night*

[*In Act II, Scene iv, the Duke Orsino, in love with the Lady Olivia, prepares once more to send his page Cesario to woo Olivia in vain. Cesario, though Orsino does not know it, is actually the young maiden Viola, who has been shipwrecked and has entered the Duke's service in masculine disguise. Viola's situation is here ironical, since she has herself fallen in love with Orsino*].

DUKE. Once more, Cesario,
Get thee to yond same sovereign cruelty.
Tell her, my love, more noble than the world,
Prizes not quantity of dirty lands.
The parts that fortune hath bestow'd upon her,
Tell her I hold as giddily as fortune;
But 'tis that miracle and queen of gems
That nature pranks her in, attracts my soul.
  VIOLA. But if she cannot love you, sir——
  DUKE. I cannot be so answer'd.
  VIOLA.   Sooth, but you must.
Say that some lady, as perhaps there is,
Hath for your love as great a pang of heart
As you have for Olivia. You cannot love her.
You tell her so. Must she not then be answer'd?
  DUKE. There is no woman's sides
Can bide the beating of so strong a passion
As love doth give my heart; no woman's heart
So big to hold so much; they lack retention.
Alas, their love may be call'd appetite—
No motion of the liver, but the palate—
That suffers surfeit, cloyment, and revolt;
But mine is all as hungry as the sea
And can digest as much. Make no compare
Between that love a woman can bear me
And that I owe Olivia.
  VIOLA.   Ay, but I know——
  DUKE. What dost thou know?
  VIOLA. Too well what love women to men may owe.
In faith, they are as true of heart as we.
My father had a daughter lov'd a man
As it might be perhaps, were I a woman,
I should your lordship.
  DUKE.   And what's her history?
  VIOLA. A blank, my lord. She never told her love,
But let concealment, like a worm i'th' bud,
Feed on her damask cheek. She pin'd in thought;
And, with a green and yellow melancholy,
She sat like Patience on a monument,
Smiling at grief. Was not this love indeed?

We men may say more, swear more; but indeed
Our shows are more than will; for still we prove
Much in our vows but little in our love.
    DUKE. But died thy sister of her love, my boy?
    VIOLA. I am all the daughters of my father's house,
And all the brothers too—and yet I know not.
Sir, shall I to this lady?
    DUKE.   Ay, that's the theme.
To her in haste! Give her this jewel. Say
My love can give no place, bide no denay.

From *Hamlet*

[*In Act III, Scene iv, Hamlet, having proof that his step-father King Claudius is guilty of the murder of King Hamlet the elder, goes to visit his mother, Queen Gertrude, to persuade her that her love for Claudius has been both adulterous and incestuous. Polonius, the king's elderly chamberlain, plants himself to discover the cause of the young Hamlet's mad behavior in the court.*]

(*Enter* QUEEN *and* POLONIUS.)
    POLONIUS. He will come straight. Look you lay home to him.
Tell him his pranks have been too broad to bear with,
And that your Grace hath screen'd and stood between
Much heat and him. I'll silence me even here.
Pray you be round with him.
    HAMLET. (*Within*) Mother, mother, mother!
    QUEEN. I'll warrant you; fear me not. Withdraw; I hear him coming.

(POLONIUS *hides behind the arras.*)
(*Enter* HAMLET.)
    HAMLET. Now, mother, what's the matter?
    QUEEN. Hamlet, thou hast thy father much offended.
    HAMLET. Mother, you have my father much offended.

QUEEN. Come, come, you answer with an idle tongue.

HAMLET. Go, go, you question with a wicked tongue.

QUEEN. Why, how now, Hamlet?

HAMLET.   What's the matter now?

QUEEN. Have you forgot me?

HAMLET.   No, by the rood, not so!
You are the Queen, your husband's brother's wife,
And (would it were not so!) you are my mother.

QUEEN. Nay, then I'll set those to you that can speak.

HAMLET. Come, come, and sit you down. You shall not budge!
You go not till I set you up a glass
Where you may see the inmost part of you.

QUEEN. What wilt thou do? Thou wilt not murther me?
Help, help, ho!

POLONIUS. *(Behind the arras)* What, ho! help, help, help!

HAMLET. *(Draws)* How now? a rat? Dead for a ducat, dead!
 (Makes a pass through the arras and kills POLONIUS.)

POLONIUS. O, I am slain!

QUEEN.   O me, what hast thou done?

HAMLET. Nay, I know not. Is it the King?

QUEEN. O, what a rash and bloody deed is this!

HAMLET. A bloody deed—almost as bad, good mother,
As kill a king and marry with his brother.

QUEEN. As kill a king?

HAMLET.   Ay, lady, it was my word.
 (Lifts the arras and sees POLONIUS' body.)
Thou wretched, rash, intruding fool, farewell!
I took thee for thy better. Take thy fortune.
Thou find'st to be too busy is some danger.
Leave wringing of your hands. Peace! sit you down
And let me wring your heart; for so I shall
If it be made of penetrable stuff;
If damned custom have not braz'd it so
That it is proof and bulwark against sense.

QUEEN. What have I done that thou dar'st wag thy tongue
In noise so rude against me?

HAMLET.   Such an act
That blurs the grace and blush of modesty;
Calls virtue hypocrite; takes off the rose
From the fair forehead of an innocent love

And sets a blister there; makes marriage vows
As false as dicers' oaths. O, such a deed
As from the body of contraction plucks
The very soul, and sweet religion makes
A rhapsody of words! Heaven's face doth glow;
Yea, this solidity and compound mass,
With tristful visage, as against the doom,
Is thought-sick at the act.

    QUEEN.   Ay me, what act,
That roars so loud and thunders in the index?

    HAMLET. Look here upon his picture, and on this,
The counterfeit presentment of two brothers.
See what a grace was seated on this brow;
Hyperion's curls; the front of Jove himself;
An eye like Mars, to threaten and command;
A station like the herald Mercury
New-lighted on a heaven-kissing hill:
A combination and a form indeed
Where every god did seem to set his seal
To give the world assurance of a man.
This was your husband. Look you now what follows.
Here is your husband, like a mildew'd ear
Blasting his wholesome brother. Have you eyes?
Could you on this fair mountain leave to feed,
And batten on this moor? Ha! have you eyes?
You cannot call it love; for at your age
The heyday in the blood is tame, it's humble,
And waits upon the judgment; and what judgment
Would step from this to this? Sense sure you have,
Else could you not have motion; but sure that sense
Is apoplex'd; for madness would not err,
Nor sense to ecstasy was ne'er so thrall'd
But it reserv'd some quantity of choice
To serve in such a difference. What devil was't
That thus hath cozen'd you at hoodman-blind?
Eyes without feeling, feeling without sight,
Ears without hands or eyes, smelling sans all,
Or but a sickly part of one true sense
Could not so mope.
O shame! where is thy blush? Rebellious hell,

If thou canst mutine in a matron's bones,
To flaming youth let virtue be as wax
And melt in her own fire. Proclaim no shame,
When the compulsive ardour gives the charge,
Since frost itself as actively doth burn,
And reason panders will.

QUEEN.   O Hamlet, speak no more!
Thou turn'st mine eyes into my very soul,
And there I see such black and grained spots
As will not leave their tinct.

HAMLET.   Nay, but to live
In the rank sweat of an enseamed bed,
Stew'd in corruption, honeying and making love
Over the nasty sty!

QUEEN.   O, speak to me no more!
These words like daggers enter in mine ears.
No more, sweet Hamlet!

HAMLET.   A murtherer and a villain!
A slave that is not twentieth part the tithe
Of your precedent lord; a vice of kings;
A cutpurse of the empire and the rule,
That from a shelf the precious diadem stole
And put it in his pocket.

QUEEN.   No more!
          (*Enter the* GHOST *in his night gown.*)

HAMLET. A king of shreds and patches!—
Save me and hover o'er me with your wings,
You heavenly guards! What would your gracious figure?

QUEEN. Alas, he's mad!

HAMLET. Do you not come your tardy son to chide,
That, laps'd in time and passion, lets go by
Th' important acting of your dread command?
O, say!

GHOST. Do not forget. This visitation
Is but to whet thy almost blunted purpose.
But look, amazement on thy mother sits.
O, step between her and her fighting soul!
Conceit in weakest bodies strongest works.
Speak to her, Hamlet.

HAMLET.   How is it with you, lady?

QUEEN. Alas, how is't with you,
That you do bend your eye on vacancy,
And with th' incorporal air do hold discourse?
Forth at your eyes your spirits wildly peep;
And, as the sleeping soldiers in th' alarm,
Your bedded hairs, like life in excrements,
Start up and stand on end. O gentle son,
Upon the heat and flame of thy distemper
Sprinkle cool patience! Whereon do you look?
HAMLET. On him, on him! Look you how pale he glares!
His form and cause conjoin'd, preaching to stones,
Would make them capable.—Do not look upon me,
Lest with this piteous action you convert
My stern effects. Then what I have to do
Will want true colour—tears perchance for blood.
QUEEN. To whom do you speak this?
HAMLET.   Do you see nothing there?
QUEEN. Nothing at all. Yet all that is, I see.
HAMLET. Nor did you nothing hear?
QUEEN.   No, nothing but ourselves.
HAMLET. Why, look you there! Look how it steals away!
My father, in his habit as he liv'd!
Look where he goes even now out at the portal!
                    (*Exit* GHOST.)
QUEEN. This is the very coinage of your brain.
This bodiless creation ecstasy
Is very cunning in.
HAMLET.   Ecstasy?
My pulse as yours doth temperately keep time
And makes as healthful music. It is not madness
That I have utter'd. Bring me to the test,
And I the matter will reword, which madness
Would gambol from. Mother, for love of grace,
Lay not that flattering unction to your soul,
That not your trespass but my madness speaks.
It will but skin and film the ulcerous place,
Whiles rank corruption, mining all within,
Infects unseen. Confess yourself to heaven;
Repent what's past; avoid what is to come;
And do not spread the compost on the weeds

To make them ranker. Forgive me this my virtue;
For in the fatness of these pursy times
Virtue itself of vice must pardon beg—
Yea, curb and woo for leave to do him good.

    QUEEN. O, Hamlet, thou hast cleft my heart in twain.

    HAMLET. O, throw away the worser part of it,
And live the purer with the other half.
Good night,—but go not to my uncle's bed.
Assume a virtue, if you have it not.
That monster, custom, who all sense doth eat
Of habits evil, is angel yet in this,
That to the use of actions fair and good
He likewise gives a frock or livery,
That aptly is put on. Refrain tonight,
And that shall lend a kind of easiness
To the next abstinence; the next more easy;
For use almost can change the stamp of nature,
And either master the devil, or throw him out
With wondrous potency. Once more, good night;
And when you are desirous to be blest,
I'll blessing beg of you.—For this same lord,
I do repent; but heaven hath pleas'd it so,
To punish me with this, and this with me,
That I must be their scourge and minister.
I will bestow him, and will answer well
The death I gave him. So again, good night.
I must be cruel, only to be kind;
Thus bad begins, and worse remains behind.

BEN JONSON

~~~~~~

From *Volpone*

[*In Act I, Scene iv, the servant Mosca admits to Volpone's presence the elderly Corbaccio, who hopes by his gifts to become Volpone's heir. But the wealthy Volpone is only pretending to be sick, and by this*

*means increases his wealth from the gifts of those who, wishing him
dead, pretend to be inquiring after his health.*]

(MOSCA *and* VOLPONE *remain.*)

MOSCA. Betake you to your silence, and your sleep.—
(To the plate) Stand there and multiply.—(*Aside*) Now shall we see
A wretch who is indeed more impotent
Than this can feign to be; yet hopes to hop
Over his grave.—

(*He admits* CORBACCIO.)

Signior Corbaccio!
You're very welcome, sir.

CORBACCIO.   How does your patron?

MOSCA. Troth, as he did, sir; no amends.

CORBACCIO.   What? mends he?

MOSCA. No, sir: he is rather worse.

CORBACCIO.   That's well. Where is he?

MOSCA. Upon his couch, sir, newly fall'n asleep.

CORBACCIO. Does he sleep well?

MOSCA.   No wink, sir, all this night,
Nor yesterday; but slumbers.

CORBACCIO.   Good! he should take
Some counsel of physicians. I have brought him
An opiate here, from mine own doctor—

MOSCA. He will not hear of drugs.

CORBACCIO.   Why? I myself
Stood by while 'twas made, saw all th' ingredients,
And know it cannot but most gently work.
My life for his, 'tis but to make him sleep.

VOLPONE. (*Aside*) Ay, his last sleep, if he would take it.

MOSCA.   Sir,
He has no faith in physic.

CORBACCIO.   Say you? say you?

MOSCA. He has no faith in physic; he does think
Most of your doctors are the greater danger,
And worse disease, t' escape. I often have
Heard him protest that your physician
Should never be his heir.

CORBACCIO.   Not I his heir?

MOSCA. Not your physician, sir.

CORBACCIO.   O, no, no, no;
I do not mean it.

MOSCA.   No, sir, nor their fees
He cannot brook; he says they flay a man
Before they kill him.

CORBACCIO.   Right, I do conceive you.

MOSCA. And then they do it by experiment;
For which the law not only doth absolve 'em,
But gives them great reward, and he is loth
To hire his death so.

CORBACCIO.   It is true, they kill
With as much license as a judge.

MOSCA.   Nay, more;
For he but kills, sir, where the law condemns,
And these can kill him too.

CORBACCIO.   Ay, or me,
Or any man. How does his apoplex?
Is that strong on him still?

MOSCA.   Most violent.
His speech is broken, and his eyes are set,
His face drawn longer than 'twas wont—

CORBACCIO.   How? how?
Stronger than he was wont?

MOSCA.   No, sir, his face
Drawn longer than 'twas wont.

CORBACCIO.   O good.

MOSCA.   His mouth
Is ever gaping, and his eyelids hang.

CORBACCIO.   Good.

MOSCA. A freezing numbness stiffens all his joints,
And makes the color of his flesh like lead.

CORBACCIO.   'Tis good.

MOSCA. His pulse beats slow, and dull.

CORBACCIO.   Good symptoms still.

MOSCA. And from his brain—

CORBACCIO.   Ha? How? Not from his brain?

MOSCA. Yes, sir, and from his brain—

CORBACCIO.   I conceive you; good.

MOSCA. Flows a cold sweat, with a continual rheum,
Forth the resolved corners of his eyes.

CORBACCIO. Is 't possible? Yet I am better, ha!
How does he with the swimming of his head?

MOSCA. O, sir, 'tis past the scotomy; he now
Hath lost his feeling, and hath left to snort;
You hardly can perceive him, that he breathes.

CORBACCIO. Excellent, excellent, sure I shall outlast him;
This makes me young again, a score of years.

MOSCA. I was a-coming for you, sir.

CORBACCIO.   Has he made his will?
What has he giv'n me?

MOSCA.   No, sir.

CORBACCIO.   Nothing? ha?

MOSCA. He has not made his will, sir.

CORBACCIO.   Oh, oh, oh.
What then did Voltore, the lawyer, here?

MOSCA. He smelt a carcass, sir, when he but heard
My master was about his testament;
As I did urge him to it for your good—

CORBACCIO. He came unto him, did he? I thought so.

MOSCA. Yes, and presented him this piece of plate.

CORBACCIO. To be his heir?

MOSCA.   I do not know, sir.

CORBACCIO.   True;
I know it too.

MOSCA. (Aside) By your own scale, sir.

CORBACCIO.   Well,
I shall prevent him yet. See, Mosca, look,
Here I have brought a bag of bright *cecchines,*
Will quite weigh down his plate.

MOSCA.   Yea, marry, sir.
This is true physic, this your sacred medicine;
No talk of opiates to this great elixir!

CORBACCIO. 'Tis *aurum palpabile,* if not *potabile.*

MOSCA. It shall be minister'd to him in his bowl!

CORBACCIO. Ay, do, do, do.

MOSCA.   Most blessed cordial!
This will recover him.

CORBACCIO.   Yes, do, do, do.

Mosca. I think it were not best, sir.

Corbaccio.   What?

Mosca.   To recover him.

Corbaccio. O, no, no, no; by no means.

Mosca.   Why, sir, this
Will work some strange effect, if he but feel it.

Corbaccio. 'Tis true; therefore forbear. I'll take my venture;
Give me 't again.

Mosca.   At no hand; pardon me,
You shall not do yourself that wrong, sir. I
Will so advise you, you shall have it all.

Corbaccio. How?

Mosca.   All, sir; 'tis your right, your own; no man
Can claim a part; 'tis yours without a rival,
Decreed by destiny.

Corbaccio.   How, how, good Mosca?

Mosca. I'll tell you, sir. This fit he shall recover—

Corbaccio. I do conceive you.

Mosca.   And, on first advantage
Of his gain'd sense, will I re-importune him
Unto the making of his testament,
And show him this. *(Points to the money.)*

Corbaccio.   Good, good.

Mosca.   'Tis better yet,
If you will hear, sir.

Corbaccio.   Yes, with all my heart.

Mosca. Now would I counsel you, make home with speed;
There, frame a will; whereto you shall inscribe
My master your sole heir.

Corbaccio.   And disinherit
My son?

Mosca. O, sir, the better; for that color
Shall make it much more taking.

Corbaccio.   O, but color?

Mosca. This will, sir, you shall send it unto me.
Now, when I come to enforce, as I will do,
Your cares, your watchings, and your many prayers,
Your more than many gifts, your this day's present,
And last, produce your will; where (without thought
Or least regard unto your proper issue,
A son so brave, and highly meriting)

The stream of your diverted love hath thrown you
Upon my master, and made him your heir;
He cannot be so stupid or stone-dead,
But, out of conscience and mere gratitude—

CORBACCIO. He must pronounce me his?

MOSCA.   'Tis true.

CORBACCIO.   This plot
Did I think on before.

MOSCA.   I do believe it.

CORBACCIO. Do you not believe it?

MOSCA.   Yes, sir.

CORBACCIO.   Mine own project.

MOSCA. Which, when he hath done, sir—

CORBACCIO.   Publish'd me his heir?

MOSCA. And you so certain to survive him—

CORBACCIO.   Ay.

MOSCA. Being so lusty a man—

CORBACCIO.   'Tis true,

MOSCA.   Yes, sir—

CORBACCIO. I thought on that too. See, how he should be
The very organ to express my thoughts

MOSCA. You have not only done yourself a good—

CORBACCIO. But multiplied it on my son!

MOSCA.   'Tis right, sir.

CORBACCIO. Still, my invention.

MOSCA.   'Las, sir! Heaven knows,
It hath been all my study, all my care,
(I e'en grow gray withal) how to work things—

CORBACCIO. I do conceive, sweet Mosca.

MOSCA.   You are he
For whom I labor here.

CORBACCIO.   Ay, do, do, do.
I'll straight about it.

MOSCA. (Aside) Rook go with you, raven.

CORBACCIO. I know thee honest.

MOSCA.   You do lie, sir—

CORBACCIO.   And—

MOSCA. Your knowledge is no better than your ears, sir.

CORBACCIO. I do not doubt to be a father to thee.

MOSCA. Nor I to gull my brother of his blessing.

CORBACCIO. I may ha' my youth restor'd to me, why not?

MOSCA. Your Worship is a precious ass—

CORBACCIO. What say'st thou?

MOSCA. I do desire your Worship to make haste, sir. *(Exit.)*

CORBACCIO. 'Tis done, 'tis done; I go.

VOLPONE. *(Leaping from his couch)* Oh, I shall burst!
Let out my sides, let out my sides—

MOSCA. Contain
Your flux of laughter, sir; you know this hope
Is such a bait, it covers any hook.

VOLPONE. O, but thy working, and thy placing it!
I cannot hold; good rascal, let me kiss thee;
I never knew thee in so rare a humor.

MOSCA. Alas, sir, I but do as I am taught;
Follow your grave instructions, give 'em words,
Pour oil into their ears, and send them hence.

VOLPONE. 'Tis true, 'tis true. What a rare punishment
Is avarice to itself!

MOSCA. Ay, with our help, sir.

VOLPONE. So many cares, so many maladies,
So many fears attending on old age.
Yea, death so often call'd on, as no wish
Can be more frequent with 'em, their limbs faint,
Their senses dull, their seeing, hearing, going,
All dead before them; yea their very teeth,
Their instruments of eating, failing them.
Yet this is reckon'd life! Nay, here was one,
Is now gone home, that wishes to live longer!
Feels not his gout, nor palsy; feigns himself
Younger by scores of years, flatters his age
With confident belying it, hopes he may
With charms like Aeson have his youth restor'd;
And with these thoughts so battens, as if fate
Would be as easily cheated on as he;
And all turns air! Who's that there, now? a third?
(Another knocks.)

MOSCA. Close; to your couch again; I hear his voice.
It is Corvino, our spruce merchant.

VOLPONE. *(Lying down)* Dead.

MOSCA. Another bout, sir, with your eyes. *(Anointing them)*—Who's
there?

WILLIAM CONGREVE

〰〰〰

From *The Way of the World*

[*In Act III, old Lady Wishfort, unwilling to act her age, awaits news from her woman Foible about an affair of the heart being arranged with Sir Rowland. Lady Wishfort does not know that Sir Rowland is in reality Waitwell, the disguised servant of Mirabell, a young man who is trying to trick Lady Wishfort into giving him the hand of her wealthy niece Millamant. Lady Wishfort has been in love with Mirabell but now hates him for having only pretended to love her. Mrs. Marwood, spurned by Mirabell, plans to expose him to Lady Wishfort. Foible is in league with Mirabell and is secretly married to Waitwell.*]

(LADY WISHFORT *at her toilet.* PEG *waiting.*)

LADY WISHFORT. Merciful! No news of Foible yet?

PEG. No, madam.

LADY WISHFORT. I have no more patience.—If I have not fretted myself till I am pale again, there's no veracity in me! Fetch me the red— the red, do you hear, sweetheart? An arrant ash-color, as I am a person! Look you how this wench stirs!—Why dost thou not fetch me a little red? Didst thou not hear me, Mopus?

PEG. The red ratafia, does your ladyship mean, or the cherry brandy?

LADY WISHFORT. Ratafia, fool? No, fool. Not the ratafia, fool—grant me patience!—I mean the Spanish paper, idiot—complexion, darling. Paint, paint, paint, dost thou understand that, changeling, dangling thy hands like bobbins before thee? Why dost thou not stir, puppet? Thou wooden thing upon wires!

PEG. Lord, madam, your ladyship is so impatient!—I cannot come at the paint, madam; Mrs. Foible has locked it up, and carried the key with her.

LADY WISHFORT. A pox take you both!—Fetch me the cherry brandy, then. (*Exit* PEG.) I'm as pale and as faint, I look like Mrs. Qualmsick, the curate's wife, that's always breeding.—Wench, come,

come, wench, what art thou doing? Sipping; tasting?—Save thee, dost thou not know the bottle?

(Re-enter PEG *with a bottle and china cup.)*

PEG. Madam, I was looking for a cup.

LADY WISHFORT. A cup, save thee! And what a cup hast thou brought!—Dost thou take me for a fairy, to drink out of an acorn? Why didst thou not bring thy thimble? Hast thou ne'er a brass thimble clinking in thy pocket with a bit of nutmeg?—I warrant thee. Come, fill, fill!—So—again—See who that is. *(One knocks.)* Set down the bottle first—here, here, under the table.—What, wouldst thou go with the bottle in thy hand, like a tapster? As I am a person, this wench has lived in an inn upon the road, before she came to me, like Maritornes the Asturian in Don Quixote!—No Foible yet?

PEG. No, madam; Mrs. Marwood.

LADY WISHFORT. Oh, Marwood. Let her come in. Come in, good Marwood.

(Enter MRS. MARWOOD. *)*

MRS. MARWOOD. I'm surprised to find your ladyship in dishabille at this time of day.

LADY WISHFORT. Foible's a lost thing; has been abroad since morning, and never heard of since.

MRS. MARWOOD. I saw her but now, as I came masked through the park, in conference with Mirabell.

LADY WISHFORT. With Mirabell!—You call my blood into my face with mentioning that traitor. She durst not have the confidence! I sent her to negotiate an affair, in which, if I'm detected, I'm undone. If that wheedling villain has wrought upon Foible to detect me, I'm ruined. O my dear friend, I'm a wretch of wretches if I'm detected.

MRS. MARWOOD. O madam, you cannot suspect Mrs. Foible's integrity.

LADY WISHFORT. Oh, he carries poison in his tongue that would corrupt integrity itself. If she has given him an opportunity she has as good as put her integrity into his hands. Ah, dear Marwood, what's integrity to an opportunity?—Hark? I hear her!—Go, you thing, and send her in. *(Exit* PEG.*)* Dear friend, retire into my closet, that I may examine her with more freedom. You'll pardon me, dear friend, I can make bold with you.—There are books over the chimney—Quarles and Prynne, and *The Short View of the Stage,* with Bunyan's works, to entertain you.

(Exit MRS. MARWOOD. *Enter* FOIBLE.*)*

LADY WISHFORT. O Foible, where hast thou been? What hast thou been doing?

FOIBLE. Madam, I have seen the party.

LADY WISHFORT. But what hast thou done?

FOIBLE. Nay, 'tis your ladyship has done, and are to do; I have only promised—But a man so enamored—so transported!—Well, here it is, all that is not left, all that is not kissed away. Well, if worshipping of pictures be a sin, poor Sir Rowland, I say.

LADY WISHFORT. The miniature has been counted like;—but hast thou not betrayed me, Foible? Hast thou not detected me to that faithless Mirabell? What hadst thou to do with him in the park? Answer me, has he got nothing out of thee?

FOIBLE. (Aside) So, the devil has been beforehand with me. What shall I say? (Aloud) Alas, madam, could I help it if I met that confident thing? Was I in fault? If you had heard how he used me, and all upon your ladyship's account, I'm sure you would not suspect my fidelity. Nay, if that had been the worst, I could have borne; but he had a fling at your ladyship, too, and then I could not hold; but i' faith I gave him his own.

LADY WISHFORT. Me? What did the filthy fellow say?

FOIBLE. Oh, madam! 'tis a shame to say what he said—with his taunts and his fleers, tossing up his nose. Humh! (says he) what, you are a-hatching some plot (says he), ferreting for some disbanded officer, I warrant.—Half pay is but thin subsistence (says he);—well, what pension does your ladyship propose? Let me see (says he), what, she must come down pretty deep now, she's superannuated (says he) and——

LADY WISHFORT. Odds my life, I'll have him, I'll have him murdered! I'll have him poisoned! Where does he eat?—I'll marry a drawer to have him poisoned in his wine. I'll send for Robin from Locket's immediately.

FOIBLE. Poison him! poisoning's too good for him. Starve him, madam, starve him; marry Sir Rowland, and get him disinherited. Oh, you would bless yourself to hear what he said!

LADY WISHFORT. A villain! Superannuated!

FOIBLE. Humh (says he), I hear you are laying designs against me too (says he), and Mrs. Millamant is to marry my uncle (he does not suspect a word of your ladyship); but (says he) I'll fit you for that, I warrant you (says he), I'll hamper you for that (says he), you and your old frippery too (says he); I'll handle you——

LADY WISHFORT. Audacious villain! Handle me! would he durst! Frippery! old frippery! Was there ever such a foul-mouthed fellow? I'll be married tomorow, I'll be contracted tonight.

FOIBLE. The sooner the better, madam.

LADY WISHFORT. Will Sir Rowland be here, sayest thou? When, Foible?

FOIBLE. Incontinently, madam. No new sheriff's wife expects the return of her husband after knighthood with that impatience in which Sir Rowland burns for the dear hour of kissing your ladyship's hand after dinner.

LADY WISHFORT. Frippery! superannuated frippery! I'll frippery the villain. I'll reduce him to frippery and rags! a tatterdemalion! I hope to see him hung with tatters, like a Long-Lane penthouse or a gibbet thief. A slander-mouthed railer! I warrant the spendthrift prodigal's in debt as much as the million lottery, or the whole court upon a birthday! I'll spoil his credit with his tailor. Yes, he shall have my niece with her fortune, he shall!

FOIBLE. He! I hope to see him lodge in Ludgate first, and angle into Blackfriars for brass farthings with an old mitten.

LADY WISHFORT. Ay, dear Foible; thank thee for that, dear Foible. He has put me out of all patience. I shall never recompose my features to receive Sir Rowland with any economy of face. This wretch has fretted me that I am absolutely decayed. Look, Foible.

FOIBLE. Your ladyship has frowned a little too rashly, indeed, madam. There are some cracks discernible in the white varnish.

LADY WISHFORT. Let me see the glass.—Cracks, say'st thou?—why, I am arrantly flayed—I look like an old peeled wall. Thou must repair me, Foible, before Sir Rowland comes, or I shall never keep up to my picture.

FOIBLE. I warrant you, madam, a little art once made your picture like you; and now a little of the same art must make you like your picture. Your picture must sit for you, madam.

LADY WISHFORT. But art thou sure Sir Rowland will not fail to come? Or will 'a not fail when he does come? Will he be importunate, Foible, and push? For if he should not be importunate, I shall never break decorums:—I shall die with confusion, if I am forced to advance. —Oh, no, I can never advance!—I shall swoon if he should expect advances. No, I hope Sir Rowland is better bred than to put a lady to the necessity of breaking her forms. I won't be too coy, neither.—I won't give him despair—but a little disdain is not amiss; a little scorn is alluring.

FOIBLE. A little scorn becomes your ladyship.

LADY WISHFORT. Yes, but tenderness becomes me best—a sort of a dyingness—you see that picture has a sort of a—ha, Foible!—a swimmingness in the eyes—yes, I'll look so—my niece affects it, but she wants features. Is Sir Rowland handsome? Let my toilet be removed—I'll dress above. I'll receive Sir Rowland here. Is he handsome? Don't answer me. I won't know. I'll be surprised. I'll be taken by surprise!

FOIBLE. By storm, madam. Sir Rowland's a brisk man.

LADY WISHFORT. Is he! O then he'll importune, if he's a brisk man. I shall save decorums if Sir Rowland importunes. I have a mortal terror at the apprehension of offending against decorums. Nothing but importunity can surmount decorums. O, I'm glad he's a brisk man. Let my things be removed, good Foible. *(Exit.)*

RICHARD BRINSLEY SHERIDAN

From *The Rivals*

[*In Act I, Scene ii, the ridiculous Mrs. Malaprop is angry with her niece, who refuses to marry the man chosen for her by her aunt. Not even Lydia realizes that Jack Absolute is actually the same Beverley whom Lydia loves. Mrs. Malaprop is meanwhile negotiating her own affair with Sir Lucius.*]

(*Enter* MRS. MALAPROP, *and* SIR ANTHONY ABSOLUTE.)

MRS. MALAPROP. There, Sir Anthony, there sits the deliberate simpleton who wants to disgrace her family, and lavish herself on a fellow not worth a shilling!

LYDIA. Madam, I thought you once——

MRS. MALAPROP. You thought, Miss! I don't know any business you have to think at all. Thought does not become a young woman. But the point we would request of you is, that you will promise to forget this fellow—to illiterate him, I say, quite from your memory.

LYDIA. Ah! Madam! our memories are independent of our wills. It is not so easy to forget.

MRS. MALAPROP. But I say it is, Miss; there is nothing on earth so easy as to *forget*, if a person chooses to set about it. I'm sure I have as much forgot your poor dear uncle as if he had never existed—and I thought it my duty so to do; and let me tell you, Lydia, these violent memories don't become a young woman.

SIR ANTHONY. Why sure she won't pretend to remember what she's ordered not!—aye, this comes of her reading!

LYDIA. What crime, Madam, have I committed to be treated thus?

MRS. MALAPROP. Now don't attempt to extirpate yourself from the matter; you know I have proof controvertible of it. But tell me, will you promise to do as you're bid? Will you take a husband of your friend's choosing?

LYDIA. Madam, I must tell you plainly, that had I no preference for anyone else, the choice you have made would be my aversion.

MRS. MALAPROP. What business have you, Miss, with *preference* and *aversion*? They don't become a young woman; and you ought to know, that as both always wear off, 'tis safest in matrimony to begin with a little *aversion*. I am sure I hated your poor dear uncle before marriage as if he'd been a blackamoor—and yet, Miss, you are sensible what a wife I made!—and when it pleased heaven to release me from him, 'tis unknown what tears I shed! But suppose we were going to give you another choice, will you promise us to give up this Beverley?

LYDIA. Could I belie my thoughts so far as to give that promise, my actions would certainly as far belie my words.

MRS. MALAPROP. Take yourself to your room. You are fit company for nothing but your own ill-humours.

LYDIA. Willingly, Ma'am—I cannot change for the worse. (*Exit* LYDIA.)

MRS. MALAPROP. There's a little intricate hussy for you!

SIR ANTHONY. It is not to be wondered at, Ma'am—all this is the natural consequence of teaching girls to read. Had I a thousand daughters, by heaven! I'd as soon have them taught the black art as their alphabet!

MRS. MALAPROP. Nay, nay, Sir Anthony, you are an absolute misanthropy.

SIR ANTHONY. In my way hither, Mrs. Malaprop, I observed your niece's maid coming forth from a circulating library! She had a book in each hand—they were half-bound volumes, with marble covers!

From that moment I guessed how full of duty I should see her mistress!

MRS. MALAPROP. Those are vile places, indeed!

SIR ANTHONY. Madam, a circulating library in a town is as an ever-green tree of diabolical knowledge! It blossoms through the year! And depend on it, Mrs. Malaprop, that they who are so fond of handling the leaves, will long for the fruit at last.

MRS. MALAPROP. Fie, fie, Sir Anthony, you surely speak laconically!

SIR ANTHONY. Why, Mrs. Malaprop, in moderation, now, what would you have a woman know?

MRS. MALAPROP. Observe me, Sir Anthony. I would by no means wish a daughter of mine to be a progeny of learning; I don't think so much learning becomes a young woman; for instance—I would never let her meddle with Greek, or Hebrew, or Algebra, or Simony, or Fluxions, or Paradoxes, or such inflammatory branches of learning—neither would it be necessary for her to handle any of your mathematical, astronomical, diabolical instruments;—but, Sir Anthony, I would send her, at nine years old, to a boarding-school, in order to learn a little ingenuity and artifice. Then, Sir, she should have a supercilious knowledge in accounts—and as she grew up, I would have her instructed in geometry, that she might know something of the contagious countries—but above all, Sir Anthony, she should be mistress of orthodoxy, that she might not misspell, and mispronounce words so shamefully as girls usually do; and likewise that she might reprehend the true meaning of what she is saying. This, Sir Anthony, is what I would have a woman know—and I don't think there is a superstitious article in it.

SIR ANTHONY. Well, well, Mrs. Malaprop, I will dispute the point no further with you; though I must confess that you are a truly moderate and polite arguer, for almost every third word you say is on my side of the question. But, Mrs. Malaprop, to the more important point in debate—you say you have no objection to my proposal.

MRS. MALAPROP. None, I assure you. I am under no positive engagement with Mr. Acres, and as Lydia is so obstinate against him, perhaps your son may have better success.

SIR ANTHONY. Well, Madam, I will write for the boy directly. He knows not a syllable of this yet, though I have for some time had the proposal in my head. He is at present with his regiment.

MRS. MALAPROP. We have never seen your son, Sir Anthony; but I hope no objection on his side.

SIR ANTHONY. Objection!—let him object if he dare! No; no, Mrs. Malaprop, Jack knows that the least demur puts me in a frenzy directly.

My process was always very simple—in their young days, 'twas "Jack do this";—if he demurred—I knocked him down—and if he grumbled at that—I always sent him out of the room.

MRS. MALAPROP. Aye, and the properest way, o' my conscience!— nothing is so conciliating to young people as severity. Well, Sir Anthony, I shall give Mr. Acres his discharge, and prepare Lydia to receive your son's invocations; and I hope you will represent *her* to the Captain as an object not altogether illegible.

SIR ANTHONY. Madam, I will handle the subject prudently. Well, I must leave you—and let me beg you, Mrs. Malaprop, to enforce this matter roundly to the girl; take my advice—keep a tight hand; if she rejects this proposal—clap her under lock and key—and if you were just to let the servants forget to bring her dinner for three or four days, you can't conceive how she'd come about! (*Exit* SIR ANTHONY.)

MRS. MALAPROP. Well, at any rate I shall be glad to get her from under my intuition. She has somehow discovered my partiality for Sir Lucius O'Trigger—sure, Lucy can't have betrayed me! No, the girl is such a simpleton, I should have made her confess it.—(*Calls*) Lucy!— Lucy—Had she been one of your artificial ones, I should never have trusted her.

(*Enter* LUCY.)

LUCY. Did you call, Ma'am?

MRS. MALAPROP. Yes, girl. Did you see Sir Lucius while you was out?

LUCY. No, indeed, Ma'am, not a glimpse of him.

MR: MALAPROP. You are sure, Lucy, that you never mentioned——

LUCY. O Gemini! I'd sooner cut my tongue out.

MRS. MALAPROP. Well, don't let your simplicity be imposed on.

LUCY. No, Ma'am.

MRS. MALAPROP. So, come to me presently, and I'll give you another letter to Sir Lucius; but mind, Lucy—if ever you betray what you are intrusted with (unless it be other people's secrets to me) you forfeit my malevolence forever, and your being a simpleton shall be no excuse for your locality. (*Exit* MRS. MALAPROP.)

LUCY. Ha! ha! ha!—So, my dear *simplicity,* let me give you a little respite—(*Altering her manner*)—let girls in my station be as fond as they please of appearing expert, and knowing in their trusts—commend me to a mask of silliness, and a pair of sharp eyes for my own interest under it! Let me see to what account have I turned my *simplicity* lately—(*Looks at a paper.*) For *abetting Miss Lydia Languish in a de-*

sign of running away with an Ensign!—in money—sundry times—twelve
pound twelve—gowns, five—hats, ruffles, caps, &c., &c.—numberless!
From the said Ensign, within this last month, six guineas and a half.—
About a quarter's pay!—Item, *from Mrs. Malaprop, for betraying the*
*young people to her—*when I found matters were likely to be discovered
*—two guineas, and a black paduasoy.—*Item, *from Mr. Acres, for carry-*
*ing divers letters—*which I never delivered—*two guineas, and a pair of*
*buckles.—*Item, *from Sir Lucius O'Trigger—three crowns—two gold*
*pocket-pieces—and a silver snuff-box!—*Well done, *simplicity!—*Yet I
was forced to make my Hibernian believe that he was corresponding,
not with the *aunt,* but with the *niece:* for, though not overrich, I found
he had too much pride and delicacy to sacrifice the feelings of a gentleman to the necessities of his fortune. *(Exit.)*

OSCAR WILDE

From *The Importance of Being Earnest*

[*Gwendolen, the daughter of the very proper Lady Bracknell, is in*
love with Jack Worthing. In the present scene, Lady Bracknell is con-
fronting her would-be son-in-law.]

LADY BRACKNELL. *(Sitting down)* You can take a seat, Mr. Worthing. *(Looks in her pocket for note-book and pencil.)*

JACK. Thank you, Lady Bracknell, I prefer standing.

LADY BRACKNELL. *(Pencil and note-book in hand)* I feel bound to
tell you that you are not down on my list of eligible young men, although I have the same list as the dear Duchess of Bolton has. We work
together, in fact. However, I am quite ready to enter your name, should
your answers be what a really affectionate mother requires. Do you
smoke?

JACK. Well, yes, I must admit I smoke.

LADY BRACKNELL. I am glad to hear it. A man should always have
an occupation of some kind. There are far too many idle men in
London as it is. How old are you?

JACK. Twenty-nine.

LADY BRACKNELL. A very good age to be married at. I have always been of the opinion that a man who desires to get married should know either everything or nothing. Which do you know?

JACK. *(After some hesitation)* I know nothing, Lady Bracknell.

LADY BRACKNELL. I am pleased to hear it. I do not approve of anything that tampers with natural ignorance. Ignorance is like a delicate exotic fruit; touch it and the bloom is gone. The whole theory of modern education is radically unsound. Fortunately in England, at any rate, education produces no effect whatsoever. If it did, it would prove a serious danger to the upper classes, and probably lead to acts of violence in Grosvenor Square. What is your income?

JACK. Between seven and eight thousand a year.

LADY BRACKNELL. *(Makes a note in her book)* In land, or in *investments*?

JACK. In investments, chiefly.

LADY BRACKNELL. That is satisfactory. What between the duties expected of one during one's lifetime, and the duties exacted from one after one's death, land has ceased to be either a profit or a pleasure. It gives one position, and prevents one from keeping it up. That's all that can be said about land.

JACK. I have a country house with some land, of course, attached to it, about fifteen hundred acres, I believe; but I don't depend on that for my real income. In fact, as far as I can make out, the poachers are the only people who make anything out of it.

LADY BRACKNELL. A country house! How many bedrooms? Well, that point can be cleared up afterwards. You have a town house, I hope? A girl with a simple, unspoiled nature, like Gwendolen, could hardly be expected to reside in the country.

JACK. Well, I own a house in Belgrave Square, but it is let by the year to Lady Bloxham. Of course, I can get it back whenever I like, at six months' notice.

LADY BRACKNELL. Lady Bloxham? I don't know her.

JACK. Oh, she goes about very little. She is a lady considerably advanced in years.

LADY BRACKNELL. Ah, now-a-days that is no guarantee of respectability of character. What number in Belgrave Square?

JACK. 149.

LADY BRACKNELL. *(Shaking her head)* The unfashionable side. I thought there was something. However, that could easily be altered.

JACK. Do you mean the fashion, or the side?

LADY BRACKNELL. (*Sternly*) Both, if necessary, I presume. What are your politics?

JACK. Well, I am afraid I really have none. I am a Liberal Unionist.

LADY BRACKNELL. Oh, they count as Tories. They dine with us. Or come in the evening, at any rate. Now to minor matters. Are your parents living?

JACK. I have lost both my parents.

LADY BRACKNELL. Both? . . . That seems like carelessness. Who was your father? He was evidently a man of some wealth. Was he born in what the Radical papers call the purple of commerce, or did he rise from the ranks of aristocracy?

JACK. I am afraid I really don't know. The fact is, Lady Bracknell, I said I had lost my parents. It would be nearer the truth to say that my parents seem to have lost me. . . . I don't actually know who I am by birth. I was . . . Well, I was found.

LADY BRACKNELL. Found!

JACK. The late Mr. Thomas Cardew, an old gentleman of a very charitable and kindly disposition, found me, and gave me the name of Worthing, because he happened to have a first-class ticket for Worthing in his pocket at the time. Worthing is a place in Sussex. It is a seaside resort.

LADY BRACKNELL. Where did the charitable gentleman who had a first-class ticket for this seaside resort find you?

JACK. (*Gravely*) In a hand-bag.

LADY BRACKNELL. A hand-bag?

JACK. (*Very seriously*) Yes, Lady Bracknell. I was in a hand-bag—a somewhat large, black leather hand-bag, with handles to it—an ordinary hand-bag, in fact.

LADY BRACKNELL. In what locality did this Mr. James, or Thomas, Cardew come across this ordinary hand-bag?

JACK. In the cloak-room at Victoria Station. It was given to him in mistake for his own.

LADY BRACKNELL. The cloak-room at Victoria Station?

JACK. Yes. The Brighton line.

LADY BRACKNELL. The line is immaterial. Mr. Worthing, I confess I feel somewhat bewildered by what you have just told me. To be born, or at any rate, bred in a hand-bag, whether it had handles or not, seems to me to display a contempt for the ordinary decencies of family life that reminds one of the worst excesses of the French Revolution. And I presume you know what that unfortunate movement led to? As for the particular locality in which the hand-bag was found, a cloak-room at a railway station might serve to conceal a social indiscretion—has probably, indeed, been used for that purpose before now—but it could hardly be regarded as an assured basis for a recognized position in good society.

JACK. May I ask you then what you would advise me to do? I need hardly say I would do anything in the world to insure Gwendolen's happiness.

LADY BRACKNELL. I would strongly advise you, Mr. Worthing, to try and acquire some relations as soon as possible, and to make a definite effort to produce at any rate one parent, of either sex, before the season is quite over.

JACK. Well, I don't see how I could possibly manage to do that. I can produce the hand-bag at any moment. It is in my dressing-room at home. I really think that should satisfy you, Lady Bracknell.

LADY BRACKNELL. Me, sir! What has it to do with me? You can hardly imagine that I and Lord Bracknell would dream of allowing our only daughter—a girl brought up with the utmost care—to marry into a cloak-room, and form an alliance with a parcel? Good morning, Mr. Worthing!

GEORGE BERNARD SHAW

From *Pygmalion*

[*Henry Higgins, on a wager with Colonel Pickering, has taken the flower-girl Liza Doolittle from the gutter and sworn to make her a lady. He has finally given her what he hopes will appear to be the speech and manners of a cultured young woman, and in the present scene is first introducing her to society in a gathering at the home of his mother. Higgins suddenly remembers during the course of the scene that Liza, as the flower-girl, was noticed in Covent Garden by Mrs. Eynsford Hill and her children.*]

THE PARLOR-MAID. *(Opening the door)* Miss Doolittle. *(She withdraws)*

HIGGINS. *(Rising hastily and running to Mrs. Higgins)* Here she is, mother.

(He stands on tiptoe and makes signs over his mother's head to Eliza to indicate to her which lady is her hostess. Eliza, who is exquisitely dressed, produces an impression of such remarkable distinction and beauty as she enters that they all rise, quite fluttered. Guided by Higgins's signals, she comes to Mrs. Higgins with studied grace.)

LIZA. *(Speaking with pedantic correctness of pronunciation and great beauty of tone)* How do you do, Mrs. Higgins? *(She gasps slightly in making sure of the H in Higgins, but is quite successful.)* Mr. Higgins told me I might come.

MRS. HIGGINS. *(Cordially)* Quite right: I'm very glad indeed to see you.

PICKERING. How do you do, Miss Doolittle?

LIZA. *(Shaking hands with him)* Colonel Pickering, is it not?

MRS. EYNSFORD HILL. I feel sure we have met before, Miss Doolittle. I remember your eyes.

LIZA. How do you do?

(She sits down on the ottoman gracefully in the place just left vacant by Higgins.)

MRS. EYNSFORD HILL. *(Introducing)* My daughter Clara.

LIZA. How do you do?

CLARA. *(Impulsively)* How do you do?

(She sits down on the ottoman beside Eliza, devouring her with her eyes.)

FREDDY. *(Coming to their side of the ottoman)* Ive certainly had the pleasure.

MRS. EYNSFORD HILL. *(Introducing)* My son Freddy.

LIZA. How do you do?

(FREDDY bows and sits down in the Elizabethan chair, infatuated.)

HIGGINS. *(Suddenly)* By George, yes: it all comes back to me! *(They stare at him.)* Covent Garden! *(Lamentably)* What a damned thing!

MRS. HIGGINS. Henry, please! *(He is about to sit on the edge of the table.)* Dont sit on my writing-table: youll break it.

HIGGINS. *(Sulkily)* Sorry.

(He goes to the divan, stumbling into the fender and over

the fire-irons on his way; extricating himself with muttered imprecations; and finishing his disastrous journey by throwing himself so impatiently on the divan that he almost breaks it. Mrs. Higgins looks at him, but controls herself and says nothing. A long and painful pause ensues.)

MRS. HIGGINS. *(At last, conversationally)* Will it rain, do you think?

LIZA. The shallow depression in the west of these islands is likely to move slowly in an easterly direction. There are no indications of any great change in the barometrical situation.

FREDDY. Ha! ha! how awfully funny!

LIZA. What is wrong with that, young man? I bet I got it right.

FREDDY. Killing!

MRS. EYNSFORD HILL. I'm sure I hope it wont turn cold. Theres so much influenza about. It runs right through our whole family regularly every spring.

LIZA. *(Darkly)* My aunt died of influenza: so they said.

MRS. EYNSFORD HILL. *(Clicks her tongue sympathetically)! ! !*

LIZA. *(In the same tragic tone)* But it's my belief they done the old woman in.

MRS. HIGGINS. *(Puzzled)* Done her in?

LIZA. Y-e-e-e-es, Lord love you! Why should she die of influenza? She come through diphtheria right enough the year before. I saw her with my own eyes. Fairly blue with it, she was. They all thought she was dead; but my father he kept ladling gin down her throat till she came to so sudden that she bit the bowl off the spoon.

MRS. EYNSFORD HILL. *(Startled)* Dear me!

LIZA. *(Piling up the indictment)* What call would a woman with that strength in her have to die of influenza? What become of her new straw hat that should have come to me? Somebody pinched it; and what I say is, them as pinched it done her in.

MRS. EYNSFORD HILL. What does doing her in mean?

HIGGINS. *(Hastily)* Oh, thats the new small talk. To do a person in means to kill them.

MRS. EYNSFORD HILL. *(To Eliza, horrified)* You surely dont believe that your aunt was killed?

LIZA. Do I not! Them she lived with would have killed her for a hat-pin, let alone a hat.

MRS. EYNSFORD HILL. But it cant have been right for your father to pour spirits down her throat like that. It might have killed her.

LIZA. Not her. Gin was mother's milk to her. Besides, he'd poured so much down his own throat that he knew the good of it.

MRS. EYNSFORD HILL. Do you mean that he drank?

LIZA. Drank! My word! Something chronic.

MRS. EYNSFORD HILL. How dreadful for you!

LIZA. Not a bit. It never did him no harm what I could see. But then he did not keep it up regular. *(Cheerfully)* On the burst, as you might say, from time to time. And always more agreeable when he had a drop in. When he was out of work, my mother used to give him fourpence and tell him to go out and not come back until he'd drunk himself cheerful and loving-like. Theres lots of women has to make their husbands drunk to make them fit to live with. *(Now quite at her ease)* You see, it's like this. If a man has a bit of conscience, it always takes him when he's sober; and then it makes him low-spirited. A drop of booze just takes that off and makes him happy. *(To Freddy, who is in convulsions of suppressed laughter)* Here! what are you sniggering at?

FREDDY. The new small talk. You do it so awfully well.

LIZA. If I was doing it proper, what was you laughing at? *(To Higgins)* Have I said anything I oughtnt?

MRS. HIGGINS. *(Interposing)* Not at all, Miss Doolittle.

LIZA. Well, thats a mercy, anyhow. *(Expansively)* What I always say is——

HIGGINS. *(Rising and looking at his watch)* Ahem!

LIZA. *(Looking round at him; taking the hint; and rising)* Well: I must go. *(They all rise. FREDDY goes to the door.)* So pleased to have met you. Goodbye.

(She shakes hands with Mrs. Higgins.)

MRS. HIGGINS. Goodbye.

LIZA. Goodbye, Colonel Pickering.

PICKERING. Goodbye, Miss Doolittle.

(They shake hands.)

LIZA. *(Nodding to the others)* Goodbye, all.

FREDDY. *(Opening the door for her)* Are you walking across the Park, Miss Doolittle? If so——

LIZA. *(With perfectly elegant diction)* Walk! Not bloody likely. *(Sensation.)* I am going in a taxi. *(She goes out.)*

EUGENE O'NEILL

From *Long Day's Journey into Night*

[*In this autobiographical play, O'Neill tells the story of the Tyrone family. James Tyrone, 65, is a rundown actor; his wife, Mary, 54, now addicted to drugs, has still some of the air of the shy convent-girl of her youth. Edmund is the younger of two sons, in his early twenties; his hypersensitiveness makes him like his mother.*]

MARY. (*Rises from her chair, her face lighting up lovingly—with excited eagerness*) I'm here, dear. In the living room. I've been waiting for you. (TYRONE *comes in through the front parlor.* EDMUND *is behind him.* TYRONE *has had a lot to drink but beyond a slightly glazed look in his eyes and a trace of blur in his speech, he does not show it.* EDMUND *has also had more than a few drinks without much apparent effect, except that his sunken cheeks are flushed and his eyes look bright and feverish. They stop in the doorway to stare appraisingly at her. What they see fulfills their worst expectations. But for the moment* MARY *is unconscious of their condemning eyes. She kisses her husband and then* EDMUND. *Her manner is unnaturally effusive. They submit shrinkingly. She talks excitedly.*) I'm so happy you've come. I had given up hope. I was afraid you wouldn't come home. It's such a dismal, foggy evening. It must be much more cheerful in the barrooms uptown, where there are people you can talk and joke with. No, don't deny it. I know how you feel. I don't blame you a bit. I'm all the more grateful to you for coming home. I was sitting here so lonely and blue. Come and sit down. (*She sits at left rear of table,* EDMUND *at left of table, and* TYRONE *in the rocker at right of it.*) Dinner won't be ready for a minute. You're actually a little early. Will wonders never cease. Here's the whiskey, dear. Shall I pour a drink for you? (*Without waiting for a reply she does so.*) And you, Edmund? I don't want to encourage you, but one before dinner, as an appetizer, can't do any harm. (*She pours a drink for him. They make no move to take the drinks. She talks on as if unaware of their silence.*) Where's Jamie? But, of course, he'll never come home so long as he has the price of a drink left. *(She reaches out and clasps her husband's hand—sadly.)* I'm afraid Jamie has been lost to us for a long time, dear. *(Her face hardens.)* But we mustn't allow him to drag Edmund down with him, as he's like to do. He's jealous because Edmund has always been the baby—just as he used to be of Eugene. He'll never be content until he makes Edmund as hopeless a failure as he is.

EDMUND. *(Miserably)* Stop talking, Mama.

TYRONE. *(Dully)* Yes, Mary, the less you say now—*(Then to EDMUND, a bit tipsily)* All the same, there's truth in your mother's warning. Beware of that brother of yours, or he'll poison life for you with his damned sneering serpent's tongue!

EDMUND. *(As before)* Oh, cut it out, Papa.

MARY. *(Goes on as if nothing has been said)* It's hard to believe, seeing Jamie as he is now, that he was ever my baby. Do you remember what a healthy, happy baby he was, James? The one-night stands and filthy trains and cheap hotels and bad food never made him cross or sick. He was always smiling or laughing. He hardly ever cried. Eugene was the same, too, happy and healthy, during the two years he lived before I let him die through my neglect.

TYRONE. Oh, for the love of God! I'm a fool for coming home!

EDMUND. Papa! Shut up!

MARY. *(Smiles with detached tenderness at Edmund)* It was Edmund who was the crosspatch when he was little, always getting up and frightened about nothing at all. *(She pats his hand, teasingly.)* Everyone used to say, dear, you'd cry at the drop of a hat.

EDMUND. *(Who cannot control his bitterness)* Maybe I guessed there was a good reason not to laugh.

TYRONE. *(Reproving and pitying)* Now, now, lad. You know better than to pay attention——

MARY. *(As if she hadn't heard—sadly again)* Who would have thought Jamie would grow up to disgrace us. You remember, James, for years after he went to boarding school, we received such glowing reports. Everyone liked him. All his teachers told us what a fine brain he had, and how easily he learned his lessons. Even after he began to drink and they had to expel him, they wrote us how sorry they were, because he was so likable and such a brilliant student. They predicted a wonderful future for him if he would only learn to take life seriously. *(She pauses—then adds with a strange, sad detachment.)* It's such a pity. Poor Jamie! It's hard to understand——*(Abruptly a change comes over her. Her face hardens and she stares at her husband with accusing hostility.*) No, it isn't at all. You brought him up to be a boozer. Since he first opened his eyes, he's seen you drinking. Always a bottle on the bureau in the cheap hotel rooms! And if he had a nightmare when he was little, or a stomach-ache, your remedy was to give him a teaspoonful of whiskey to quiet him.

TYRONE. *(Stung)* So I'm to blame because that lazy hulk has made a drunken loafer of himself? Is that what I came home to listen to? I might have known! When you have the poison in you, you want to blame everyone but yourself!

EDMUND. Papa! You told me not to pay attention. *(Then, resentfully)* Anyway, it's true. You did the same thing with me. I can remember that teaspoonful of booze every time I woke up with a nightmare.

MARY. *(In a detached reminiscent tone)* Yes, you were continually having nightmares as a child. You were born afraid. Because I was so afraid to bring you into the world. *(She pauses—then goes on with the same detachment.)* Please don't think I blame your father, Edmund. He didn't know any better. He never went to school after he was ten. His people were the most ignorant kind of poverty-stricken Irish. I'm sure they honestly believed whiskey is the healthiest medicine for a child who is sick or frightened.

(TYRONE is about to burst out in angry defense of his family, but EDMUND intervenes.)

EDMUND. *(Sharply)* Papa! *(Changing the subject)* Are we going to have this drink, or aren't we?

TYRONE. *(Controlling himself—dully)* You're right. I'm a fool to take notice. *(He picks up his glass listlessly.)* Drink hearty, lad.

(EDMUND drinks but TYRONE remains staring at the glass in his hand. EDMUND at once realizes how much the whiskey has been watered. He frowns, glancing from the bottle to his mother—starts to say something but stops.)

MARY. *(In a changed tone—repentently)* I'm sorry if I sounded bitter, James. I'm not. It's all so far away. But I did feel a little hurt when you wished you hadn't come home. I was so relieved and happy when you came, and grateful to you. It's very dreary and sad to be here alone in the fog with night falling.

TYRONE. *(Moved)* I'm glad I came, Mary, when you act like your real self.

MARY. I was so lonesome I kept Cathleen with me just to have someone to talk to. (*Her manner and quality drift back to the shy convent girl again.*) Do you know what I was telling her, dear? About the night my father took me to your dressing room and I first fell in love with you. Do you remember?

TYRONE. (*Deeply moved—his voice husky*) Can you think I'd ever forget, Mary?

(EDMUND *looks away from them, sad and embarrassed.*)

MARY. (*Tenderly*) No. I know you still love me, James, in spite of everything.

TYRONE. (*His face works and he blinks back tears—with quiet intensity.*) Yes! As God is my judge! Always and forever, Mary!

MARY. And I love you, dear, in spite of everything. (*There is a pause in which* EDMUND *moves embarrassedly. The strange detachment comes over her manner again as if she were speaking impersonally of people seen from a distance.*) But I must confess, James, although I couldn't help loving you, I would never have married you if I'd known you drank so much. I remember the first night your barroom friends had to help you up to the door of our hotel room, and knocked and then ran away before I came to the door. We were still on our honeymoon, do you remember?

TYRONE. (*With guilty vehemence*) I don't remember! It wasn't on our honeymoon! And I never in my life had to be helped to bed, or missed a performance!

MARY. (*As though he hadn't spoken*) I had waited in that ugly hotel room hour after hour. I kept making excuses for you. I told myself it must be some business connected with the theater. I knew so little about the theater. Then I became terrified. I imagined all sorts of horrible accidents. I got on my knees and prayed that nothing had happened to you—and then they brought you up and left you outside the door. (*She gives a little, sad sigh.*) I didn't know how often that was to happen in the years to come, how many times I was to wait in ugly hotel rooms. I became quite used to it.

MAXWELL ANDERSON

~~~~~~

From *Key Largo*

[*On Key Largo, looking out over the Gulf of Mexico, live the sightless d'Alcala and his daughter Alegre. To them comes King Mc-Cloud, driven by the knowledge that during the Spanish Civil War he fled too quickly from a battle where Victor, d'Alcala's son, died for his principles. Now once again, in Act II of the play, King faces death, this time at the hands of the gangster-killer Murillo, who tells King that he will accuse him of a murder unless King allows Murillo to pin it on two innocent Indian fugitives. King says to Alegre "Then what you mean is/ I should strike an attitude of what the hell/ and walk off gallantly to a death on the gallows/ to save two drones from a reservation?" and Alegre replies to him:*]

ALEGRE. No,
I haven't said that. But can you stand face to face
with two innocent fugitives, and stand there silent
and load them with a crime to save yourself?
How could one do it and live? Would you wish to live
after they were gone?
    KING. How else can I live?
    ALEGRE. Any way that squares
with what a man, waking, may think of himself in the night
and not want to die before morning.
    KING. But no way squares—
no way I could possibly think of, squares with the rules;
you're thinking of the old rules, the ancient code
established by the knights in the middle ages,
the old authentic code. And men don't live
by faith or honor or justice. That's revoked.
They live as they can, as the animals they are,
because it's impossible to arrange a life
by these fantastic, inexcusable rules.

Look at these laws of chivalry as they're laid
upon my soul tonight. Half an hour ago
I'm asked to die to protect a woman's choice
of the man she'll have. That's understandable.
All right, one can die for that. But now I'm asked
to forget about you, because that was less important,
and die for a couple of Indians out on the beach
that I don't know—meanwhile leaving the woman
to the mercy of the same scoundrel it was my job
to save her from before. Isn't it a question
whether I'm more useful here, and alive, and trying,
at least, to ward off Murillo?

    ALEGRE. But we cannot choose,
either you or I, to purchase your safety or mine,
by offering up those two poor, wandering children
to Murillo and the sheriff. We simply can't,
whatever happens to us.

    KING. Whatever happens?
Have you envisioned that?

    ALEGRE. I have a revolver,
and I can use it.

    KING. And would you?

    ALEGRE. Do you doubt it?

    KING. Then we both die—as a sacrifice to the rules.
It would be something to know who it is arranges
these little ironies.
I came here running from a civil war
where madmen and morons tore a continent
apart to share it, where death and rape were common
as flies on a dead soldier, and alien men
were weary of native women. I ran from that storm
of rape and murder, because I couldn't help
and nobody could help, and I wanted at least
to save my life, in any crawling way,
and the great master of the laboratory,
(wearing spectacles, probably) drives me down
to this bloody wharf, where I must choose again
between death and the rape of a woman, between death
and the murder of innocent men. I made my choice
long ago, and ran, and left them bleeding

there in the field. And I say it's better to live—
if one could live alone in the Everglades
and fill his stomach with fish, and sleep at night,
and knock his oysters from the mangrove roots,
and let the dead bury their dead, for there's no faith sure,
no magnanimity that won't give way
if you test it often enough, no love of woman
or love of man, that won't dry up in the end
if the drouth lasts long enough, no modesty
that isn't relative. There's no better than you
among all women—and yet when you envisioned
the choice between Murillo and your death
there was a flash when your mind asked itself,
must it be death? Is even the man Murillo
worse than death? And if you can ask the question
then there's more than one answer.

    ALEGRE. How did you know that!

    KING. Because the mind, the bright, quick-silver mind,
has but one purpose, to defend the body
and ward off death. Because it's the law of earth
where life was built up from the very first
on rape and murder—where the female takes what she gets
and learns to love it, and must learn to love it,
or the race would die! Show me one thing secure
among these names of virtues—justice and honor
and love and friendship—and I'll die for it gladly,
but where's justice, and where's honor, and where's friendship,
and what's love, under the rose?

    ALEGRE. Then you've never loved.

    KING. Not as you've loved, perhaps, for you assume
that it's forever, and I've known, and know,
that it's till the fire burns down, till the stimulant
of something new or something stolen's gone,
till you know all the intimate details
and the girl's with child, and cries. And if that's true
of love, it's true of all the other doors—
the doors of all the illusions, and one by one
we all jump at them. We jump first at the door
with Christ upon it, hanging on the cross,
then the door with Lenin, legislating heaven,

then the emblem of social security, representing
eighteen dollars a week, good luck or bad,
jobs or no jobs—then the door with the girl expectant,
the black triangle door, and they all give meaning
to life, and mental sustenance, but then
there comes a day when there's no sustenance,
and you jump, and there's nothing you want to buy with money,
and Christ hangs dead on the cross, as all men die,
and Lenin legislates a fake paradise,
and the girl holds out her arms, and she's made of sawdust,
and there's sawdust in your mouth!
    ALEGRE. But if this were true,
then why would one live—woman or man or beast,
or grub in the dark?
    KING. To eat and sleep and breed
and creep in the forest.
    ALEGRE. Answer him, father, answer,
because it sounds like truth—but if it were true
one couldn't live! There is something in women
that is as he says, and there is something in men
that merely wants to live, but answer him!
We're not like this!
    D'ALCALA. Why, girl, we're all alone,
here on the surface of a turning sphere
of earth and water, cutting a great circle
round the sun, just as the sun itself
cuts a great circle round the central hub
of some great constellation, which in turn
wheels round another. Where this voyage started
we don't know, nor where it will end, nor whether
it has a meaning, nor whether there is good
or evil, whether man has a destiny
or happened here by chemical accident—
all this we never know. And that's our challenge—
to find ourselves in this desert of dead light-years,
blind, all of us, in a kingdom of the blind,
living by appetite in a fragile shell
of dust and water; yet to take this dust
and water and our range of appetites
and build them toward some vision of a god

of beauty and unselfishness and truth—
could we ask better of the mud we are
than to accept the challenge, and look up
and search for god-head? If it's true we came
from the sea-water—and children in the womb
wear gills a certain time in memory
of that first origin—we've come a long way;
so far there's no predicting what we'll be
before we end. It may be women help
this progress choosing out the men who seem
a fractional step beyond sheer appetite—
and it may be that's sacred, though my values
are hardly Biblical—and perhaps men help
by setting themselves forever, even to the death,
against cruelty and arbitrary power,
for that's the beast—the ancient, belly-foot beast
from which we came, which is strong within us yet,
and tries to drag us back down. Somehow or other,
in some obscure way, it's the love of woman
for man, and a certain freedom in her love
to choose tomorrow's men, and the leverage
in the interplay of choice between men and women,
that's brought us here—to this forking of the roads—
and may take us farther on.

    KING. And where are we going?

    D'ALCALA. To a conquest of all there is, whatever there is
among the suns and stars.

    KING. And what if it's empty—
what if the whole thing's empty here in space
like a vast merry-go-round of eyeless gods
turning without resistance—Jupiter
and Mars and Venus, Saturn and Mercury,
carved out of rock and trailed with cloud and mist,
but nothing, and in all the constellations,
no meaning anywhere, nothing? Then if man gets up
and makes himself a god, and walks alone
among these limitless tensions of the sky,
and finds that he's eternally alone,
and can mean nothing, then what was the use of it,

why climb so high, and set ourselves apart
to look out on a place of skulls?

    D'ALCALA. Now you want to know
what will come of us all, and I don't know that.
You should have asked the fish what would come of him
before the earth shrank and the land thrust up
between the oceans. You should have asked the fish
or asked me, or asked yourself, for at that time
we were the fish, you and I, or they were we—
and we, or they, would have known as much about it
as I know now—yet it somehow seems worth while
that the fish were not discouraged and did keep on—
at least as far as we are.—For conditions
among the fish were quite the opposite
of what you'd call encouraging. They had
big teeth and no compunction. Bigger teeth
than Hitler or Murillo.
Over and over again the human race
climbs up out of the mud, and looks around,
and finds that it's alone here; and the knowledge
hits it like a blight—and down it goes
into the mud again.
Over and over again we have a hope
and make a religion of it—and follow it up
till we're out on the topmost limb of the tallest tree
alone with our stars—and we don't dare to be there,
and climb back down again.
It may be that the blight's on the race once more—
that they're all afraid—and fight their way to the ground.
But it won't end in the dark. Our destiny's
the other way. There'll be a race of men
who can face even the stars without despair,
and think without going mad.

JOHN STEINBECK

~~~~~~

From *Of Mice and Men*

[*In Act I, Scene 1, George and Lennie appear with their blanket rolls on the bank of the Salinas River in Central California. They are transients, but out of a job.*]

GEORGE. There's enough beans for four men.

LENNIE. (*Sitting on the other side of the campfire, speaks patiently*) I like 'em with ketchup.

GEORGE. (*Explodes*) Well, we ain't got any. Whatever we ain't got, that's what you want. God Almighty, if I was alone, I could live so easy. I could go get a job of work and no trouble. No mess . . . and when the end of the month come, I could take my fifty bucks and go into town and get whatever I want. Why, I could stay in a cat-house all night. I could eat any place I want. Order any damn thing.

LENNIE. (*Plaintively, but softly*) I didn't want no ketchup.

GEORGE. (*Continuing violently*) I could do that every damn month. Get a gallon of whiskey or set in a pool room and play cards or shoot pool. (LENNIE *gets up to his knees and looks over the fire, with frightened face.*) And what have I got? (*Disgustedly*) I got *you*. You can't keep a job and you lose me every job I get!

LENNIE. (*In terror*) I don't mean nothing, George.

GEORGE. Just keep me shovin' all over the country all the time. And that ain't the worst—you get in trouble. You do bad things and I got to get you out. It ain't bad people that raises hell. It's dumb ones. (*He shouts.*) You crazy son-of-a-bitch, you keep me in hot water all the time. (LENNIE *is trying to stop* GEORGE's *flow of words with his hands. Sarcastically.*) You just wanta feel that girl's dress. Just wanta pet it like it was a mouse. Well, how the hell'd she know you just wanta feel her dress? How'd she know you'd just hold onto it like it was a mouse?

LENNIE. (*In panic*) I didn't mean to, George.

GEORGE. Sure you didn't mean to. You didn't mean for her to yell bloody hell, either. You didn't mean for us to hide in the irrigation ditch all day with guys lookin' for us with guns. Alla time it's something you didn't mean. God damn it, I wish I could put you in a cage with a million mice and let them pet *you*. (GEORGE's *anger leaves him suddenly. For the first time, he seems to see the expression of terror on* LENNIE's *face. He looks down ashamedly at the fire, and maneuvers some beans onto the blade of his pocket-knife and puts them into his mouth.*)

LENNIE. *(After a pause)* George! (GEORGE *purposely does not answer him.*) George?

GEORGE. What do you want?

LENNIE. I was only foolin', George. I don't want no ketchup. I wouldn't eat no ketchup if it was right here beside me.

GEORGE. *(With a sullenness of shame)* If they was some here you could have it. And if I had a thousand bucks I'd buy ya a bunch of flowers.

LENNIE. I wouldn't eat no ketchup, George. I'd leave it all for you. You could cover your beans so deep with it, and I wouldn't touch none of it.

GEORGE. *(Refusing to give in from his sullenness, refusing to look at* LENNIE*)* When I think of the swell time I could have without you, I go nuts. I never git no peace!

LENNIE. You want I should go away and leave you alone?

GEORGE. Where the hell could you go?

LENNIE. Well, I could . . . I could go off in the hills there. Some place I could find a cave.

GEORGE. Yeah, how'd ya eat? You ain't got sense enough to find nothing to eat.

LENNIE. I'd find things. I don't need no nice food with ketchup. I'd lay out in the sun and nobody would hurt me. And if I found a mouse—why, I could keep it. Wouldn't nobody take it away from me.

GEORGE. *(At last he looks up)* I been mean, ain't I?

LENNIE. *(Presses his triumph)* If you don't want me, I can go right in them hills and find a cave. I can go away any time.

GEORGE. No. Look! I was just foolin' ya. 'Course I want you to stay with me. Trouble with mice is you always kill 'em. *(He pauses.)* Tell you what I'll do, Lennie. First chance I get I'll find you a pup. Maybe you wouldn't kill it. That would be better than mice. You could pet it harder.

LENNIE. *(Still avoiding being drawn in)* If you don't want me, you only gotta say so. I'll go right up on them hills and live by myself. And I won't get no mice stole from me.

GEORGE. I want you to stay with me. Jesus Christ, somebody'd shoot you for a coyote if you was by yourself. Stay with me. Your Aunt Clara wouldn't like your runnin' off by yourself, even if she is dead.

LENNIE. George?

GEORGE. Huh?

LENNIE. *(Craftily)* Tell me—like you done before.

GEORGE. Tell you what?

LENNIE. About the rabbits.

GEORGE. *(Near to anger again)* You ain't gonna put nothing over on me!

LENNIE. *(Pleading)* Come on, George . . . tell me! Please! Like you done before.

GEORGE. You get a kick out of that, don't you? All right, I'll tell you. And then we'll lay out our beds and eat our dinner.

LENNIE. Go on, George. *(Unrolls his bed and lies on his side, supporting his head on one hand.* GEORGE *lays out his bed and sits cross-legged on it.* GEORGE *repeats the next speech rhythmically, as though he had said it many times before.)*

GEORGE. Guys like us that work on ranches is the loneliest guys in the world. They ain't got no family. They don't belong no place. They come to a ranch and work up a stake and then they go in to town and blow their stake. And then the first thing you know they're poundin' their tail on some other ranch. They ain't got nothin' to look ahead to.

LENNIE. *(Delightedly)* That's it, that's it! Now tell how it is with us.

GEORGE. *(Still almost chanting)* With us it ain't like that. We got a future. We got somebody to talk to that gives a damn about us. We don't have to sit in no barroom blowin' in our jack, just because we got no place else to go. If them other guys gets in jail, they can rot for all anybody gives a damn.

LENNIE. *(Who cannot restrain himself any longer. Bursts into speech)* But not us! And why? Because . . . because I got you to look after me . . . and you got me to look after you . . . and that's why! *(He laughs.)* Go on, George!

GEORGE. You got it by heart. You can do it yourself.

LENNIE. No, no. I forget some of the stuff. Tell about how it's gonna be.

GEORGE. Some other time.

LENNIE. No, tell how it's gonna be!

GEORGE. Okay. Some day we're gonna get the jack together and we're gonna have a little house, and a couple of acres and a cow and some pigs and . . .

LENNIE. (*Shouting*) And live off the fat of the land! And have rabbits. Go on, George! Tell about what we're gonna have in the garden. And about the rabbits in the cages. Tell about the rain in the winter . . . and about the stove and how thick the cream is on the milk, you can hardly cut it. Tell about that, George.

GEORGE. Why don't you do it yourself—you know all of it!

LENNIE. It ain't the same if I tell it. Go on now. How I get to tend the rabbits.

GEORGE. (*Resignedly*) Well, we'll have a big vegetable patch and a rabbit hutch and chickens. And when it rains in the winter we'll just say to hell with goin' to work. We'll build up a fire in the stove, and set around it and listen to the rain comin' down on the roof—Nuts! (*Begins to eat with his knife.*) I ain't got time for no more. (*He falls to eating. . . .*)

WILLIAM SAROYAN

From *The Time of Your Life*

[*From Act II, in Nick's Pacific Street saloon, San Francisco, 1939. Of Joe, Saroyan writes, "always calm, always quiet, always thinking, always eager, always bored, always superior." He dresses expensively and youthfully. Just now he is being joined by a stranger.*]

KIT CARSON. Murphy's the name. Just an old trapper. Mind if I sit down?

JOE. Be delighted. What'll you drink?

KIT CARSON. (*Sitting down*) Beer. Same as I've been drinking. And thanks.

JOE. (*To* NICK) Glass of beer, Nick.

KIT CARSON. (*Moving in*) I don't suppose you ever fell in love with a midget weighing thirty-nine pounds?

JOE. *(Studying the man)* Can't say I have, but have another beer.

KIT CARSON. *(Intimately)* Thanks, thanks. Down in Gallup, twenty years ago. Fellow by the name of Rufus Jenkins came to town with six white horses and two black ones. Said he wanted a man to break the horses for him because his left leg was wood and he couldn't do it. Had a meeting at Parker's Mercantile Store and finally came to blows, me and Henry Walpal. Bashed his head with a brass cuspidor and ran away to Mexico, but he didn't die. Couldn't speak a word. Took up with a cattlebreeder named Diego, educated in California. Spoke the language better than you and me. Said, Your job, Murph, is to feed them prize bulls. I said, Fine, what'll I feed them? He said, Hay, lettuce, salt, beer, and aspirin. Came to blows two days later over an accordion he claimed I stole. I had *borrowed* it. During the fight I busted it over his head; ruined one of the finest accordions I ever saw. Grabbed a horse and rode back across the border. Texas. Got to talking with a fellow who looked honest. Turned out to be a Ranger who was looking for me.

JOE. Yeah. You were saying a thirty-nine-pound midget?

KIT CARSON. Will I ever forget that lady? Will I ever get over that amazon of small proportions?

JOE. Will you?

KIT CARSON. If I live to be sixty.

JOE. *Sixty?* You look more than sixty now.

KIT CARSON. That's trouble showing in my face. Trouble and complications. I was fifty-eight three months ago.

JOE. That accounts for it, then. Go ahead, tell me more.

KIT CARSON. Told the Texas Ranger my name was Rothstein, mining engineer from Pennsylvania, looking for something worth while. Mentioned two places in Houston. Nearly lost an eye early one morning, going down the stairs. Ran into a six-footer with an iron claw where his right hand was supposed to be. Said, You broke up my home. Told him I was a stranger in Houston. The girls gathered at the top of the stairs to see a fight. Seven of them. Six feet and an iron claw. That's bad on the nerves. Kicked him in the mouth when he swung for my head with the claw. Would have lost an eye except for quick thinking. He rolled into the gutter and pulled a gun. Fired seven times. I was back upstairs. Left the place an hour later, dressed in silk and feathers, with a hat swung around over my face. Saw him standing on the corner, waiting. Said, Care for a wiggle? Said he didn't. I went on down the street and left town. I don't suppose you ever had to put a dress on to save your skin, did you?

JOE. No, and I never fell in love with a midget weighing thirty-nine pounds. Have another beer?

KIT CARSON. Thanks. Ever try to herd cattle on a bicycle?

JOE. No. I never got around to that.

KIT CARSON. Left Houston with sixty cents in my pocket, gift of a girl named Lucinda. Walked fourteen miles in fourteen hours. Big house with barb-wire all around, and big dogs. One thing I never could get around. Walked past the gate, anyway, from hunger and thirst. Dogs jumped up and came for me. Walked right into them, growing older every second. Went up to the door and knocked. Big negress opened the door, closed it quick. Said, On your way, white trash. Knocked again. Said, On your way. Again. On your way. Again. This time the old man himself opened the door, ninety, if he was a day. Sawed-off shotgun, too. Said, I ain't looking for trouble, Father. I'm hungry and thirsty, name's Cavanaugh. Took me in and made mint juleps for the two of us. Said, Living here alone, Father? Said, Drink and ask no questions. Maybe I am and maybe I ain't. You saw the lady. Draw your own conclusions. I'd heard of that, but didn't wink out of tact. If I told you that old Southern gentleman was my grandfather, you wouldn't believe me, would you?

JOE. I might.

KIT CARSON. Well, it so happens he wasn't. Would have been romantic if he had been, though.

JOE. Where did you herd cattle on a bicycle?

KIT CARSON. Toledo, Ohio, 1918.

JOE. Ohio? They don't herd cattle in Toledo.

KIT CARSON. They don't anymore. They did in 1918. One fellow did, leastaways. Bookkeeper named Sam Gold. Straight from the East Side, New York. Sombrero, lariats, Bull Durham, two head of cattle and two bicycles. Called his place The Gold Bar Ranch, two acres, just outside the city limits. That was the year of the War you'll remember.

JOE. Yeah, I remember, but how about herding them two cows on a bicycle? How'd you do it?

KIT CARSON. Easiest thing in the world. Rode no hands. Had to, otherwise couldn't lasso the cows. Worked for Sam Gold till the cows ran away. Bicycles scared them. They went into Toledo. Never saw hide nor hair of them again. Advertised in every paper, but never got them back. Broke his heart. Sold both bikes and returned to New York. Took four aces from a deck of red cards and walked to town. Poker. Fellow in the game named Chuck Collins, liked to gamble. Told him with a smile I didn't suppose he'd care to bet a hundred dollars I wouldn't hold four aces the next hand. Called it. My cards were red on the blank side. The other cards were blue. Plumb forgot all about it. Showed him four aces. Ace of spades, ace of clubs, ace of diamonds, ace of hearts. I'll remember them four cards if I live to be sixty. Would have been killed on the spot except for the hurricane that year.

JOE. Hurricane?

KIT CARSON. You haven't forgotten the Toledo hurricane of 1918, have you?

JOE. No. There was no hurricane in Toledo in 1918, or any other year.

KIT CARSON. For the love of God, then what do you suppose that commotion was? And how come I came to in Chicago, dreamwalking down State Street?

JOE. I guess they scared you.

KIT CARSON. No, that wasn't it. You go back to the papers of November 1918, and I think you'll find there was a hurricane in Toledo. I remember sitting on the roof of a two-story house, floating northwest.

JOE. (*Seriously*) Northwest?

KIT CARSON. Now, son, don't tell me *you* don't believe me, either?

JOE. (*Pause. Very seriously, energetically and sharply*) Of course I believe you. Living is an art. It's not bookkeeping. It takes a lot of rehearsing for a man to get to be himself.

KIT CARSON. (*Thoughtfully, smiling, and amazed*) You're the first man I've ever met who believes me.

JOE. (*Seriously*) Have another beer.

TENNESSEE WILLIAMS

∿∿

From *A Streetcar Named Desire*

[*In the opening scene of the play, Blanche du Bois is talking with her sister Stella, married to Stanley Kowalski. Stella is about 25, gentle in contrast to her rough husband. Blanche is about 30, with delicate beauty and an uncertain manner which seems somehow mothlike.*]

BLANCHE. *(In an uneasy rush)* I haven't asked you the things you probably thought I was going to ask. And so I'll expect you to be understanding about what *I* have to tell *you.*

STELLA. What, Blanche? *(Her face turns anxious.)*

BLANCHE. Well, Stella—you're going to reproach me, I know that you're bound to reproach me—but before you do—take into consideration—you left! I stayed and struggled! You came to New Orleans and looked out for yourself! I stayed at Belle Reve and tried to hold it together! I'm not meaning this in any reproachful way, but *all* the burden descended on *my* shoulders.

STELLA. The best I could do was make my own living, Blanche.

(BLANCHE *begins to shake again with intensity.*)

BLANCHE. I know, I know. But you are the one that abandoned Belle Reve, not I! I stayed and fought for it, bled for it, almost died for it!

STELLA. Stop this hysterical outburst and tell me what's happened? What do you mean fought and bled? What kind of——

BLANCHE. I knew you would, Stella. I knew you would take this attitude about it!

STELLA. About—what?—please!

BLANCHE. *(Slowly)* The loss—the loss . . .

STELLA. Belle Reve? Lost, is it? No!

BLANCHE. Yes, Stella.

(They stare at each other across the yellow-checked linoleum of the table. BLANCHE *slowly nods her head and* STELLA *looks slowly down at her hands folded on the table. The music of the "blue piano" grows louder.* BLANCHE *touches her handkerchief to her forehead.)*

STELLA. But how did it go? What happened?

BLANCHE. *(Springing up)* You're a fine one to ask me how it went!

STELLA. Blanche!

BLANCHE. You're a fine one to sit there *accusing me* of it!

STELLA. *Blanche!*

BLANCHE. I, I, *I* took the blows in my face and my body! All of those deaths! The long parade to the graveyard! Father, mother! Margaret, that dreadful way! So big with it, it couldn't be put in a coffin! But had to be burned like rubbish! You just came home in time for the funerals, Stella. And funerals are pretty compared to deaths. Funerals are quiet, but deaths—not always. Sometimes their breathing is hoarse, and sometimes it rattles, and sometimes they even cry out to you, "Don't let me go!" Even the old, sometimes, say, "Don't let me go." As if you were able to stop them! But funerals are quiet, with pretty flowers. And, oh, what gorgeous boxes they pack them away in! Unless you were there at the bed when they cried out, "Hold me!" you'd never suspect there was the struggle for breath and bleeding. You didn't dream, but I saw. *Saw! Saw!* And now you sit there telling me with your eyes that I let the place go! How in hell do you think all that sickness and dying was paid for? Death is expensive, Miss Stella! And old Cousin Jessie's right after Margaret's, hers! Why, the Grim Reaper had put up his tent on our doorstep! . . . Stella. Belle Reve was his headquarters! Honey— that's how it slipped through my fingers! Which of them left us a fortune? Which of them left a cent of insurance even? Only poor Jessie— one hundred to pay for her coffin. That was all, Stella! And I with my pitiful salary at the school. Yes, accuse me! Sit there and stare at me, thinking I let the place go! *I* let the place go? Where were *you?* In bed with your—Polack!

STELLA. *(Springing)* Blanche! You be still! That's enough. *(She starts out.)*

BLANCHE. Where are you going?

STELLA. I'm going into the bathroom to wash my face.

BLANCHE. Oh, Stella, Stella, you're crying!

STELLA. Does that surprise you?

BLANCHE. Forgive me—I didn't mean to—.

(The sound of men's voices is heard. STELLA goes into the bathroom, closing the door behind her.)

Index of Authors

71 460 55